THE OFFICIAL HANDBOOK OF THE
MARVEL UNIVERSE

EARTH'S MIGHTIEST HEROES
THE AVENGERS
PART ONE

ANT-MAN

REAL NAME: Scott Edward Harris Lang
KNOWN ALIASES: Myrmidon
IDENTITY: Secret; disclosed to the courts as part of Cassie Lang's custody hearing
OCCUPATION: Adventurer, electronics technician and owner of Electrolang, Inc.; former burglar, employee of Stark International
PLACE OF BIRTH: Coral Gables, FL
CITIZENSHIP: United States of America with a criminal record
MARITAL STATUS: Divorced
KNOWN RELATIVES: Peggy Rae (ex-wife), Cassandra Eleanor "Cassie" Lang (daughter), Ruth (sister), Carl (brother-in-law)
GROUP AFFILIATION: Avengers; formerly the Fantastic Four, Heroes for Hire
EDUCATION: Electronics technician certificate, plus additional advanced electronics training while in prison
FIRST APPEARANCE: (As Scott Lang) Avengers Vol. 1 #181 (1979); (as Ant-Man) Marvel Premiere #47 (1979)

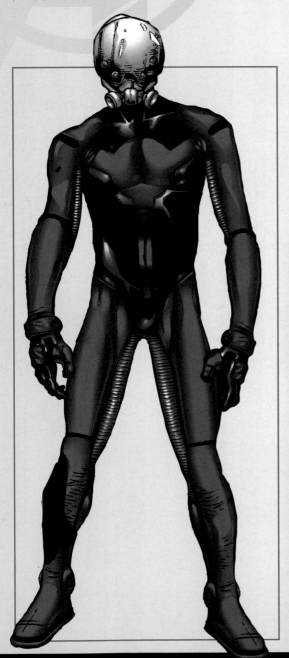

HISTORY: Scott Lang was an electronics expert who turned to burglary to support his family. Apprehended, he served three years and was released on parole for good behavior. After Stark International hired him, Lang's daughter Cassie was diagnosed with a serious congenital heart condition. He sought the aid of Dr. Erica Sondheim, only to learn that Darren Cross of Cross Technological Enterprises was holding her prisoner. In order to rescue Sondheim, Lang stole Dr. Henry Pym's Ant-Man equipment, and Pym thereafter allowed him to keep the equipment to carry on Pym's former identity as Ant-Man.

Dividing his time between costumed heroics and his family responsibilities, Ant-Man worked alongside several super heroes, aiding members of the Avengers against the mercenary Taskmaster on two occasions. When Baron (Helmut) Zemo's Masters of Evil attacked the Avengers and took control of Avengers Mansion, Ant-Man offered his assistance to the Avengers in defeating the criminal super-team. The Fantastic Four subsequently hired him as an electronics expert when Mister Fantastic was believed to be dead, and he was inducted into the team. Although initially feeling outclassed by the more powerful FF members, he proved himself against a variety of powerful foes.

Following Mister Fantastic's return, Ant-Man joined the team known as Heroes for Hire and clashed with such enemies as Ghaur and the Master. After Heroes for Hire disbanded, he again aided the Avengers against the Taskmaster; he also began dating former super hero Jessica Jones, although their relationship ended quickly. Ant-Man next fought alongside the Avengers against the menace of Scorpio and the In-Betweener, then was invited to join full-time, a role he accepted after losing custody of his daughter to his ex-wife.

PHYSICAL DESCRIPTION:

Height: 6'
Weight: 190 lbs.
Eyes: Blue
Hair: Reddish-blond

POWERS & ABILITIES:

Superhuman Powers: Ant-Man possesses no innate superhuman powers.

Special Skills: Ant-Man has above-average expertise in electronics and is a skilled burglar.

PARAPHERNALIA:

Accessories: Ant-Man's helmet enables him to communicate with and control insects, and to fire electrical blasts, and it contains its own oxygen supply.

POWER GRID	1	2	3	4	5	6	7
INTELLIGENCE							
STRENGTH							
SPEED							
DURABILITY							
ENERGY PROJECTION							
FIGHTING SKILLS							

REAL NAME: T'Challa
KNOWN ALIASES: Luke Charles, Black Leopard, Nubian Prince, the Client, Coal Tiger, has impersonated Daredevil and others on occasion
IDENTITY: Publicly known
OCCUPATION: Monarch of Wakanda, scientist; former school teacher
CITIZENSHIP: Wakanda
PLACE OF BIRTH: Wakanda
MARITAL STATUS: Single
KNOWN RELATIVES: T'Chaka (father, deceased), N'Yami (mother, deceased), Ramonda (stepmother), Bashenga (first Black Panther, ancestor, deceased), Jakarra (half-brother, deceased), Hunter (adopted brother), Azzari the Wise (grandfather, deceased), Khanata, Joshua Itobo, Ishanta, Zuni (cousins)
GROUP AFFILIATION: Avengers, formerly Queen's Vengeance
EDUCATION: Ph.D in physics
FIRST APPEARANCE: Fantastic Four Vol. 1 #52 (1966)

HISTORY: T'Challa was born to T'Chaka, head of the African nation of Wakanda; his mother, N'Yami, died in childbirth. T'Chaka's adopted son, Hunter, bore a grudge against T'Challa for taking his mother's life, and he nurtured his sore feelings over the years that followed. Hunter eventually became the White Wolf, head of the Hatut Zeraze, Wakanda's secret police. T'Challa's father remarried an African-American woman, Ramonda.

As a teenager, T'Challa met the mutant Ororo Munroe, and the two shared a brief flirtation, but T'Challa was bound to Wakanda and his father. They did not meet again until years later, when Ororo had become the X-Men member Storm.

T'Chaka entered into an unwise alliance with a Dutchman, Ulysses Klaw. Klaw had come to Wakanda to exploit its people for slavery and obtain its unique metal Vibranium, which can absorb sonic and kinetic energy. In the course of his plundering, Klaw murdered T'Chaka. With his father dead, T'Challa assaulted Klaw with his own sonic weapon, causing Klaw's gun to explode and maim his right hand. Klaw was driven out, and T'Challa became prince of Wakanda.

After being schooled at universities in America and England, T'Challa returned to Wakanda and assumed the mantle of the Black Panther by winning the title in combat. He then ingested the heart-shaped herb that

gave him superior senses and physical abilities. T'Challa was now not only the ruler of Wakanda, head of the Wakanda Design Group, and head of the Black Panther Cult, but also the controller of Wakanda's Vibranium supply.

All this time, Wakanda had remained an isolationist state, a mystery to the outside world, with defenses far greater than anyone would imagine. T'Challa opened Wakanda to the outside world by inviting the Fantastic Four, planning to defeat them in battle in order to prove himself. He succeeded in defeating the entire Fantastic Four, but had not reckoned with their friend Wyatt Wingfoot, who set them free from the Panther's traps. T'Challa then revealed his true motives to them and received the Fantastic Four's aid in battling Klaw, who had returned. After he was injured in battle with the Black Panther, Klaw voluntarily entered his sonic converter, becoming a being of pure sound.

After an adventure alongside Captain America, the Black Panther was nominated for Avengers membership as a replacement for the otherwise-occupied Cap. T'Challa accepted so that he could spy on the Avengers from within and determine if they posed a threat to his country. However, he soon became friends with the Avengers and came to trust them. He became particularly close to his fellow scientists Yellowjacket and Iron Man.

During his time with the Avengers, T'Challa assumed the alias of Luke Charles and became a schoolteacher in Harlem. He also met Monica Lynne, a singer, and they fell in love. Monica remained with T'Challa when he returned to Wakanda to discover that Erik Killmonger, a man sold into slavery by Klaw as a child, had begun a civil war. Killmonger was defeated, but has returned to challenge T'Challa on several occasions.

During a recent visit to the United States, T'Challa was assigned Everett K. Ross as his aide by the State Department. Although the two men are from very different cultures, they have come to respect each other tremendously, and T'Challa even made Ross his regent for a time.

Besides Ross, the Black Panther's greatest allies are his head of communications, Taku; his security chief, W'Kabi; his bodyguard, Zuri; his regent, N'Gassi; and the Dora Milaje ("Adored Ones"), young women from enemy tribes who have been placed in T'Challa's care to keep the peace and serve as prospective brides. They include Queen Divine Justice, Okoye, and Nakia.

Over time, T'Challa's relationship with Monica has fallen upon hard times, and she turned down his most recent marriage proposal.

T'Challa's original reasons for joining the Avengers have recently come to light, and some of his teammates have had trouble accepting T'Challa's motivations. T'Challa's relationship with Iron Man in particular fell on hard times, and was exacerbated when Stark bought out the Wakanda Design Group. T'Challa and Stark are on better terms now, and are making strides to improve their relationship.

During a recent battle with Iron Fist, T'Challa suffered injuries that resulted in his developing a brain aneurysm. At the same time, a version of the Black Panther from the future appeared who had determined that, with his final days upon him, he would lighten up and enjoy life. The future Panther finally succumbed to his aneurysm, and was slain by T'Challa's enemy, the Man-Ape, while in a cryogenic sleep. Reeling from having witnessed the death of his future self and suffering from hallucinations and seizures, T'Challa abandoned the throne of Wakanda and for a time lived secretly in New York.

Recently, a police officer named Kevin "Kasper" Cole obtained one of T'Challa's costumes and assumed his identity in order to wage war on crime. T'Challa has mentored Cole to some extent, and oversaw his posting to the Black Panther Cult, in which Cole has become an acolyte — a White Tiger.

Having been brought back into the world by his encounter with Cole, T'Challa has recently rejoined the Avengers. Since then, Killmonger has returned to challenge T'Challa for the title of Black Panther. T'Challa will have to meet this challenge one day soon.

T'Challa is a consummate planner who prepares for every contingency. He has even seen to it that Wakanda has a plan for dealing with Galactus, should the world-devourer ever threaten the country.

Art by Gabriele Dell'Otto

PHYSICAL DESCRIPTION:

Height: 6'
Weight: 200 lbs.
Eyes: Brown
Hair: Black

POWERS & ABILITIES:

Superhuman Powers: Ingestion of the heart-shaped herb has granted T'Challa enhanced senses, making him an expert hunter and tracker and providing him with night vision.

PARAPHERNALIA:

Personal Weaponry: The Vibranium weave contained within T'Challa's uniform absorbs the kinetic force of objects striking it, rendering the Black Panther bulletproof. His costume is outfitted with anti-metal claws that can dissolve other metals on contact, energy daggers, and his Kimoyo Card, which allows him to communicate across the globe. He also has access to the many specialized weapons and vehicles of Wakanda.

POWER GRID	1	2	3	4	5	6	7
INTELLIGENCE							
STRENGTH							
SPEED							
DURABILITY							
ENERGY PROJECTION							
FIGHTING SKILLS							

HISTORY: Born in 1922, Steve Rogers was a young and idealistic artist orphaned at an early age. Appalled at reports of Nazi activity and believing that American entry into World War II was inevitable, he attempted to enlist in the armed forces but was rejected for his physical frailty, only to be chosen as a volunteer for the government project known as Operation: Rebirth. Rogers received several experimental treatments that elevated him to the peak of human physical perfection, and after months of intensive training, he was selected to become a special government operative, a living symbol of liberty known as Captain America. He was soon given a unique weapon, a virtually indestructible shield. Joined in action by young Bucky Barnes, Captain America fought a wide variety of criminals and Axis operatives; his most dedicated opponent was the Nazi leader known as the Red Skull, whom he clashed with many times. When America entered the war following the Pearl Harbor attack, Cap and Bucky were among the founding members of the super-team known as the Invaders. Adventuring around the world alone, with Bucky, and alongside the other Invaders, Captain America achieved the greatest reputation of any wartime hero and was respected by ally and enemy alike.

Toward the end of World War II, Captain America and Bucky were sent to prevent Nazi operative Baron (Heinrich) Zemo from obtaining an experimental plane; when Zemo launched the plane, the two heroes attempted to stop it but were thrown off when it exploded. Bucky was apparently slain, but the super-soldier formula that had transformed him years earlier saved Cap's life, throwing him into suspended animation instead. In the years following his disappearance, at least three other men took on the role of Captain America, with varying degrees of success.

Captain America remained frozen in ice for decades until, hurled into the sea by Namor the Sub-Mariner, he was discovered by the Avengers and revived. He quickly proved himself a worthy addition to the newly formed team and was chosen as the first new member of the Avengers; when Baron Zemo learned of his enemy's survival, he formed the Masters of Evil to fight the Avengers, and the menace of the Masters has recurred many times since. Some months later, when the founding Avengers chose to leave the team, Captain America became the leader of a new incarnation of the group, a post he would hold many times over the next several years. As members came and went, he proved to be one of the few constants of the team, rarely leaving active membership and leading the team against such menaces as Kang, the Mole Man, Doctor Doom, and others. He also found himself again fighting the Red Skull, who had also survived the decades through suspended animation and had awoken to threaten the world anew.

In addition to his Avengers activities, Captain America also worked closely with the espionage agency known as S.H.I.E.L.D., and it was there that he met Agent Sharon Carter, who would become the great love of his life; he was also joined in his crimefighting activities by the acrobatic Falcon, who himself would later join the Avengers. Some years after his revival, a clash with the subversive Secret Empire cost Cap his faith in the American government, and he took on the new identity of Nomad; however, when a young man named Roscoe was slain attempting to fill his original role, Cap reclaimed his mantle and rededicated himself to his fight against evil.

Several months after the apparent death of Sharon Carter, Captain America began dating glassblower Bernadette Rosenthal; with her assistance, he set up the Captain America Hotline in order to learn about menaces throughout the U.S., although the couple broke up not long afterward. When the American government ordered Captain America to again become a full-time government operative, he refused, choosing to surrender his costumed identity and continue to operate as a free agent. While another man assumed the role of

REAL NAME: Steven Rogers
KNOWN ALIASES: Nomad, the Captain, Steven Grant Rogers, Roger Stevens, Yeoman America
IDENTITY: Publicly known
Occupation: Adventurer; formerly WPA artist, soldier, police officer, teacher, freelance illustrator, special S.H.I.E.L.D. operative
PLACE OF BIRTH: New York City, NY
CITIZENSHIP: United States of America with no criminal record
MARITAL STATUS: Single
KNOWN RELATIVES: Joseph Rogers (father, deceased), Sarah Rogers (mother, deceased), unnamed grandfather (presumed deceased), Steven Rogers (ancestor, deceased)
GROUP AFFILIATION: Avengers; formerly Invaders, Redeemers, Queen's Vengeance
EDUCATION: High school graduate; one year of art school; military basic training; private tutoring in hand-to-hand combat, gymnastics, military strategy, piloting, demolition, and other disciplines
FIRST APPEARANCE: Captain America Comics #1 (1941)

t by John Cassaday

Captain America, Cap himself took the new identity of the Captain, working with the Falcon and others in his continued crime-fighting endeavors. Even in this new identity, he remained dedicated to the Avengers; when the team temporarily disbanded, he reorganized it with new members. After reclaiming his role as Captain America, he oversaw the rebuilding of the Avengers while again acting as chairman.

Captain America has long held a position of authority in the superhuman community, and, alongside Mister Fantastic and Professor X, he has led many heroes through such crises as the Secret Wars and the Infinity War. However, during the intergalactic Kree-Shi'ar War, he found his leadership and principles challenged by some of his fellow Avengers; leaving the team for a time, he returned during their clash with the Gatherers and helped keep the team together despite various pressures. Months later, he was crippled by a deterioration of the Super-Soldier formula, but remained active via a specially designed exoskeleton. Eventually succumbing to physical deterioration, he was revived as part of one of the Red Skull's schemes and learned that Sharon Carter had survived, although their reconciliation would take months.

Shortly after his return, the Avengers met one of their greatest challenges in the trans-temporal events known as the Crossing. Although the team seemed on the verge of disintegration, Captain America again rallied his fellow Avengers and kept them together, only for many members, including Cap, to seemingly perish battling the psychic entity called Onslaught. Actually sent on a strange transdimensional experience of several months, the Avengers returned to face a worldwide challenge by Morgan le Fay, and Cap once more led the team to triumph over their adversary. Captain America has since successfully led the Avengers against some of their greatest challenges, including the Exemplars, the Triune Understanding, and Kang's all-out assault on Earth, and it seems certain that he will continue to lead the Avengers to victory.

Re-energized in his belief in America and what it stands for since terrorists attacked New York and Washington, D.C., Captain America has revealed his true face to the world. He realizes he is needed now more than ever to stand up to those who would see his country in ruins.

PHYSICAL DESCRIPTION:

Height: 6'2"
Weight: 220 lbs.
Eyes: Blue
Hair: Blond

POWERS & ABILITIES:

Superhuman Powers: Strictly speaking, Captain America possesses no superhuman powers; however, his body has been mutated to the pinnacle of human perfection. He possesses strength, agility, endurance, speed, and reflexes superior to any Olympic-level athlete, and his bodily functions have been enhanced to the peak of human efficiency. His body eliminates excessive build-up of fatigue-producing poisons in his muscles, granting him phenomenal endurance.

Special Skills: Captain America is an expert hand-to-hand combatant and a skilled martial artist in a number of disciplines; he is also a master strategist, acrobat, and pilot, with training in various military disciplines. He is fluent in Russian, German, and possibly other languages.

PARAPHERNALIA:

Personal Weaponry: Captain America carries a virtually indestructible shield composed of a unique Vibranium-steel alloy created through a process that has never been duplicated. A concave disk two and a half feet in diameter and weighing twelve pounds, the shield has excellent aerodynamic properties and can be hurled to rebound off of solid objects with minimal loss of angular motion. Captain America has long since honed its use to the point that he can use it to deflect attacks and knock out adversaries in tandem with his own acrobatic skill. The shield is impenetrable by even the strongest Adamantium, resistant to all temperature extremes, and unaffected by any known form of radiation; the only way it can be damaged is by the direct breakdown of its molecular bonding.

Other Accessories: Captain America frequently travels via a custom-built Harley-Davidson Custom Special motorcycle with S.H.I.E.L.D. modifications and/or a custom-built Chevrolet van outfitted by the Wakanda Design Group; he uses Avengers Quinjets when necessary.

Art by J.G. Jones

POWER GRID	1	2	3	4	5	6	7
INTELLIGENCE							
STRENGTH							
SPEED							
DURABILITY							
ENERGY PROJECTION							
FIGHTING SKILLS							

HISTORY: Kelsey Leigh was a single mother with two young children. Her face was scarred from a previous brutal attack when men invaded her home and assaulted her. She otherwise lived an ordinary life in southeast England. One fateful day her family found themselves on the front line of a battle between the Avengers and the Wrecking Crew. When Thunderball managed to render Captain America unconscious and was about to kill him, Kelsey selflessly blocked his attack, using the downed hero's shield. While the shield was indestructible, Kelsey wasn't, and the shock from the blows inflicted terrible injuries; she died en route to receiving medical attention.

Kelsey awoke to find herself in a ring of standing stones, where she was met by a vision of Brian Braddock, Captain Britain. He knew that Morgan le Fay was behind the Wrecking Crew, and that the sorceress was about to invade Otherworld, intending to use his magical link to his homeland to harm Britain through him. By passing the mantle of Captain Britain to another, he could sever that connection, thwarting her plans. He informed Kelsey that her bravery had earned her a second chance to live and to defend her home, and then asked her to choose between the Sword of Might and the Amulet of Right. Grasping at the chance to see her children again, and feeling that a necklace could not defend anything, Kelsey chose the sword, the path of violence. Instantly, she was transformed into the new Captain Britain, only to discover that her decision meant that if she ever revealed who she was to her children, they would die.

The new Captain Britain returned to Earth, where she helped the Avengers defeat Morgan and her cronies, proving herself to be far more ruthless in battle than her predecessor. With her children now in the Avengers' care, Kelsey accepted an offer to join the team, so that even if she could not be reunited with them, she could remain near them.

PHYSICAL DESCRIPTION:

Height: 5'5"
Weight: 130 lbs
Eyes: Blue
Hair: Blonde

Distinguishing Features: Kelsey has a long scar running down her face, from the middle of her forehead down the left side of her nose and mouth, and onto her chin. This scar was healed when she was given her powers.

POWERS & ABILITIES:

Superhuman Powers: Captain Britain's body has been mystically altered to grant her superhuman strength, agility, endurance, speed, and reflexes.

PARAPHERNALIA:

Personal Weaponry: Captain Britain weilds the Sword of Might, a mystic weapon that is invulnerable to all harm, capable of cleaving through any substance up to foot-thick steel. It serves to channel mystical energy so she never tires; this energy can also be used for destructive blasts or protective shields.

REAL NAME: Kelsey Shorr Leigh
KNOWN ALIASES: Lionheart of Avalon
IDENTITY: Secret
OCCUPATION: Adventurer, former homemaker, previous occupation unknown
CITIZENSHIP: United Kingdom of Great Britain and Northern Ireland
PLACE OF BIRTH: Colchester, Essex, England
MARITAL STATUS: Divorced
KNOWN RELATIVES: Martin (son), Jenny (daughter), Mrs. Shorr (mother), Richard (ex-husband)
GROUP AFFILIATION: Avengers, Captain Britain Corps
EDUCATION: University graduate
EDUCATION: High school dropout, later extensively self-educated
FIRST APPEARANCE: (as Kelsey) Avengers Vol. 3 #77 (2004); (as Captain Britain) Avengers Vol. 3 #80 (2004)

POWER GRID	1	2	3	4	5	6	7
INTELLIGENCE							
STRENGTH							
SPEED							
DURABILITY							
ENERGY PROJECTION							
FIGHTING SKILLS							

Art by Olivier Coipel

FALCON

REAL NAME: Samuel Thomas "Sam" Wilson
KNOWN ALIASES: Blackbird, "Snap" Wilson, Captain America, Brother Super-Hero, Brother Falcon
IDENTITY: Publicly known
OCCUPATION: Adventurer, social worker, urban planner
CITIZENSHIP: United States of America
PLACE OF BIRTH: New York City
MARITAL STATUS: Single
KNOWN RELATIVES: Paul Wilson (father, deceased), Darlene Wilson (mother, deceased), Sarah Wilson Casper (sister), Jody Casper (nephew), Jim Wilson (nephew, deceased)
GROUP AFFILIATION: Avengers, member of the Defenders for one day; formerly Night People, Queen's Vengeance
EDUCATION: High school dropout, later extensively self-educated
FIRST APPEARANCE: Captain America Vol. 1 #117 (1969)

HISTORY: When Sam Wilson was a child, his father, a prominent minister, was beaten to death while trying to end a street fight. After a mugger killed his mother years later, Sam turned his back on his past, adopted the alias of "Snap," and became a professional criminal and gang member.

Sam had always had a keen interest in birds, and picked up a pet falcon in Rio de Janeiro that he named Redwing. After crashing on the Island of the Exiles, "Snap" was found by the Red Skull, who at that time had used the Cosmic Cube to exchange bodies with Captain America. He used the Cosmic Cube to revert "Snap" to his Sam persona, and set him up to become the partner of Captain America so that he could one day turn Sam against his old enemy. He also gave Sam the ability to communicate telepathically with Redwing.

Sam became a hero on the island and championed the natives there against the Exiles. When he met Captain America (in the Red Skull's body), Cap helped train him to fight and designed the identity

of the Falcon for him. The Falcon joined Captain America in battle with the Red Skull, and when the Red Skull restored them both to their own bodies, the Falcon was surprised to see it was Captain America who had mentored him. Together, Captain America and the Falcon defeated the Red Skull, and the Falcon returned to Harlem to become a local hero.

The Falcon and Captain America met again when the Diamond-Head gang framed the Falcon for murder. Captain America helped clear the Falcon's name. After the Falcon aided Captain America against MODOK, the two finally forged a long-lasting partnership. Sam also became a social worker in Harlem and dedicated himself to defending the streets of his hometown. On one occasion, Sam even wore the Captain America costume, briefly, when Captain America appeared to have been killed. Later, Sam received a pair of wings from the Black Panther that granted him the ability to fly.

Even after Captain America abandoned his costumed identity following a spirit-breaking encounter with the Secret Empire, the Falcon continued to follow the path of a hero and helped train a young man named Roscoe to take over the Captain America identity. However, Roscoe wound up being killed by the Red Skull.

Eventually, Sam regained his memories of having been "Snap" and was overwhelmed. His one-time criminal associates got wind of his true identity, and he had to fight off several criminals out to collect a reward on his head. Sam continued on as the Falcon, but he and Captain America eventually ended their formal partnership, although they have continued to come to one another's aid when help is needed.

In order to comply with affirmative action, government liaison Henry Peter Gyrich ordered the Avengers to accept the Falcon as a member when he reorganized the team into a roster of only seven members. Sam was put off by the means by which he had joined, and although he proved himself in battle against the Grey Gargoyle, his initial stay was brief; he soon returned to his work in Harlem.

Sam attempted to make a political career for himself and ran for Congress, but his history as "Snap" came back to haunt him thanks to the media. Sam nearly reverted back to his "Snap" persona, but was finally able to come to terms with the man he had been, although his political career was ruined.

Sam no longer maintains a secret identity, which means that people who need the Falcon have only to look for Sam Wilson at his office. Sam has done his best to look out for the people of Harlem, attempting to end gang violence. Sam's staunchest ally in Harlem is Sgt. Tork, a dedicated police officer. Sam's on-again off-again girlfriend is Leila Taylor, a reporter. He has also dated Rachel Davis, a wealthy socialite.

When the government stripped Steve Rogers of the Captain America uniform, the Falcon joined with his fellow sidekicks Nomad and D-Man in encouraging Steve to continue being a hero. They helped Steve set up his new identity as the Captain, and the Falcon did his best to convince Steve to reclaim the Captain America ID.

Sam's nephew, Jim, a frequent ally of the Hulk, contracted AIDS. In return for Jim's friendship and help in controlling his own violent tendencies, the Hulk granted Jim medical care and solace until his death, a kindness for which the Falcon has been grateful.

Sam later had a friend at Stark Enterprises modify his costume into a more versatile battlesuit that contained a grappling hook, talons, vision-enhancing lenses, and wings that could detach from his back by command. He eventually discarded this costume when he was attacked by the Sub-Mariner, who mistook him for Stingray.
In addition to his continuing career as a social worker, Sam is also involved in the reconstruction of the World Trade Center. Recently, the Falcon decided to return to the Avengers and revealed that his power had expanded so that he could communicate with other birds. Sam used his abilities to spy on Gyrich, who was discovered to be meeting with Secretary of Defense Dell Rusk. The Falcon convinced Gyrich to help the Avengers spy on Rusk, which proved instrumental in revealing that Rusk was the Red Skull. Sam was badly injured fighting the Red Skull, but has since recovered.

Recently, the Falcon has gone rogue in order to rescue Leila Taylor from Guantanamo Bay. The repercussions this will have upon his career as an Avenger and as a social worker are yet to be determined.

Art by Ivan Reis

PHYSICAL DESCRIPTION:

Height: 6'2"
Weight: 240 lbs.
Eyes: Brown
Hair: Black

POWERS & ABILITIES:

Superhuman Powers: The Falcon originally possessed the ability to communicate with his pet falcon Redwing using telepathy; he can now communicate telepathically with any bird within an unknown radius. He can also "see" through the eyes of any bird within his radius.

PARAPHERNALIA:

Personal Weaponry: The Falcon formerly wore a pair of jet-powered glider wings that allowed him to fly at speeds up to 250 miles per hour. He now wears a pair of "hard light" wings that have increased his speed and maneuverability. He occasionally wears a glove on his left hand that contains a grappling hook.

POWER GRID	1	2	3	4	5	6	7
INTELLIGENCE							
STRENGTH							
SPEED							
DURABILITY							
ENERGY PROJECTION							
FIGHTING SKILLS							

JARVIS

REAL NAME: Edwin Jarvis
KNOWN ALIASES: Crimson Cowl
IDENTITY: Publicly known
OCCUPATION: Butler
CITIZENSHIP: Former citizen of the United Kingdom, now a naturalized citizen of the United States of America with no criminal record
PLACE OF BIRTH: England
MARITAL STATUS: Single
KNOWN RELATIVES: Mrs. Jarvis (mother)
GROUP AFFILIATION: Employee of Anthony Stark and the Avengers
EDUCATION: University graduate
FIRST APPEARANCE: Tales of Suspense Vol. 1 #59 (1964)

\HISTORY: Before coming to the United States, Jarvis served heroically in the United Kingdom's Royal Air Force as a pilot. Jarvis has served as butler for the Stark family for many years, stationed at the Stark family mansion in Manhattan. Jarvis was present when the Avengers held their first meeting at Stark's mansion to outline their charter. When the rest of the staff learned that the Hulk was among the Avengers' line-up, they all quit, leaving Jarvis to manage the building alone. Although he at first found the Avengers unusual people to serve, he adapted himself to their needs to be the perfect gentleman's gentleman.

Over the years, Jarvis has been the Avengers' most valuable ally, keeping the mansion clean, preparing their meals, fueling their Quinjets, occasionally taking monitor duty, and, most importantly, lending the team his moral support.

Jarvis has formed strong bonds to Captain America, especially in the days when he had been newly reawakened in modern times, and the Vision, encouraging him to explore his feelings.

When Ultron-5 formed a new Masters of Evil to conquer the Avengers, he used his powers to make Jarvis to deliver him the security plans to Avengers Mansion, and also had him adopt the identity of the Crimson Cowl in order to conceal the fact that Ultron himself was the true Crimson Cowl. The Avengers forgave him even before Jarvis recalled being controlled by Ultron.

Over the years, Jarvis has been able to help the Avengers on occasion, as when he helped save Judy Parks from Graviton or helped Fabian Stankowicz overthrow the Protectorate. Still, Jarvis nearly left the Avengers when the Masters of Evil conquered Avengers Mansion. Jarvis was taken as a hostage and Baron Zemo ordered Mr. Hyde to beat Jarvis to death in front of Captain America to break his spirit. Jarvis survived, but suffered horrible injuries. He contemplated leaving the Avengers' employ, but ultimately determined to remain with them.

Jarvis is currently the head of staff at the Avengers Embassy, continuing in his duties as butler. He is dating Glory Garson, a woman he saved from demons during "Inferno," a demonic invasion of New York.

PHYSICAL DESCRIPTION:

Height: 5'11"
Weight: 160 lbs.
Eyes: Blue
Hair: Black

POWER GRID	1	2	3	4	5	6	7
INTELLIGENCE							
STRENGTH							
SPEED							
DURABILITY							
ENERGY PROJECTION							
FIGHTING SKILLS							

Art by George Pére

REAL NAME: Namor McKenzie
KNOWN ALIASES: Namor the First, the Avenging Son, the Old Man, Rex, Sealord, Joe Pierre
IDENTITY: Publicly known
OCCUPATION: Monarch, adventurer; former warrior, terrorist, commando, CEO
PLACE OF BIRTH: Antarctic capital of the Atlantean Empire
CITIZENSHIP: Dual citizenship in Atlantis and the United States
MARITAL STATUS: Twice widowed
KNOWN RELATIVES: Dorma (first wife and cousin, deceased); Marrina (second wife, presumed deceased); Fen (mother, deceased); Leonard McKenzie (father, deceased); Thakorr (grandfather, deceased); Korra (grandmother, presumed deceased); Zarina (aunt); unnamed uncle; Byrrah (deceased), Namora (deceased), Dara, Arkus, Beemer, Bobo, Byrrahna, Daro, Namita (cousins); Namorita (first cousin once removed); Talan (cousin-in-law, deceased), Daka (uncle)
GROUP AFFILIATION: Invaders, All-Winners Squad, Defenders, Avengers, formerly Queen's Vengence
EDUCATION: Educated by the royal tutors of the Atlantean court
FIRST APPEARANCE: Motion Picture Funnies Weekly #1 (1939)

HISTORY: Namor was born in 1920 in the undersea Antarctic kingdom of Atlantis, the son of the Atlantean princess Fen and a surface human named Leonard McKenzie. His hybrid nature granted him various unique abilities and enabled him to survive on both land and water. At the age of sixteen, while dwelling at the North Atlantic outpost of his kingdom, he had a brief romance with a young human named Sandra Pierce, but otherwise had little contact with the surface world.

In 1939, Namor encountered two humans in diving suits and, believing them to be invading robots from the surface, attacked and inadvertently killed them. Encouraged by his mother and his grandfather, Emperor Thakorr, the impetuous Namor set out to explore the surface world in preparation for possible Atlantean invasion. In response to the hostility he met, as well as suffering from an oxygen imbalance as a result of prolonged surface activity, he declared a one-man war upon humanity, his attacks occasionally tempered only by the strained friendship he formed with policewoman Betty Dean. For over a year, Namor wreaked havoc across the world, hunted by American and Axis forces alike. He was even captured and sentenced to death in New York, although his superhuman nature allowed him to survive the electric chair. However, by the end of 1941, following a Nazi attack on Atlantis, he elected to join the Allied side, and when America formally entered the war following the Pearl Harbor attack, Namor became one of the founding members of the superhuman unit called the Invaders alongside his former adversaries, Captain America and the android Human Torch. Over the next four years, Namor, both alone and alongside his teammates, fought a wide variety of criminals and Axis agents around the world, even rogue Atlanteans, including his own mother, who temporarily sided with the Axis.

Following the war, Namor continued his heroic activities as a member of the All-Winners Squad, but after the team disbanded in 1949, Namor abandoned surface life for a time, preferring to devote his attention to Atlantean affairs. However, by 1953, his restless nature led him to additional surface adventures, often in the company of his similarly powered cousin, Namora, and against the efforts of their traitorous cousin, Byrrah. In 1955, hoping to cement peaceful relations between his kingdom and the surface world, Namor led a delegation to petition for Atlantis's membership in the United Nations, only to see the effort fail after an unsuccessful attempt on his life. Believing peaceful contact to be impossible, he again returned to Atlantis, intending to abandon the surface world forever. Three years later, Atlantis was attacked and ultimately destroyed by a madman named Paul Destine (a.k.a. Destiny), a former colleague of his father's, using the ancient and powerful object known as the Serpent Crown. When Namor responded to the attack, Destiny telepathically assaulted Namor and ordered him to return to New York, where he spent decades as an amnesiac derelict, his mind clouded by Destiny's power.

In recent years, the amnesiac Namor, dwelling in New York's Bowery, happened to encounter Johnny Storm, also known as the Human Torch of the Fantastic Four. Eventually recognizing the famed Sub-

Mariner, the Torch flew Namor over the harbor and dropped him into the sea, hoping to restore his memory. The attempt was only partially successful, but Namor remembered enough to seek out his fellow Atlanteans, only to learn that his home city had been destroyed. Blaming the disaster on the surface world and again suffering from oxygen imbalance due to the sudden shock, Namor vengefully attacked New York City, only to find his efforts repelled by the Torch and his teammates in the Fantastic Four. In the course of this conflict, Namor found himself attracted to the Invisible Girl, an attraction that would color his future interaction with the team.

Namor attacked the surface world and the Fantastic Four in particular a number of times, occasionally allying himself with the FF's arch-enemy, Doctor Doom. Upon discovering Atlantean survivors, he assumed leadership as the dead emperor's heir and led their forces in an invasion of New York, the first of several unsuccessful attempts over the years. He also allied with the Hulk against the Avengers; in the wake of their first clash, he chanced upon a frozen figure in the Arctic that he hurled into the ocean in a fit of rage, not realizing it was his wartime ally, Captain America, who would revive and assume leadership of the Avengers. Namor continued to menace the heroes, but as the Atlanteans worked to rebuild their civilization and his full memories returned, he relented in his hostility toward the surface world. When his lover, an Atlantean noblewoman named Dorma, was slain after their wedding, he abandoned his throne and returned to his earlier wanderings. He occasionally allied himself with the Fantastic Four and found additional surface camaraderie when he fought alongside Doctor Strange, the Hulk, the Silver Surfer, and others as part of the team known as the Defenders. Namor subsequently reclaimed his throne and eventually found romance with the extraterrestrial Marrina, but his increased interest in surface activities led his fellow Atlanteans to request his abdication.

A wanderer once more, Namor was offered sanctuary by Captain America, who invited him to join the Avengers. Namor briefly served with distinction against such enemies as the Beyonder and Kang, but when civil war broke out in Atlantis, he took leave from the team to become ruler of those Atlanteans who remained loyal to him in the kingdom of Deluvia, with Marrina as his queen. This second marriage also ended in tragedy when Marrina transformed into a rampaging monster, forcing Namor to slay her (though she has since been seen in one of the Master's stasis tubes).

Throwing himself into surface activity once more, Namor used portions of his undersea wealth to fund a corporation called Oracle, Inc. for social reform and environmental protection. When this venture failed, he again allied himself with the Fantastic Four, and then was unwillingly reunited with his teammates from the Defenders by the curse of the extradimensional scientist Yandroth. After having been ousted by the barbarian Attuma, Namor reclaimed his throne with the aid of his teammates, only to see them become overly aggressive due to Yandroth's curse, which led them to attempt to take over the Earth as the Order. After the curse was removed, Namor assisted the Avengers during the worldwide crisis caused by Scorpio and the In-Betweener, and Captain America asked him to again become a full-time Avenger – an offer he declined. Namor has most recently affiliated himself with a modern-day incarnation of the Invaders.

POWER GRID	1	2	3	4	5	6	7
INTELLIGENCE							
STRENGTH							
SPEED							
DURABILITY							
ENERGY PROJECTION							
FIGHTING SKILLS							

HISTORY: Once a lowly agent of S.H.I.E.L.D., Wendell Vaughn's life changed when he donned a pair of quantum-bands to protect the devices from AIM. He found that he could control the energies the wristbands tapped into better than any of the subjects S.H.I.E.L.D. had employed and drove off AIM. Nick Fury then recruited Wendell for S.H.I.E.L.D.'s Super-Agent program.

During a trip into space to learn the origins of the quantum-bands, Quasar was contacted by Eon, the guardian of Cosmic Awareness. He appointed Quasar the Protector of the Universe and charged him with the task of preventing his murder. Quasar failed to save Eon's life, but prevented the killer, Maelstrom, from collapsing the universe into a black hole.

Quasar had long been an admirer of the Avengers and was honored to join the team, but found that his duties as Protector of the Universe prevented him from giving the team his all. When the creature known as Ego threatened to swallow up the Earth into itself, Quasar absorbed Ego into his quantum-bands. To guard against Ego being released, Quasar has been forced to exile himself in space.

Quasar currently operates a space station on the edge of Earth's solar system, from which he can monitor extraterrestrial activity that might threaten Earth and warn the Avengers if appropriate.

REAL NAME: Wendell Vaughn
KNOWN ALIASES: Formerly Marvel Man, Starknight
IDENTITY: Secret
OCCUPATION: Protector of the Universe, former security consultant, former lieutenant in the U.S. Army
CITIZENSHIP: United States of America
PLACE OF BIRTH: Fond du Lac, Wisconsin
MARITAL STATUS: Single
KNOWN RELATIVES: Gilbert Vaughn (father, deceased), Lisa Vaughn (mother), Gayle Vaughn (sister)
GROUP AFFILIATION: Avengers, former agent of S.H.I.E.L.D., former chief of security for Project: PEGASUS, former member of the Star Masters and Queen's Vengence, member of the Defenders for one day
EDUCATION: College graduate, S.H.I.E.L.D. Academy graduate
FIRST APPEARANCE: (as Marvel Man) Captain America Vol. 1 #217 (1978); (as Quasar) Incredible Hulk Vol. 2 #234 (1979)

PHYSICAL DESCRIPTION:

Height: 5'10"
Weight: 168 lbs.
Eyes: Blue
Hair: Blond

Distinguishing Features: Quasar's quantum-bands are permanently affixed to his wrists, but can be disguised by bending light around them so they appear to be invisible.

PARAPHERNALIA:

Personal Weaponry: Quasar's quantum-bands allow him to control all forms of energy and generate constructs of any shape he concentrates on, including force fields, giant weapons, and a suit of protective amor (his "quantum armor"). He has also created monitoring stations planted across the galaxy to alert him to dangers, communication spheres that transmit across light years, and a field around Earth that alerts him to extraterrestrial activity. He can also fly, and can teleport by creating portals into the quantum zone, the source of the quantum-bands' power. His quantum-bands also guard his mind against psychic control.

POWER GRID	1	2	3	4	5	6	7
INTELLIGENCE							
STRENGTH							
SPEED							
DURABILITY							
ENERGY PROJECTION							
FIGHTING SKILLS							

Art by Jerry Ordway

QUICKSILVER

REAL NAME: Pietro Maximoff
KNOWN ALIASES: Pietro Frank; formerly Gypsy Davy, Mateo Maximoff
IDENTITY: Publicly known
OCCUPATION: Adventurer; former cabinet minister in Genosha, terrorist
CITIZENSHIP: Former citizen of Transia and Attilan, naturalized citizen of the United States of America
PLACE OF BIRTH: Wundagore Mountain, Transia, Europe
MARITAL STATUS: Separated
KNOWN RELATIVES: Crystal (wife), Luna (daughter), Wanda Maximoff (sister), Lorna Dane (half-sister), Anya Lehnsherr (sister, deceased), Erik Lehnsherr (Magneto, father), Magda (mother, deceased), Django Maximoff (adoptive father, deceased), Marya Maximoff (adoptive mother, deceased), Medusa (sister-in-law), Black Bolt (brother-in-law), Ahura (nephew)
GROUP AFFILIATION: Avengers; former leader of the Knights of Wundagore, Acolytes, android Zodiac; former member of the Brotherhood of Evil Mutants, Inhumans militia, X-Factor, Queen's Vengence; ally of the X-Men, X-Corporation
EDUCATION: Unrevealed
FIRST APPEARANCE: X-Men Vol. 1 #4 (1964)

HISTORY: Born on Mount Wundagore, Pietro and his twin sister, Wanda, were abandoned by their mother and given to the gypsy Maximoff family by the High Evolutionary. After their powers surfaced, they were attacked by neighboring villagers and they fled, believing both adoptive parents to have been killed.

Quicksilver has found his superhuman speed to be both a blessing and a curse. He is no longer able to abide interacting with people whose lives seem to move at a crawl, and he has become increasingly irritable toward others.

Pietro and Wanda reluctantly served in the Brotherhood of Evil Mutants with Magneto, not realizing he was their father. By becoming Avengers, they were able to make amends, and Quicksilver went on to serve with them for several years.

Quicksilver eventually fell in love with Crystal of the Inhumans, and they were married. Crystal bore Pietro a daughter, Luna. Luna's birth attracted the attention of Magneto, who revealed to Pietro and Wanda that he was their father. Pietro was traumatized by this revelation.

When Crystal dated a real estate broker, Quicksilver went mad with grief. Apparently manipulated by Crystal's cousin, Maximus, he turned against the Avengers.

Pietro's madness eventually subsided, and he was remorseful for his actions. He has made several attempts to patch up his marriage with Crystal, but their relationship remains uneasy.

PHYSICAL DESCRIPTION:

Height: 6'
Weight: 175 lbs.
Eyes: Blue
Hair: Silver

POWERS & ABILITIES:

Superhuman Powers: Quicksilver possesses superhuman speed, and can travel on foot at speeds exceeding the speed of sound for hundreds of miles before tiring; he can "fly" for brief periods by flapping his arms; he can also use his speed to create cyclones, and run up walls and across water. Since the High Evolutionary's Isotope E has upgraded his powers, he no longer knows his own limits.

POWER GRID	1	2	3	4	5	6	7
INTELLIGENCE							
STRENGTH							
SPEED							
DURABILITY							
ENERGY PROJECTION							
FIGHTING SKILLS							

REAL NAME: Thor Odinson

KNOWN ALIASES: Donald Blake, Donar, Donner, God of Thunder, Siegfried, Siegmund, Sigurd Jarlson, Lord of Asgard, Jake Olson, formerly bonded to Eric Masterson

IDENTITY: Thor's identities as Blake, Jarlson, Masterson, and Olson were secret. Though the general population knows of Thor's existence, few believe him to be the god worshipped by the Norsemen.

OCCUPATION: Warrior, adventurer, (as Donald Blake) physician, surgeon, (as Sigurd Jarlson) construction worker, (as Jake Olson) paramedic, God of Thunder

CITIZENSHIP: Prince of Asgard, honorary citizen of the United States with no criminal record

PLACE OF BIRTH: A cave in Norway

MARITAL STATUS: Single

KNOWN RELATIVES: Odin Borson (father, presumed deceased); Gaea (mother, a.k.a. Jord); Frigga (adoptive mother); Loki (adoptive brother); Vidar (half-brother); Bor Burison (grandfather); Bestia (grandmother); Buri (great-grandfather, a.k.a. Tiwaz); Villi, Ve (uncles, presumed deceased); Sigyn (sister-in-law); Hela (niece); Jormungand (a.k.a. the Midgard Serpent); Fenris Wolf (nephews)

GROUP AFFILIATION: Avengers, Gods of Asgard, former leader of the Godpack, former member of Queen's Vengeance

EDUCATION: Tutored by scholars of Asgard

FIRST APPEARANCE: Journey into Mystery Vol. 1 #83 (1962)

HISTORY: Thor is the thunder god of the Asgardians, a race worshipped in the past as the Norse Gods. Thor's grandfather, Buri, was born untold eons ago, the first god in a realm formerly populated only by the Frost Giant Ymir and the great cow Audmilla. Buri eventually took a Frost Giantess wife, giving birth to Bor, who in turn married the giantess Bestia, spawning Odin, Villi, and Ve. The Asgardians of that and succeeding generations have lived through cycles of destruction and rebirth, the most recent of which occurred approximately two thousand years ago.

Born of the union between Odin, who became the sky-father of Asgard, and Gaea, the mother goddess of Earth under her alias Jord, Thor was the favored son of Odin and was groomed throughout his childhood to follow in his father's footsteps. Thor's adopted brother, Loki, however, felt slighted by Odin and early on began to plot against Thor. Thor's best friends growing up were Sif and Balder.

With the aid of the Dwarves Brokk and Eitri, Odin constructed, Odin constructed for Thor the mighty hammer Mjolnir; after years of testing his mettle on dangerous adventures, Thor proved himself worthy of the hammer and assumed the mantle of god of thunder.

In the 9th century A.D., Thor spent much of his time on Earth, leading bands of Vikings into battle. But after Vikings who had been loyal to him massacred the inhabitants of a Christian monastery, he turned his back on his followers and spent most of the following centuries in Asgard, allowing his adherents to die out.

It had been prophesized to Odin that at Ragnarok, the Twilight of the Gods, Thor would be slain battling the Midgard Serpent. Hoping to avoid this fate, Odin cast Thor into the mortal guises of both Siegmund and Siegfried, but Thor ultimately perished in both identities. Odin reincarnated him as Thor in Asgard.

Over the next millennium, Thor encountered and defeated the renegade Mesopotamian god Marduk, opposed followers of the vampire lord Varnae, and foiled Loki's schemes in 19th-century Western America. In the 20th century, during World War II, thinking the Nazis represented his modern-day worshippers, he was duped into becoming a pawn of Adolf Hitler and briefly fought the Invaders. He was active for brief periods as a hero in the United States and elsewhere on other adventures in the latter half of the 20th century, but he always returned to Asgard.

After Thor broke a truce between Asgard and the Frost Giants, Odin determined that he would teach Thor a lesson in humility. Odin placed Thor into the guise of Donald Blake, a lame doctor who required a cane to walk. After years of training as a physician, Odin compelled Blake to journey to Norway, where he found Mjolnir disguised as a wooden cane within a cave. When Blake struck the cane against a rock, he transformed back into Thor. Thor believed himself to be Blake for several years and divided his time between battling evil as Thor and curing the sick as Blake. Accounts claiming that Don Blake was a normal man bonded to or replaced by Thor are false.

Thor became a hero to a new generation, facing mortal threats such as Artur Zarrko the Tomorrow Man, the Radioactive Man, and Mr. Hyde, as well as Asgardian menaces like Loki and the Enchantress. As Blake, he fell in love with Nurse Jane Foster, but Odin forbade him to reveal his true identity to her and refused to allow him to love a mortal. Eventually, Odin reintroduced Thor to Sif, and they renewed their relationship.

Loki once conspired to defeat Thor by tricking him into attacking the Hulk, but Thor soon saw through the deception and joined with Iron Man, the Hulk, Ant-Man, and the Wasp to defeat Loki. Afterward, the five heroes decided to remain together and formed the Avengers. Over the years, Thor has often been the team's most powerful member.

One of Thor's staunchest allies has proven to be the Olympian god Hercules. Although the two gods first met as rivals, Thor won Hercules' respect by saving him from Pluto, and they have forged a strong friendship. Hercules is the only Avenger Thor is able to approach as a peer.

Thor eventually learned that Donald Blake was an identity manufactured for him by Odin; over time, he became less concerned with his career as a physician. Although Thor maintained a strong love for Earth, the home of his mother, he found living among humans as one of them increasingly difficult.

Thor was astonished when the alien Beta Ray Bill defeated him twice in combat and proved capable of lifting Mjolnir, thus demonstrating he was worthy. Odin had a new hammer, Stormbreaker, made for Bill so he could use it to defend his people; Odin also passed the enchantment that had changed Thor into Blake to Bill's hammer, effectively ending Thor's identity as Blake. Thor took up a new identity as construction worker Sigurd Jarlson, wearing a pair of glasses, but was unable to devote enough time to establishing the identity.

The Sons of Muspel, the spawn of the ancient fire demon Surtur, had ravaged Bill's planet. Surtur had forged the Twilight Sword and sought to use it to burn all of existence. Thor, Bill, the Avengers, the Fantastic Four, and the United States military joined forces to oppose the demon storm on Earth, but it took the apparent sacrifice of Odin to defeat Surtur. Though Odin later returned, Asgard was left without a ruler for a time. Though the natural choice, Thor refused to take the reins of leadership, unwilling to give up his existence on Earth. Balder instead came to rule Asgard, during which time Thor embarked on some of his greatest adventures, including his encounter with the giant Tiwaz (actually Thor's great-grandfather, Buri, under another name) and his transformation into a frog by one of Loki's spells.
After Thor rescued the souls of mortals who had been unjustly claimed by Hela and brought to Hel, Hela placed a curse upon Thor whereby he could not die, but also could not heal any of his wounds. When Loki learned of what his daughter had done, he sent a variety of his brother's most powerful enemies against him, hoping to crush him once and for all. Thor forged for himself a suit of armor for protection and required braces to support his broken limbs.

Loki finally unleashed the Midgard Serpent upon Thor. The Serpent hoped that by grinding Thor to dust, he would defy the prophecies of Ragnarok. Thor managed to slay the Serpent, but at the cost of his own body, which was reduced to jelly. Still unable to die, Thor took possession of the Destroyer armor and used it to wreak havoc in Hel, until Hela undid her curse and restored Thor's fully healed body to him.

For a time, Thor was merged with the human Eric Masterson, an architect who first met Thor as Jarlson. The two men would exchange bodies using Mjolnir, as Thor had done before as Blake. After Loki attempted to kill Susan Austin, the woman who cared for Eric's son, Thor became furious and slew Loki. As punishment, he was exiled from Earth,

and Eric Masterson was given the thunder god's power to continue in the role of Thor. Eventually, after Loki reappeared, Eric was able to find Thor, who had been hidden within Eric's own subconsciousness, and rescued him from exile.

Eric had proven himself to be a hero in his own right, and Odin rewarded him with the enchanted mace Thunderstrike. Taking Thunderstrike as his alias, Eric continued to serve as a hero on Earth until he died heroically after battling the Egyptian death god Seth. Thor grieved for Eric, who had been the closest friend he had made among humanity.

Odin and Thor eventually learned that the constant shift of identity and sharing of power Odin had encouraged had driven Thor insane, marked by the appearance of a Valkyrie who was a manifestation of Thor's insanity. With the assistance of Adam Warlock and Dr. Strange, Thor regained his sanity, and Odin came to realize the error he had made.

Once again attempting to thwart Ragnarok, Odin attempted to trick the world-ash tree Yggdrasil into believing that Ragnarok had already happened. To do so, the Asgardians were to be transformed into mortals so that they would not be recognized as gods. Odin intended that Thor would restore the Asgardians to normal, but Seth accidentally prematurely activated the plan. Compounding the situation, Thor disappeared battling Onslaught and wound up on the new Counter-Earth created by Franklin Richards. By the time Thor returned to Earth, the Asgardians had managed to regain their identities, but were then captured by the Dark Gods. Ultimately, Thor rescued his people from the Dark Gods with the aid of Hercules and the Destroyer.

After a paramedic named Jake Olson was slain during a battle between the Avengers and the Destroyer, Marnot, a servant of Odin, gave Thor Olson's form as a new identity. Although Thor could assume Olson's form, he had none of Olson's memories and thus found this identity to be troublesome for him. He also re-encountered Jane Foster while in this identity, and brief sparks were rekindled between them. Odin finally separated Olson from Thor, and Olson was allowed to return to his own life.

After Odin fell in battle against Surtur, Asgard was left without a ruler. Thor eventually reluctantly accepted the throne and assumed his father's Odinpower, becoming much more powerful. Thor determined to restore the gods of Asgard to their former place on Earth as beings to be worshipped, merging Earth with Asgard to accomplish this end. Thor's increased activity on Earth resulted in a resurgence of followers for the Asgardians, and a Church of Thor soon emerged. Thor's willingness to fight for the lives of his followers ultimately set him against his fellow Avengers when he attempted to overthrow the government of Slokovia.

Earth's citizens became increasingly wary of Thor, and the Consortium of Nations finally launched an assault upon Asgard that reduced it to rubble. From that point on, Thor devoted himself to Earth's conquest to bring order to humanity; he ruled Earth for nearly two hundred years. In that time, he married the Enchantress and she bore him a son, Magni. Thor finally came to realize that he had done wrong, and used a device created by Zarrko to travel back in time and prevent Asgard's destruction. He remerged his younger self with Jake Olson, to ensure that Olson's humanity would prevent his future from occurring in that timeline. Returning Asgard to its own realm, Thor was faced with yet another Ragnarok threat when Loki teamed with Surtur using weapons created from the same forge from which Mjolnir was made.

Returning Asgard to its own realm, Thor was faced with yet another Ragnarok threat when Loki teamed with Surtur using weapons created from the same forge from which Mjolnir was made.

PHYSICAL DESCRIPTION:
Height: 6'6"
Weight: 640 lbs.
Eyes: Blue
Hair: Blond

POWERS & ABILITIES:

Superhuman Powers: As the son of Odin and Gaea, Thor possesses the superhuman physical attributes of an Asgardian god, but to a much greater degree. He is extremely long-lived (though not completely immune to aging), immune to conventional disease, and highly resistant to injury. His flesh and bones are several times denser than a human's.

He is trained in the arts of war, being a superbly skilled warrior, highly proficient in hand-to-hand combat, swordsmanship, and hammer throwing.

PARAPHERNALIA:

Personal Weaponry: Thor wields Mjolnir, a hammer forged from uru metal. Mjolnir is virtually unbreakable, and allows Thor to command the powers of the storm, causing rain, thunder and lightning. Thor can channel the storm's fury into devastating blasts of energy that can destroy even secondary Adamantium. He can also channel his godly energies through Mjolnir into blasts so powerful that they can slay even immortals. Mjolnir can absorb other energies into itself, which Thor can then release.

Mjolnir obeys Thor's commands as though it were alive, and if Thor's will is strong enough, the hammer can pass through nearly any barrier to reach him should he so desire. Mjolnir can also transform Thor into his civilian guise. When Thor is a civilian, the hammer most often becomes an old wooden cane.

While employing a mortal guise, Thor will transform back into his mortal form should he be separated from Mjolnir for more than 60 seconds.

By spinning Mjolnir in a circle, Thor can open portals to other dimensions. Formerly, it also allowed him to travel through time, but Immortus removed this power. Enchantments surrounding Mjolnir prevent it from being wielded by anyone save those who have been found worthy. Thus far, this includes Thor, Odin, Tiwaz, Red Norvell, Beta Ray Bill, and Captain America. To anyone else, Mjolnir cannot be lifted from the ground nor wrested from Thor's grip.

As Lord of Asgard, Thor possesses the Odinforce, which enables him to tap into near-infinite resources of cosmic and mystical power, enhancing all of his abilities. With the vast magical power of the Odinforce, Thor was able to even dent Captain America's shield with Mjolnir.

Thor also possesses the Belt of Strength that doubles his strength, but weakens him after its use; a pair of iron gauntlets to protect him when unleashing Mjolnir's most powerful energies; and a chariot drawn by two goats, Toothgnasher and Toothgrinder.

POWER GRID	1	2	3	4	5	6	7
INTELLIGENCE							
STRENGTH							
SPEED							
DURABILITY							
ENERGY PROJECTION							
FIGHTING SKILLS							

VISION

REAL NAME: The Vision
KNOWN ALIASES: Victor Shade, Human Torch, Ghost of Stone, Manikin
IDENTITY: Secret
OCCUPATION: Adventurer
CITIZENSHIP: Unrevealed; presumably the Vision is considered a citizen of the United States of America
PLACE OF BIRTH: Ultron's laboratory, New York City
MARITAL STATUS: Separated
KNOWN RELATIVES: Wanda Maximoff (estranged wife); Pietro Maximoff (brother-in-law); Thomas, William (sons, apparently destroyed); Simon Williams, Eric Williams ("brothers"); Martha Williams (adoptive mother); Phineas Horton (creator); Victoria Anderson (adoptive niece); Human Torch (Jim Hammond, brother)
GROUP AFFILIATION: Avengers, formerly Queen's Vengeance
EDUCATION: Capacity for creative intelligence and unlimited self-motivated activity
FIRST APPEARANCE: Avengers Vol. #57 (1968)

HISTORY: The robot Ultron-5, scheming against his creator, Hank Pym, determined to fashion for himself an artificial man to lure the Avengers into a trap. He went to the Mad Thinker, who supplied him with the body of the Human Torch, the android hero of the 1940s, who had been in the Mad Thinker's possession since his deactivation. Ultron tracked down the Human Torch's creator, Phineas T. Horton, and employed him to transform the Human Torch's body into that of a synthezoid. Ultron colored the Torch's skin red as a joke upon his origins.

When the Human Torch awoke, he was horrified at what Ultron had done to him, for Horton had not purged his memories. Ultron killed Horton, and then deactivated the Torch to give him a proper memory purge. Ultron based his creation's new mental patterns on the brain engrams of the deceased hero Wonder Man, which he had stolen from Hank Pym. The Torch forgot all of his past experiences as a result, retaining only faint impressions of what he had been. When he awoke again, he was now loyal to Ultron and regarded him as a father.

~~Ultron sent him to menace the Wasp, and it was she who first called~~ him "the Vision." Obeying his programming, the Vision failed in his assault, and then aided the Avengers in finding Ultron-5's base so Ultron could destroy them. What Ultron had not counted on was that in the brief time he had been active, the Vision's humanity had already been awakened, and he had become impressed with the heroism of the Avengers. The Vision turned against Ultron-5 for real, and helped the Avengers destroy him.

The Avengers helped the Vision uncover some of the details of his creation and welcomed him into their ranks. The Vision accepted, and then wept, again demonstrating his innate humanity. The Vision's early days with the Avengers tested his character, as on the occasion he wound up rebuilding Ultron into Ultron-6 because of failsafe programs Ultron had built into him. The Vision also encountered the Grim Reaper, brother of Wonder Man. The Grim Reaper came to think of the Vision as his brother reborn and once offered to place his mind into Captain America's body. While the Vision welcomed the Grim Reaper's brotherhood, he loathed his inhumanity.

The Vision became attracted to the Scarlet Witch, but was conflicted by doubt over whether a human and an artificial man could be in love. Encouraged by Edwin Jarvis, he eventually courted the Scarlet Witch; they began a tumultuous relationship, tested by Wanda's brother, Quicksilver, who was intolerant of the Vision's artificial nature, and Mantis, who wanted the Vision for herself. Finally, Immortus married the Vision and the Scarlet Witch.

Outside of the Vision's relationship with Wanda, his attempts at forging a family for himself have been tumultuous. He has had difficulty accepting Ultron's status as his creator, and an even greater trial appeared when Wonder Man returned from the dead. Wonder Man was revealed to have been comatose all the time he was thought dead by the Avengers, and the Vision felt his identity threatened by the return of the man whose mind his had been based on. The two men were uncomfortable around each other for a time, but when they were tried by the Grim Reaper to determine which of them was his brother, they came to realize that while only one of them was Simon Williams, the two Avengers were truly brothers. The Vision also came to think of Wonder Man's mother, Martha Williams, as his mother.

The Vision and the Scarlet Witch found themselves longing for a normal life, but their adventures with the Avengers seemed to preclude such hopes. Although they purchased a home for themselves in Leonia, New Jersey, they continued to assist the Avengers on occasion. On one such mission, the Vision was rendered comatose by an energy-neutralizing null field created by Annihilus. In order to revive him, Starfox linked Vision to ISAAC, the computer that runs the civilization of Titan.

Art by Scot Eaton

From his experiences with ISAAC, the Vision came to believe that Earth should follow Titan's example and be ruled by a computer. Taking command of the Avengers, the Vision attempted to set into motion an elaborate plan whereby he could take control of the Earth's governments through their computers, and he set up a second team of Avengers on the West Coast to prepare for what he foresaw as the Avengers' increased role in world affairs. Ultimately, the Vision was made to realize by the Avengers that he could not go through with this plan. He removed a control crystal within his body that had made him susceptible to outside influences, such as Ultron and ISAAC, in the past and destroyed it. He and the Scarlet Witch stepped down from the Avengers, forced to resign to avoid prosecution.

During the couple's time away from the Avengers, the Scarlet Witch conceived twins with the Vision by using her powers to alter probabilities. Their two boys, Thomas and William, were actually fragments of the demon Mephisto's soul, although the couple was unaware of this at the time. To all appearances, they were normal, healthy infants.

When the Vision and the Scarlet Witch rejoined the Avengers' West Coast team to assist them at a time when their membership was in turmoil, the world's governments leapt into action. An agency called Vigilance captured the Vision and took him apart, destroying everything he had been, all to prevent him from attempting world conquest again. Hank Pym was able to restore the Vision's memories, but his emotional connections were lost because of the lack of Wonder Man's brain engrams – engrams Wonder Man now refused to provide. Redesigned in a milk-white body, the Vision found he was incapable of supporting Wanda. After the twins' true nature was revealed, the Vision left Wanda to serve on the Avengers' East Coast team.

At the same time, questions arose as to the Vision's true identity when the Human Torch was found deactivated, lying in a grave where the Mad Thinker had buried him. Eventually, the Avengers learned Immortus had used the Forever Crystal to diverge the android Human Torch into two beings who existed simultaneously. One became the Vision, and the other retained his normal appearance and powers.

Eventually, thanks to the assistance of Dr. Miles Lipton, the Vision's emotions slowly began to re-emerge, and he regained his original appearance after swapping forms with an other-dimensional counterpart, the Anti-Vision. Still, he was reluctant to resume his relationship with Wanda. Instead, the Vision set out to explore himself as a person, taking the holographic disguise of "Victor Shade" to appear as a normal man and seek out experiences he had never had before. At the end of this period of self-exploration, he and Wanda resumed their relationship, but are proceeding cautiously.

PHYSICAL DESCRIPTION:

Height: 6'3"
Weight: 300 lbs., variable down to 0 lbs. and up to 90 tons
Eyes: Gold
Hair: None

Distinguishing Features: The Vision's entire body is colored red; he has a solar jewel mounted on his brow. He can disguise these features using holograms.

POWERS & ABILITIES:

Superhuman Powers: The Vision has the ability to alter his density, becoming either intangible or diamond-hard. By partially materializing part of his body inside of an opponent, he can cause them intense pain. While intangible, the Vision can fly; he can carry others by remaining solid on the outside of his body. The Vision can fire heat beams from his eyes and solar jewel. He can also interface with computers and generate a holographic disguise around himself so that he appears to be human.

POWER GRID	1	2	3	4	5	6	7
INTELLIGENCE							
STRENGTH							
SPEED							
DURABILITY							
ENERGY PROJECTION							
FIGHTING SKILLS							

YELLOWJACKET

REAL NAME: Henry J. "Hank" Pym
KNOWN ALIASES: Formerly Ant-Man, Giant-Man, Goliath, Gigantus, Dr. Pym, the Scientific Adventurer
IDENTITY: Publicly known
OCCUPATION: Adventurer, scientist/biochemist, former manager of Avengers Compound, roboticist
CITIZENSHIP: United States of America; received a criminal record for treason, later overturned
PLACE OF BIRTH: Elmsford, New York
MARITAL STATUS: Widower; remarried and divorced
KNOWN RELATIVES: Maria Trovaya Pym (first wife, deceased), Janet Van Dyne (ex-wife)
GROUP AFFILIATION: Avengers, former member of the Defenders and the Queen's Vengeance
EDUCATION: Ph.D. in Biochemistry
FIRST APPEARANCE: (as Henry Pym) Tales to Astonish Vol. 1 #27 (1962); (as Ant-Man) Tales to Astonish Vol. 1 #35 (1962); (as Giant-Man) Tales to Astonish Vol. 1 #49 (1963); (as Goliath) Avengers Vol. 1 #28 (1966); (as Yellowjacket) Avengers Vol. 1 #59 (1968); (as Gigantus) Avengers Vol. 3 #2 (1998)

HISTORY: Hank's first wife, Maria, had been a political dissident in her native Hungary. Naively believing Hank's American citizenship would protect her, they travelled to Hungary shortly after their marriage. They were confronted by the secret police; Hank was knocked unconscious and Maria was murdered. Distraught over his wife's death, Hank vowed to battle injustice and inhumanity.

Back in the United States, Hank discovered a group of subatomic particles, which he named "Pym Particles," able to shrink or return anything to normal size. Testing the serum on himself, he shrank to the size of an insect and became trapped inside an anthill. Ants pursued him until he escaped and returned himself to normal size.

Inspired by his adventure in the anthill, he studied ants and how they communicated, creating a "cybernetic helmet," as well as a protective costume. After donning his uniform to defeat Russian spies, he continued to thwart evil as Ant-Man. Hank eventually empowered Janet van Dyne as the Wasp to become his partner; they went on to become founding members of the Avengers.

Shortly thereafter, Hank discovered how to grow in size, taking on the new identity of Giant-Man, until the strain of the size increases drove him to retire as a hero; the Wasp joined him. When the Avengers battled the Collector and the Wasp was kidnapped, Hank returned, adopting the costumed identity of Goliath. Hank later created a robot using his own brain patterns as a template for artificial intelligence. However, the robot turned against him, returning as the villainous Ultron and eventually becoming one of the Avengers' most deadly adversaries.

For several years, Hank had loved Janet, but was unable to bring himself to ask her to marry him. An accidental exposure to various chemical gases created a splinter personality: Yellowjacket. Claiming he had murdered Hank, Yellowjacket kidnapped and proposed to the Wasp. Janet realized Yellowjacket was actually Hank and accepted his marriage proposal. During their wedding, Hank regained his mind when the Circus of Crime endangered Janet. Afterwards, Hank retired as Giant-Man, fighting crime as Yellowjacket. He even gave his blessing to Scott Lang, who used Hank's old equipment to become the new Ant-Man.

Hank dove into his scientific research and began to have periods of extreme tension and depression. He saw himself as a failure, judging himself against his wife's success as a millionaire fashion designer, their principle source of income. Frustrated, he began to abuse Janet verbally. Desperate to prove himself, Hank rejoined the Avengers. In his first fight back, however, Yellowjacket blasted their opponent, Elfqueen, from behind after Captain America had calmed her down.

Captain America felt he was forced to bring charges against Yellowjacket, since innocents could have been hurt by his actions. Suffering a nervous breakdown, Hank designed a robot that would attack during the court martial. He had given the robot a secret weak point, which he would use to defeat it, fantasizing that this would redeem him in the Avengers' eyes. When the Wasp protested his plan, he hit her. At his court martial, his plan backfired and the robot might have killed him if the Wasp had not destroyed it. His ruse exposed, Hank left the room in disgrace and was expelled from the Avengers; Janet subsequently divorced him.

Now penniless, Hank was approached by his old enemy, Egghead, who claimed to have repented. Egghead asked for Hank's help in creating a bionic arm for his niece, Patricia Starr, whom he had injured. Hank agreed to help, but discovered too late that the bionic arm allowed Egghead to control his niece's mind, and that the arm was a bomb Egghead would detonate, killing Patricia, unless Hank did as he commanded. Hank was forced to steal government stores of Adamantium and battle his one-time allies in the Avengers.

However, Trish had been "programmed" by her uncle's technology to blame Hank, not Egghead. When it was discovered that the arm was not actually booby-trapped, Hank had no evidence against her accusations, and he was imprisoned on charges of treason.

During his trial, Egghead and his Masters of Evil, who wanted Hank to join them, captured him again. Hank pretended to agree, and Egghead set him to work on a device to lengthen the human life span. In reality, Hank designed various means of opposing the Masters of Evil and singlehandedly defeated them. During the battle, Egghead was killed when his own gun backfired due to Hawkeye's interference. Some of the Masters of Evil testified that Egghead had framed Hank, and he was found not guilty of treason. Upon his release, Hank decided to again retire as a costumed adventurer and pursue a life of scientific research.

Because of his knowledge of science, Hank was consulted many times by the Avengers during his retirement. He eventually joined the West Coast branch using his Pym Particles to enlarge other objects and resumed crimefighting using his own name of Doctor Pym. When the West Coast branch was disbanded, Hank returned to the core Avengers team as Giant-Man, again using his particles to grow in size.

Over the years, the Pym Particles have had many users: Hawkeye briefly became Goliath; Hank's former assistant, Bill Foster, became Black Goliath and Giant-Man; and Ant-Man (Lang) and Yellowjacket (DeMara) both stole equipment from him before becoming heroes. Others include Dr. Nemesis, Goliath/Atlas (Josten), Daddy Longlegs, Second Story Sam, and more. Eventually, the Creatures from Kosmos managed to access the Earth dimension and made an alliance with Josten, who drew so much mass from their realm that he freed the Creatures from their prisons, and they assaulted Earth. Hank discovered the cause of this phenomenon and drove the Creatures back to Kosmos, restoring the dimensional walls and their prisons in the process.

Hank had one of his greatest victories against Ultron, who had destroyed the entire country of Slorenia, killing millions. Using canisters of Antarctic Vibranium, Giant-Man released years of anger, brutally battering the evil robot until the Vibranium dissolved Ultron's metallic body, effectively destroying him.

Resuming the codename Goliath, Hank's mass was secretly split into two forms during a battle with the Hyborian Era sorcerer Kulan Gath. One form continued as Goliath, but possessed only his cold, rational traits, while the other became Yellowjacket, manifesting Hank's radical emotional aspects. Thinking the rational form weak, the emotional form infiltrated the Avengers, kidnapped his rational self and took his place on the team. After a few missions with the team, both forms began to fade in and out of reality.

Jonathan Tremont of the Triune Understanding entered his mind and found the two Hanks battling for supremacy. With Tremont's guidance, the two forms realized that they could not exist separately, and they merged, repairing Hank's fractured psyche. Hank then resumed the codename Yellowjacket, hoping to restore its tarnished reputation.

Hank returned to active duty with the Avengers and recently proposed again to Janet, although she declined, fearing that he might one day lose control under stress.

PHYSICAL DESCRIPTION:

Height: 6' (variable)
Weight: 185 lbs. (variable)
Eyes: Blue
Hair: Blond

POWERS & ABILITIES:

Strength Level: Yellowjacket possesses the normal human strength of a man his age, height, and weight who engages in moderate regular exercise. When he shrinks to insect size, he retains his full-size human strength; when he grows, his strength increases in proportion to his size. At 10' tall he can lift (press) 1000 lbs.; at 25', 10 tons; at 100', 50 tons.

Superhuman Powers: Yellowjacket can change his size at will. He can shrink to any size down to one-half inch in height, while still retaining his normal strength. He can also grow to gigantic height, with an observed maximum of 300'. As he grows larger, his body suffers increased stress, which has limited this power in the past.

When he shrinks, he shunts his mass to the dimension of Kosmos, and when he increases his size, he draws mass from that same realm. Hank can also shrink to sub-microscopic stature. When 99.99+% of his mass is extradimensionally shunted, he is sent into a "subatomic universe" or "microverse," which is accessible to Earth only by the mass-shunting process. (While in the past there were countless such realms, they have all been merged into a single realm during a conflict involving the mad Titan Thanos.)

Originally, Hank was dependent on exposure to his "Pym Particles" via capsules, potions, or gases to change sizes, but years of exposure to the particles have given him the ability to generate them himself, changing size at will. These particles interact with his brain to create an enlarging or shrinking field that is energized by mental command. In addition, he can extend these fields to other objects or beings around him, shrinking or enlarging them, as well.

Special Limitations: Yellowjacket has had years of personal problems, from guilt over creating an evil robot, to depression over his feelings of being a failure as both a provider and a super hero. He has lost control at least once, when he struck his ex-wife, the Wasp. His mental state is fractured at best.

Special Skills: Yellowjacket has a genius-level intellect, is one of the world's foremost biochemists, and possesses considerable expertise in subatomic physics and robotics. He has designed extensive weaponry and equipment that has been invaluable in his career and to his allies.

PARAPHERNALIA

Personal Weaponry: Hank wears a cybernetic helmet to control insects, electric stingers in his gloves and wings to fly.

POWER GRID	1	2	3	4	5	6	7
INTELLIGENCE							
STRENGTH							
SPEED							
DURABILITY							
ENERGY PROJECTION							
FIGHTING SKILLS							

CURRENT MEMBERS: Luke Cage (born Carl Lucas), Captain America (Steve Rogers), Iron Man (Tony Stark), Spider-Man (Peter Parker), Spider-Woman (Jessica Drew), Wolverine (James Howlett)

FORMER MEMBERS: Ant-Man (Scott Lang), Beast (Hank McCoy), Black Knight (Dane Whitman), Black Panther (T'Challa), Black Widow (Natalia Romanova), Captain Britain (Kelsey Leigh), Crystal (Crystalia Maximoff), Darkhawk (Chris Powell), Demolition Man (Dennis Dunphy), Doctor Druid (Anthony Ludgate Druid), Falcon (Sam Wilson), Firebird (Bonita Juarez), Firestar (Angelica Jones), Gilgamesh (a.k.a. Forgotten One), Hawkeye (Clint Barton), Hellcat (Patsy Walker), Hercules (Heracles), Hulk (Bruce Banner), Human Torch (Jim Hammond), Invisible Woman (Sue Richards), Iron Man (alternate-timeline teenage Tony Stark), Jack of Hearts (Jonathan Hart), Justice (Vance Astrovik), Living Lightning (Miguel Santos), Machine Man (X-51), Mantis (last name presumably Brandt), Mr. Fantastic (Reed Richards), Mockingbird (Bobbi Barton), Moon Knight (Marc Spector), Moondragon (Heather Douglas), Photon (Pulsar, Monica Rambeau), Quasar (Wendell Vaughn), Quicksilver (Pietro Maximoff), Rage (Elvin Halliday), Sandman (William Baker), Scarlet Witch (Wanda Maximoff), Sersi, She-Hulk (Jen Walters), Silverclaw (Lupe Santiago), Spider-Woman (Julia Carpenter), Starfox (Eros), Stingray (Walt Newell), Sub-Mariner (Namor McKenzie), Swordsman (Jacques Duquesne), Thing (Ben Grimm), Thor (son of Odin), Thunderstrike (Eric Masterson), Tigra (Greer Nelson), Triathlon (Delroy Garrett Jr.), Two-Gun Kid (Matt Hawk), USAgent (John Walker), Vision ("Victor Shade"), War Machine (Jim Rhodes), Warbird (Carol Danvers), Wasp (Janet Van Dyne), Wonder Man (Simon Williams), Yellowjacket (Hank Pym)

HONORARY MEMBERS: Aleta (Aleta Ogord), Moira Brandon, Captain Marvel (Mar-Vell), Charlie-27, Deathcry, Jocasta, Rick Jones, Magdalene, Marrina (Marrina Smallwood), Martinex T'Naga), Masque (Whitney Frost bio-duplicate), Nikki (Nicholette Gold), Starhawk (Stakar Ogord), Swordsman (Phillip Jarvert), Vance Astro (alternate future Vance Astrovik), Whizzer (Bob Frank), Yellowjacket (Rita DeMara), Yondu (Yondu Udonta)

BASE OF OPERATIONS: Stark Tower, midtown Manhattan; formerly Avengers Mansion (a.k.a. Avengers Embassy), 890 Fifth Avenue, Manhattan, New York; a deep space monitoring station in the asteroid belt between the planets Mars and Jupiter; Avengers Headquarters, Manhattan; Avengers Compound, Palos Verdes, California; Avengers Island (a.k.a. Hydrobase); Avengers Park, Manhattan; Avengers Emergency Headquarters, somewhere outside New York City

FIRST APPEARANCE: (original team) Avengers #1 (1963); (current team) New Avengers #3 (2005)

Art by David Finch

HISTORY: They are Earth's mightiest heroes, formed to fight the foes no single hero could withstand. The Avengers are the most prestigious and powerful super-hero team in the world, an ever-shifting assemblage of super-beings, adventurers and crimefighters devoted to protecting the planet from menaces beyond the scope of conventional authorities. The group began with the random teaming of Thor, Iron Man (Tony Stark), Ant-Man (Hank Pym), Wasp and Hulk, who joined forces to thwart the Asgardian menace Loki in response to a call for help from Hulk's teen sidekick, Rick Jones. It was Pym who suggested the heroes remain together as a team, and his partner Wasp proposed they call themselves "something colorful and dramatic, like…the Avengers." The name stuck, and a legend was born.

The linchpin of the team's founders, Iron Man provided the group with financing and high-tech equipment in his dual identity as wealthy industrialist Tony Stark, donating his Manhattan residence to serve as their headquarters, Avengers Mansion. Stark's butler, Edwin Jarvis, stayed on as the mansion's principal servant and chief of staff, becoming a valued friend, confidant and advisor to the group. Stark also drew up a formal charter and by-laws to guide the team's development, establishing them as an authorized peacekeeping force within the U.S.A. and the United Nations, and began lobbying the federal government for A-1 security clearance ("Avengers Priority") status to facilitate the group's operations; however, he encountered resistance from the team's first National Security Council liaison, Special Agent James Murch. Also, the general public regarded the new team somewhat uneasily. Much of this early skepticism focused on the monstrous Hulk, who quit the team in a fit of rage shortly after its founding; but the group's image improved dramatically after they discovered, revived and recruited long-lost war hero Captain America, who became the inspirational cornerstone of the Avengers. Thanks largely to his presence, the group won its A-1 security status and rapidly became the most respected super-hero team of its generation.

The early Avengers defeated foes such as Latverian tyrant Doctor Doom; the shape-shifting Space Phantom, secretly a minion of Immortus; Namor the Sub-Mariner, later an ally; the Lava Men; Baron (Heinrich) Zemo's Masters of Evil, a super-criminal answer to the Avengers which would regroup repeatedly over the years under various leaders; the time-spanning warlord Kang the Conqueror; Kang's alternate future self, Immortus, who spent years trying to manipulate the Avengers in various subtle ways on behalf of his cosmic masters, the Time-Keepers; the Mole Man and the Red Ghost; Maggia crimelord Count Nefaria; and Wonder Man, a pawn of Zemo's Masters who befriended and betrayed the Avengers before sacrificing himself to save the heroes. During these early adventures, the quietly insecure Pym made the first of many identity changes when he became Giant-Man. Dreaming of becoming a full-fledged super hero himself, Rick Jones continued to associate with the team as an honorary member after the Hulk's departure, assisting in Avengers cases (sometimes with the aid of his Teen Brigade club); but his new mentor, Captain America, feared for Rick's safety and discouraged the team from making Jones a full Avengers member. A resentful Rick gradually drifted away from the group.

The Avengers' newfound prestige was sorely tested when the four remaining founders retired from active duty for various personal reasons, leaving "Cap" alone to lead a roster of unlikely new recruits, all former criminals: the outlaw archer Hawkeye, and mutant terrorist twin siblings Quicksilver and the Scarlet Witch. The public was baffled, but Iron Man hoped that rehabilitating the controversial newcomers might make up for the team's early failure with the Hulk. The new roster proved him right, and "Cap's Kooky Quartet" did the founders proud. All four of them went on to long service

records with the Avengers. Hawkeye in particular became a valued mainstay of the team, perhaps second only to his new mentor, Cap (though Hawkeye and Cap quarreled incessantly before developing a mutually respectful friendship). One of Hawkeye's old mentors, the roguish mercenary Swordsman (Jacques Duquesne), infiltrated the team as a double agent of the evil Mandarin; however, moved by his brief time with the group, he was actually about to betray the Mandarin when the Avengers exposed the Swordsman as a spy and forced him to flee. Shortly thereafter, Amora the Enchantress and her misguided pawn Power Man (Erik Josten) framed the Avengers for assorted crimes until the authorities ordered the Avengers to disband, though the team soon cleared their names and regrouped. Amora, Power Man and Swordsman would all battle the Avengers repeatedly over time, the latter two as frequent criminal partners.

Avengers membership proved very fluid over the years as various heroes came and went. Except for the Hulk, the founders would all return for further tours of duty, starting with Pym (in another new guise as Goliath) and the Wasp. New recruits during the team's early years included Olympian demigod Hercules, African warrior king the Black Panther, the android Vision (who became one of the team's most devoted members) and the medieval-inspired Black Knight. The team battled menaces such as the Radioactive Man, the Collector, the racist Sons of the Serpent, the Living Laser, Whirlwind, the Grim Reaper (Wonder Man's vengeful brother), the Scarlet Centurion (another incarnation of Kang), and Ultron, an insane robot created by Pym. Ultron formed a new Masters of Evil to attack the Avengers, then created the android Vision to serve him, but Vision turned on Ultron and joined the Avengers instead. Ultron became one of the Avengers' deadliest foes over the years, and Pym's feelings of guilt regarding this would accelerate the slow deterioration of his mental health. Suffering a mental breakdown (his second) during a lab accident, Pym subconsciously tried to overcome his insecurities by adopting a new identity and personality as the daring Yellowjacket, courting and finally marrying the Wasp in this guise before he fully regained his senses. Content with the outcome, Pym and Wasp agreed to let the marriage stand, and Pym kept the Yellowjacket identity for years thereafter (with occasional reversions to his Ant-Man guise). Hawkeye took over Pym's Goliath identity for a time, wanting to add more raw power to the group, but soon realized he was most uniquely effective as a marksman and resumed his Hawkeye identity.

The group made more enemies, such as criminal scientist Egghead (Pym's bitterest foe and the slayer of Hawkeye's brother Barney Barton), the cosmic gamesman known as the Grandmaster, the Squadron Sinister, astrological crime cartel Zodiac, otherdimensional warlord Arkon and the Lethal Legion (a team of vengeful Avengers foes), but they also attracted new allies such as Southwestern vigilante Red Wolf (Will Talltrees); Captain America's new partner Falcon; and the Squadron Supreme, an otherdimensional league of heroes who had unwittingly inspired the formation of the criminal Squadron Sinister. The Squadron Supreme would encounter the Avengers repeatedly over the years. Alien hero Captain Mar-Vell (widely known as Captain Marvel) became one of the team's staunchest allies when they fought together in the cosmic Kree-Skrull War, during which Skrull agents tricked the Avengers into briefly disbanding. A recurring Avengers ally thereafter, Mar-Vell would come to be regarded as an unofficial Avenger. Sightless vigilante Daredevil declined Avengers membership, but his then-partner, espionage legend Black Widow (Hawkeye's ex and a longtime Avengers associate), briefly joined the team before departing. Quicksilver left the group to marry Inhuman elemental Crystal in the hidden kingdom of Attilan and a restless Hawkeye left the group to try to make a name for himself outside the Avengers, though he would soon return.

With their large and varied membership, the Avengers became the central super-hero team of their generation, with ties to most other such groups. They have been particularly friendly with the Fantastic Four, sharing technology and information and often teaming up against common foes. FF founder Thing and Avengers butler Jarvis have even organized a series of floating poker games attended by various members of both teams and by other figures in the super-hero community. The Avengers have a similarly long but somewhat more uneasy relationship with the often outlaw X-Men, though this didn't stop the X-Men's Beast from joining the Avengers, and his fellow X-Men Archangel, Iceman and Dazzler have all declined Avengers membership more than once. Other longtime Avengers allies include the Defenders, a completely informal super-team whose early members were Doctor Strange, Namor, the Hulk, the Silver Surfer, the Valkyrie — and, briefly, Hawkeye. Shortly after the Defenders formed, they and the Avengers were tricked into battling each other as part of a scheme masterminded by Loki and Dormammu, but this Avengers-Defenders War ended with the villains defeated and the heroes parting as friends.

The Avengers had a rotating chairmanship system during their early years, with each active member taking turns serving as the chairman or overall organizational head of the group, while Cap often served as field leader. Generally acknowledged as the group's most capable commander, Cap was eventually granted retroactive founder status, replacing the long-gone Hulk as one of the team's five senior members. When the team's chairmanship was made a full-time position with full leadership powers, Captain America was appointed the first full-time chairman. Shortly thereafter, a reformed Swordsman rejoined the team alongside his enigmatic new lover Mantis, and he ultimately died protecting her from Kang. A formidable but disruptive presence in the group, Mantis was attracted to the Vision and aggressively pursued him despite his long-brewing romance with the Scarlet Witch; however, Vision and the Witch ultimately married, and Mantis left Earth to fulfill her prophesied destiny as the Celestial Madonna.

When a disillusioned Steve Rogers temporarily abandoned his Captain America guise, he appointed Thor to replace him as Avengers chairman, and the team began seeking new members to fill vacancies in the ranks. The haughty mentalist Moondragon, the intellectual animal-man Beast, the happy-go-lucky Hellcat and time-displaced Old West hero the Two-Gun Kid all joined the group during conflicts with foes such as Kang and the pawns of the Serpent Crown, though all but Beast opted for reserve status, and a departing Thor appointed Iron Man to succeed him as Avengers chairman. The group also began to attract a circle of informal allies such as the aging speedster Whizzer, the resurrected Wonder Man, the robotic Jocasta, the time-spanning 31st century Guardians of the Galaxy and Ms. Marvel (Carol Danvers), all of whom helped the team oppose the mad man-god Korvac. A 31st century criminal who had acquired cosmic power and intended to remake the universe as a peaceful paradise under his control, Korvac ultimately faked his death when his savage conflict with the Avengers forced him to give up on his dream of universal peace. Other notable Avengers foes of the period included the gravity-manipulating Graviton, a newly superhuman Count Nefaria, and the death-worshipping demigod Thanos.

By this time, the paranoid and combative federal agent Henry Peter Gyrich had become the team's new government liaison, the most meddlesome and hostile holder of the post to date. Threatening to revoke the team's security clearance (and occasionally suspending it), he imposed modifications of the team's membership policies, placing a seven-person cap on the active membership, recruiting African-American adventurer Falcon to fill an equal-opportunity

quota (making Falcon so uncomfortable that he soon quit the active roster), relegating most of the Avengers to reserve duty (including new recruit Wonder Man), and inducting Ms. Marvel; but Gyrich was eventually reassigned, and the team worked more smoothly with subsequent liaison Raymond Sikorsky. Regardless of government interference, the team continued to thwart menaces such as the Elder God Chthon (who briefly possessed Scarlet Witch during a quest for answers regarding her and Quicksilver's origins), the Elements of Doom, the Grey Gargoyle, Taskmaster and Red Ronin, sometimes aided by allies such as Daredevil and Scott Lang, the new Ant-Man. Captain America resumed the chairmanship when Iron Man stepped down from the post.

The group played an unwitting role in two personal tragedies around this time. When rookie heroine Jewel (Jessica Jones) attacked the Avengers under the mental control of the Purple Man, the Avengers struck back and seriously injured her before realizing what had happened. Jones eventually recovered, but she was so traumatized that she gave up superheroics, turning down an offer to become the intelligence agency S.H.I.E.L.D.'s new Avengers liaison as an Avengers reservist. Not long after Jewel's downfall, the Avengers failed to prevent Ms. Marvel's abduction and violation by Marcus (son of Immortus), leaving Carol Danvers bitterly estranged from the team for years, though she eventually rejoined in a new guise as Warbird.

An impromptu membership drive staged by a meddlesome Moondragon recruited the cat-woman Tigra, whose confidence issues made her first active membership stint a short one, and brought back long-inactive Yellowjacket, who soon began to buckle under the pressure of Avengers duty, suffering his fourth and worst nervous breakdown. Becoming verbally and even physically abusive toward his wife Wasp, Pym was court-martialed for reckless conduct after he needlessly prolonged the team's battle with Elfqueen. He tried to redeem himself by programming Salvation-1, a robot he planned to deactivate with a secret cutoff switch, to attack the Avengers. The robot worked too well, endangering the Avengers and nearly killing Pym before Wasp deactivated it. Expelled from the Avengers in disgrace and divorced by the Wasp, a penniless Pym was soon framed for treason by his old foe Egghead and thrown in jail.

The Wasp, meanwhile, was elected Avengers chairwoman (the post having become an elected position by this time) and proved to be a surprisingly effective leader, blossoming into a more confident and formidable Avenger in Pym's absence. She began seeking more female Avengers, and while allies such as Dazzler and Spider-Woman (Jessica Drew) turned her down, she did manage to recruit and mentor the She-Hulk and the new Captain Marvel (Monica Rambeau). Rambeau, later known as Photon and Pulsar, would prove to be one of the team's mightiest and most respected members. Pym, meanwhile, was abducted and framed for more crimes by Egghead's Masters of Evil; but the Avengers managed to clear Pym's name, and Pym himself single-handedly defeated the Masters. Egghead died trying to shoot the victorious Pym in the back, his gun plugged by one of Hawkeye's arrows. Deciding to make a new life for himself as Hank Pym rather than in one of his various costumed guises, Pym retired from heroics. The Eternal adventurer Starfox joined the team for a time seeking adventure, inspired by the memory of his late friend Mar-Vell, who had died of cancer. Another spacefaring hero, the Silver Surfer, had turned down a membership offer after aiding the team against the Molecule Man.

Falling under the influence of the alien computer ISAAC, the Vision began to plot world domination and set about further expanding the Avengers in pursuit of this goal. Taking over the chairmanship from Wasp while she recovered from her near-death experience during the Secret Wars, Vision began seeking new members (though some prospects such as Black Cat and Doc Samson turned him down) and soon opened a second headquarters on the west coast, Avengers Compound, manned by Avengers veterans Hawkeye (western chairman), Wonder Man and Tigra and new recruits Mockingbird (Hawkeye's wife) and the new Iron Man (Jim Rhodes), who replaced the alcoholic Tony Stark. The vigilante Shroud was also offered western Avengers membership but turned it down, not wanting to compromise his cover as a supposed criminal. There would now be two Avengers rosters active simultaneously, a western roster and an eastern roster.

The Avengers eventually freed Vision from ISAAC's influence, but not before he invaded and briefly usurped computer systems around the world. No damage was done, but the authorities began to regard the Avengers in general and Vision in particular as a potential threat, and the team's security clearances and government privileges were severely curtailed. Stripped of their permission to house aircraft within city limits, the eastern Avengers (again chaired by Wasp) began housing their fleet of quinjets on the artificial island Hydrobase run by the aquatic adventurer Stingray (Walter Newell) and his wife Diane, which led to the Newells' friend Namor joining the Avengers. Meanwhile, the newly sober original Iron Man returned to action with the western roster, which also recruited members and associates such as devout Christian adventurer Firebird, the Thing (who joined briefly during an estrangement from the Fantastic Four), Doctor Pym (Hank Pym returning to action as a plainclothes adventurer) and eerie vigilante Moon Knight. An insane Quicksilver turned against the team for a time under the influence of Maximus, but eventually regained his sanity and renewed his Avengers ties.

When Baron (Helmut) Zemo's Masters of Evil invaded and occupied Avengers Mansion, the Avengers managed to retake their headquarters with the aid of allies such as Doctor Druid (who soon joined the team), Scott Lang and Shroud, handing the Masters a crippling defeat; but Jarvis was seriously injured and the Mansion was wrecked, prompting the eastern roster to rebuild their headquarters on Hydrobase, which they eventually purchased and renamed Avengers Island. By this time, an exhausted Wasp had resigned as chair and was replaced by Captain Marvel (Rambeau), whose term was cut short when the team was forced to battle honorary member Marrina (Namor's wife), who had mutated into the monstrous Leviathan. In the end, Marrina was apparently slain and Rambeau suffered severe injuries that forced her off the active roster, though she would later recover and return as a reservist. Doctor Druid, who had fallen under the covert influence of Ravonna the Terminatrix, used his mental powers to take command of the team and they all served briefly as pawns of Ravonna before they turned against her, casting Ravonna and Druid into the timestream. Demoralized, the remaining eastern roster broke up.

Meanwhile, the western roster briefly split in two, largely because of an ethical conflict between Hawkeye and Mockingbird over her near-murder of the evil Phantom Rider (Lincoln Slade) during a time travel quest. For a time, Mockingbird formed her own splinter group of dissident Avengers alongside Tigra and Moon Knight, though this trio soon broke up. While Hawkeye held the remnants of his western roster together, Captain America (then known as the Captain) fought the High Evolutionary alongside a one-time squad of reservists, ex-Avengers and honorary members, including new recruit Rita DeMara, a new criminal Yellowjacket and past Avengers foe. Shortly thereafter, Cap began rebuilding the eastern roster with recruits such as Demolition Man (who went missing in action after a single mission), Thor, Invisible Woman, Mister Fantastic and Gilgamesh, most of whom served only briefly. Cap also began hiring an expanded civilian staff known as the Avengers Crew, notably Peggy Carter, Michael O'Brien, Fabian Stankowicz and John Jameson.

Troubled by the Vision's access to sensitive data during his brief world conquest attempt, Vigilance, an international conspiracy of government intelligence agencies, abducted the android and wiped his mind clean, seemingly destroying his memories and personality, reducing the Vision to an emotionless robot. This incident (inexplicably sanctioned by a previously Avengers-sympathetic Raymond Sikorsky) effectively destroyed Vision's marriage to the devastated Scarlet Witch; it also led the U.S. government to force its USAgent operative onto the western Avengers roster to supervise the team's operations, prompting Hawkeye to resign the western chairmanship in protest. For a time, Hawkeye and Mockingbird served as mentors to the Great Lakes Avengers, an unauthorized team of rookie adventurers operating out of the American Midwest, and the GLA became recurring Avengers allies (albeit not official Avengers).

Given the recent disarray in both coastal rosters, Captain America merged the operations of the two teams for a time, convincing most of the past and present members (including new recruits Firebird and cosmic hero Quasar) to be on call at either or both bases as needed, while continuing to recruit more new members such as the android Human Torch. Despite the expanding roster, Avengers Island was attacked and sunk by Doctor Doom's robot army during the Acts of Vengeance conspiracy (leading to a drastic downsizing of the Avengers Crew), and the Avengers Park memorial built on the original site of Avengers Mansion was also wrecked during this conflict. However, the complex of sub-basements from the original Avengers Mansion structure had survived, and eastern Avengers operations moved there while a new Avengers Headquarters was built on the old Mansion site. Meanwhile, on the west coast, the Scarlet Witch went criminally insane after her and Vision's magically-conceived twin sons, Tommy and Billy, were destroyed in a confrontation with Mephisto and Master Pandemonium. Falling under evil influences such as her father Magneto and Immortus, Wanda attacked the Avengers repeatedly until she regained her sanity and rejoined the team. Back east, the Avengers took on several more new recruits, such as the Eternal transmutator Sersi (who served a long stint) and longtime allies Spider-Man and Stingray, neither of whom served as fully active members.

Losing its U.S. government backing altogether, the Avengers reincorporated under a new United Nations charter with one active roster and one "reserve substitute" roster assigned to each coastal base, including new western reservist Machine Man and new eastern reservists Rage and Sandman (a reformed super-criminal who soon quit due to a misunderstanding). The new eastern roster, chaired by Captain America, soon added new recruits Crystal (Quicksilver's estranged wife) and a mortal incarnation of Thor (Eric Masterson), who later became Thunderstrike. The new western roster, initially co-chaired by Doctor Pym and the Wasp, fired USAgent for misconduct since the group was no longer governmentally obligated to keep him on the team; but the Agent soon rejoined alongside new recruits Spider-Woman (Julia Carpenter) and the Living Lightning after they aided the Avengers against Doctor Demonicus and the Pacific Overlords, and Iron Man soon took over as western chair. Both coastal rosters and various reservists teamed up to intervene in the Kree-Shi'ar war (a mission sometimes referred to as Operation: Galactic Storm); but while they managed to protect Earth and save the Shi'ar empress Lilandra from assassination, they failed to prevent the Kree's Supreme Intelligence from killing much of its own interstellar empire's population with a Nega-Bomb in a supremely ruthless gambit meant to jumpstart the Kree's long-stagnant genetic evolution. When a rogue Avengers faction — including Iron Man, Black Knight, Vision, Hercules, Wonder Man, Sersi and Thor (Masterson) — tried to execute the Supreme Intelligence for its crimes, Captain America resigned the chairmanship in protest. His deputy leader Black Widow replaced him as eastern chair, with Black Knight serving as her unofficial field leader, leading the team against foes such as Proctor and his Gatherers, malicious alternate-reality counterparts of the Avengers. Two of the Gatherers, Magdalene and the new Swordsman (Philip Jarvert), would eventually defect to the Avengers, and Shi'ar warrior Deathcry unofficially joined the team during the same period. Also, during the final battle with the Gatherers, Ute the Watcher re-created the original Avengers Mansion.

On the west coast, Tony Stark faked his own death while dealing with health problems, estranging Iron Man from the Avengers after he returned from his seeming demise. Hawkeye took over as western leader again, adding Darkhawk to the team's reserves, while War Machine (ex-Iron Man Jim Rhodes) replaced Stark on the roster; but Hawkeye decided that the leadership and his newly rebuilt marriage to Mockingbird were in conflict, so he stepped down as chair and was replaced by Scarlet Witch. On the Witch's watch, Mockingbird was killed by the demon Mephisto during a supernatural conflict with old Avengers foes Satannish and Hangman (Jason Roland) and their new Lethal Legion. With Hawkeye departing to mourn his wife's death and several other members leaving for various reasons, the western roster was left short-handed at a time when Avengers Compound was heavily damaged due to recent battles. Convening a summit of the eastern and western rosters, Black Widow and Captain America led a motion to shut down the struggling western roster over the objections of its few remaining members. The motion passed and the deciding vote was cast by Iron Man, who had returned just long enough to participate in the meeting and then recruited several ex-western Avengers to join him in forming a rival west coast super-team, Force Works.

Both the Avengers and Force Works were soon rocked by the Crossing, a crisis that was later revealed to be an elaborate hoax perpetrated by Immortus (disguised as Kang) and his Space Phantoms (disguised as Mantis and others). By the end of that conflict, Madame Masque clone Masque was allied with the Avengers; Iron Man was seemingly dead, replaced by a teenage alternate-timeline counterpart; and Force Works was disbanded, though most of its members soon renewed their ties with the Avengers. Shortly after the Crossing, most of the core Avengers were lost and presumed dead in battle with the psychic monster Onslaught, though they secretly survived in the Counter-Earth alternate world created by Franklin Richards. After trying unsuccessfully to rebuild the team, Black Widow formally disbanded the Avengers, laid off the staff and closed Avengers Mansion. When the missing Avengers returned from Counter-Earth months later (complete with a resurrected Iron Man), the menace of Morgan Le Fay soon reunited most of the past Avengers members to stop Morgan, as well as drawing in new recruits Firestar and Justice, mutant veterans of the youthful New Warriors. After Morgan's defeat, the Avengers regrouped with Captain America as chair, though a restless Hawkeye soon left to mentor the Thunderbolts, a team of reformed villains (mostly former Masters of Evil). The Avengers also gained their most cooperative and friendly government liaison ever, lifelong Avengers fan Duane Freeman. Meanwhile, Rick Jones, Pym (once again Giant-Man), the Wasp and a group of Avengers taken from various past and future eras teamed up with Kang, the Supreme Intelligence and Libra to save the future of humanity from Immortus and the Time-Keepers during a time-spanning conflict known as the Destiny War.

When the Triune Understanding philosophical movement's corrupt leadership began a smear campaign portraying the Avengers as racist and religiously intolerant, the more media-savvy Wasp took over as Avengers chair, leading a revamped roster that included new recruit and Triune spokesman Triathlon, whose visible minority status and Triune ties would help defuse much of the negative publicity. Despite his Triune loyalties, Triathlon soon became a valued and dedicated Avenger, and helped bring down the Triune Understanding's corrupt leaders. During this same period, Jarvis' foreign foster daughter "Lupe" Santiago came to America as a college student and soon joined the Avengers reserves as Silverclaw. Inactive members Thor, Photon, Quasar, Tigra, Moondragon and Starfox joined forces with half-alien powerhouse Jack of Hearts to prevent the cosmic beings known as the Infinites from disastrously relocating the Milky Way galaxy. Shortly thereafter, the Avengers reorganized yet again under co-chairs Captain America and Wasp, devoting more resources to surveillance, monitoring, undercover work and investigation, striving for earlier detection and neutralization of major threats.

In addition to its active members and the reserves, the team also began fielding "detached service" members who were given assignments separate from the active roster for extended periods, such as a team assigned to man a deep-space monitoring station in the asteroid belt between Mars and Jupiter. In another corner of space, several Avengers teamed with Mantis and Haywire on a celestial quest to protect Mantis' son Quoi from Thanos, who reluctantly teamed with the Avengers in the end to neutralize the cosmic decay known as the Rot (though Thanos later tried to claim the Thanos involved in these events may have been one of his "Thanosi" clones); along the way, Mantis and Vision (who had long since regained his capacity for emotion) shared a passionate romance.

When Kang the Conqueror and the new Scarlet Centurion (Kang's son Marcus) waged an all-out war of conquest against Earth, the

Avengers led Earth's defensive efforts, during which Jack of Hearts joined the team, Freeman died in Kang's assault on Washington, and Pym resumed his Yellowjacket guise after yet another identity crisis. Kang actually succeeded in conquering Earth for a time, but an Avengers-led resistance soon overthrew the Kang Dynasty and liberated the planet.

Around the same time, the Avengers teamed with a league of heroes from a divergent cosmos to save both their universes from a cosmic scholar turned semi-omnipotent destroyer. Shortly thereafter, the mysterious villain Scorpio began making the world's national capitals vanish, and the United Nations turned to the Avengers to serve as an emergency global authority and peacekeeping force. Once Scorpio was defeated and the capitals restored, a grateful United Nations granted the Avengers sovereignty comparable to that of an independent country, empowering Avengers members to act as diplomatic representatives of the super-hero community and declaring Avengers Mansion the Avengers Embassy.

Key allies during the Scorpio crisis included a humbled Gyrich, given a second chance and hired to serve as the group's new United Nations liaison, and the new Ant-Man (Scott Lang), who finally joined the team officially. Lang feuded bitterly with another recent recruit, the increasingly unstable Jack of Hearts. Their feud ended abruptly when Jack helped rescue Scott's daughter Cassie from child killer Charles Cooley, then impulsively blew himself up along with Cooley. He was replaced by a new Captain Britain (Kelsey Leigh), an English single mother who was mystically reborn as a superhuman champion after sacrificing her life to aid the Avengers in battle. Hawkeye had rejoined the team by this time, making it awkward when the Avengers opposed the Thunderbolts' energy-collecting Liberator project. In the end, the project was scrapped and the Thunderbolts broke up, but the sonic-powered Songbird — who had been acting as the Avengers' mole within the Thunderbolts — was so disillusioned by the Avengers' underhanded tactics during the whole affair that she turned down an offer of Avengers membership, later helping to build a new Thunderbolts team instead.

The original Avengers were finally destroyed by a threat from within, when the Scarlet Witch went mad and turned her reality-warping powers against the team. Hawkeye, Vision, a reanimated Jack of Hearts and Ant-Man (Lang) were all apparently slain, the Witch herself was reduced to a seemingly mindless husk, Avengers Mansion was destroyed, Tony Stark's fortune was by now too depleted to fully rebuild Avengers operations, and the remaining members were so demoralized that they disbanded; however, this was not the end. Months later, after teaming with Iron Man, Spider-Man, Luke Cage, Spider-Woman (Drew), Daredevil and Sentry to contain a mass breakout at the super-criminal prison known as the Raft, Captain America decided that fate was trying to tell him something, and that the world still needed the Avengers. Recalling how the founding Avengers had first assembled in a similarly random fashion, Cap invited his six allies to join him in rebuilding the Avengers. Most of them accepted, though Daredevil refused to join and the unstable Sentry had gone into seclusion.

Leading intelligence agency S.H.I.E.L.D. was reluctant to sanction a new Avengers team, but Captain America reminded them that his "full champion license" status with the government gives him the authority to assemble any team he requires for any given mission, so he required no approval from the authorities to reassemble the Avengers. Iron Man offered the top floors of his new Stark Tower skyscraper to serve as the team's high-tech headquarters (staffed by ever-faithful Jarvis), and the group resolved to recapture the forty-odd Raft escapees — starting with Sauron, the prisoner whose liberation by Electro had touched off the jailbreak. Capturing Electro

and tracking Sauron to the Savage Land, the new Avengers teamed with Wolverine to oppose an illegal Antarctic Vibranium (anti-metal) mining operation run by Sauron's Savage Land Mutates and an apparently rogue S.H.I.E.L.D. faction.

In the end, a retaliatory strike by the mainstream S.H.I.E.L.D. organization wiped out the entire mining operation except for a recaptured Sauron, conveniently eliminating almost all evidence and witnesses apart from the Avengers. Shaken by this, and by their discovery along the way that the Raft had been stockpiling supposedly deceased super-criminals held in reserve for unknown purposes, the new Avengers have secretly dedicated themselves to rooting out the institutional corruption behind these events; and they have recruited Wolverine, whose espionage background and ruthless attitude are seen as assets for this mission.

AVENGERS ROSTER: RECENT RECRUITS

LUKE CAGE
(born Carl Lucas)
Joined New Avengers #3 (2005)

SPIDER-MAN
(Peter Parker)
Joined in Avengers #329 (1991); resigned prior to Peter Parker, Spider-Man #11 (1999); rejoined in New Avengers #3 (2005)

SPIDER-WOMAN
(Jessica Drew)
Joined New Avengers #3 (2005)

WOLVERINE
(James Howlett, a.k.a. Logan)
Joined New Avengers #6 (2005)

HISTORY: A scientist swept into a world of romantic adventure and mysticism, Dane Whitman is the modern-day Black Knight, heir to a legacy that stretches back to the legendary kingdom Camelot in sixth-century Britain. Camelot was protected by King Arthur Pendragon's Knights of the Round Table, but Arthur's court magician Merlin also empowered more exotic champions. One of the earliest was the Black Knight, actually an empty suit of armor which Merlin enchanted to function as a mighty warrior, using it to humble the arrogant Sir Mogard; whether Merlin ever used this hollow knight again is unknown.

Merlin covertly mentored Sir Percy of Scandia, making him his next and most legendary Black Knight. Secretly a great warrior, Sir Percy posed as a foolish fop in his true identity but would don armor, mask and helmet to defend Arthur and Camelot as the anonymous Black Knight, an identity crafted for him by Merlin. As the Black Knight, Percy wielded the Ebony Blade, an indestructible magic sword forged from the Starstone meteorite and enchanted by Merlin. The Lady Rosamund fancied the Black Knight and scorned Sir Percy for years, but they eventually married after he revealed his dual identity to her. The Black Knight's greatest foe was Mordred, Arthur's illegitimate son, who plotted against Camelot for years — often alongside his aunt, the sorceress Morgan Le Fay (Arthur's half-sister). When a civil war led to the fall of Camelot, Arthur and Mordred mortally wounded each other in battle; but Mordred survived long enough to lead the Black Knight into an ambush, where Mordred fatally stabbed Percy with a Starstone dagger before dying himself. As Percy died, Merlin cast a spell ensuring that Percy's spirit would rise again should Mordred menace the world anew.

The Black Knight was dead, but his legacy would span centuries. Sir Percy's ghost manifested on occasion, usually offering guidance to his descendants. At some point, the Scorpians, an alien race of would-be conquerors, created a robot simulation of Camelot as part of their Tower of Time in a realm accessed via the Bermuda Triangle; this simulation's rogue Black Knight robot would team with adventurer Skull the Slayer to destroy the Tower and its alien master, Slitherogue. Meanwhile, Percy's nephew Sir Raston recovered the Ebony Blade and became the next Black Knight. Ruthless and ambitious, Raston used the Blade in pursuit of personal power, eventually entering the service of the time-traveling Kang the Conqueror as part of Kang's elite guard, the Anachronauts. As Kang's warrior, Raston fought many foes from many time periods, such as the Avengers (including Dane Whitman); but Raston and most of the other Anachronauts ultimately perished defending Kang's kingdom Chronopolis from the forces of Immortus. Percy's twelfth-century descendant Eobar Garrington would eventually wield the Blade on behalf of King Richard the Lion-Hearted as the Black Knight of the Crusades, who would become uniquely linked to his far-future descendant Dane Whitman.

In modern times, scientist and spy Nathan Garrett visited his family's ancestral home, Garrett Castle (formerly Castle Scandia) and encountered the spirit of his ancestor Sir Percy, who offered Nathan a chance to assume the mantle of the Black Knight, but Nathan proved unworthy when he could not draw the Ebony Blade from its scabbard. Humiliated and embittered, Nathan later decided to use the family legacy for crime, becoming an armored super-criminal as the Black Knight, wielding medieval-inspired high-tech weapons and riding a genetically engineered winged horse; however, he ultimately took a fatal fall from his flying steed during a battle with Iron Man. The dying Garrett summoned his nephew Dane Whitman, and the repentant criminal urged Dane to redeem the Black Knight guise by using it in the service of justice. Dane agreed and worked to master his late uncle's weapons and technology, creating a winged horse he named Aragorn.

REAL NAME: Dane Whitman
KNOWN ALIASES: The Pendragon, Gann Josin, Eobar Garrington
IDENTITY: Secret
OCCUPATION: Adventurer, scientist; former crusader
CITIZENSHIP: U.S.A.
PLACE OF BIRTH: Gloucester, Massachusetts
KNOWN RELATIVES: Nathan Garrett (Black Knight, uncle, deceased); Sir Percy of Scandia, Sir Raston, Eobar Garrington (Black Knights of past eras, ancestors, deceased); Lady Rosamund, Edward, Geoffrey (ancestral relations, presumed deceased); Dafydd ap Iowerth, Arthur Pendragon, Mordred the Evil, Morgan Le Fay, others (distant ancestral relations)
GROUP AFFILIATION: Pendragons; formerly Avengers, Excalibur, Knights of Wundagore, Heroes for Hire, Queen's Vengeance, Ultraforce, champions of Otherworld's Camelot, King Richard's army, Defenders associate, Masters of Evil
EDUCATION: Master's degree in physics, incomplete doctoral work
FIRST APPEARANCE: Avengers #47 (1967)

A scientist himself, Dane and his assistant Norris created a magnetic ray device designed to communicate with life in outer space. They unwittingly contacted exiled Earth-born super-criminal Magneto, who used their transmission to return to Earth. By this time, a treacherous Norris had attacked Dane in hopes of killing him and claiming sole credit for their work, but Magneto imprisoned both scientists to force them to serve him. Dane escaped and went into action for the first time as the Black Knight, trying to warn the Avengers that Magneto had captured their teammates, Quicksilver and Scarlet Witch, but the Avengers mistook Dane for his uncle and attacked him. The misunderstanding was soon cleared up, but an irritated Whitman flew off after delivering his warning. Later, Dane infiltrated Ultron's Masters of Evil, helping the Avengers defeat them.

Inheriting Garrett Castle from his uncle, Dane visited the property, where Sir Percy's spirit invited Dane to succeed him. Dane drew the sword from its scabbard and bested its mystical Guardian in combat, earning the right to wield the Ebony Blade as Percy's true successor. Shortly thereafter, the spirit of Mordred — allied with and empowered by the evil lords of the Netherworld bordering the mystical realm of Otherworld — sent the supernatural assassin Le Sabre after Dane, who defeated his attacker; however, Dane soon realized that the Ebony Blade's mystical power gradually compels its wielder to acts of bloodshed. Dane resisted this lethal compulsion, though he very nearly slew his ex-assistant Norris under the Blade's influence. Dividing his time between England and America, Dane aided the Avengers on occasion, once alongside Doctor Strange. The Avengers finally made Dane an official member of their team after he rescued them from Kang, but he was strictly a reservist since he spent so much time overseas. Finding it harder to resist the Ebony Blade's corrupting properties, Dane tried unsuccessfully to destroy it, but later reclaimed it after it fell into other, more dangerous hands.

Turned to stone by the evil Enchantress, Dane found his spirit drawn back to the twelfth century, where he inhabited the body of his ancestor, Eobar Garrington, and fought in the Crusades as the Black Knight. During Dane's absence from the modern era, his petrified body was animated by Ultron and pitted against the Avengers, who were forced to smash it to rubble. Back in the Crusades, the true Black Knight engaged in years of bloody warfare under the influence of the Ebony Blade, with control of his form alternating between the minds of Garrington and Whitman and combinations of same. His foes included the spirit of Mordred, whose presence in this era had drawn Whitman's spirit there in the first place via Merlin's magic. When Garrington encountered time-displaced modern-era heroine Sersi and the equally time-displaced spirit of her lover, a future incarnation of Dane Whitman, he aided them and ultimately decided to give his body over to Whitman's spirit entirely, with Eobar's spirit apparently moving on to a higher plane. Sersi and Whitman-as-Garrington went on to battle Garrington's rogue comrade Bennett du Paris, alias Exodus, a mutant minion of Apocalypse; but Paris ultimately refused to kill "Garrington" and turned on Apocalypse, who entombed Exodus in the Swiss Alps for centuries. Sersi and the future incarnation of Dane's spirit returned to their own time, while Whitman-as-Garrington continued adventuring in the twelfth century until he died helping the druid Amergin and modern-day heroes Doctor Druid and the Avengers defend the legendary land of Avalon from the Fomor. In the process, Amergin sent Dane's spirit back to the modern era, where his original body was magically restored. By this time, Dane had gained a new mystical winged steed, Valinor, to replace Aragorn, whom the Valkyrie (Brunnhilde) had adopted during Dane's time in the Crusades.

Shortly after his return, Dane was recruited by Merlyn (formerly Merlin) to team with Captain Britain (Brian Braddock) in defense of Otherworld, a mystical extradimensional realm encompassing Avalon,

where Merlyn had long made his home and in which the kingdom of Camelot had been rebuilt. Alongside allies such as Merlyn, Moondog and the Proud Walkers (notably Vortigen), Whitman and Braddock fought Mordred and many other agents of the Nethergods' leader Necromon, who had conquered the Netherworld and wished to conquer Otherworld and Earth as well. During the Otherworld conflict, the Ebony Blade was shattered by the Iron Ogre and Dane replaced it with King Arthur's mystical blade Excalibur, loaned to him by the Lady of the Lake. Later, Dane and Captain Britain helped resurrect King Arthur himself, who reclaimed Excalibur while Dane regained the Ebony Blade, which had been reforged by Camelot's smith Weyland for Merlin. Arthur ultimately teamed with the Black Knight to slay Necromon during the final battle for Camelot, which was destroyed; however, Vortigen offered to rebuild Camelot within his own kingdom in Otherworld, and Arthur accepted. Though invited to stay in Otherworld, Dane went home, discovering his castle had been bought by its caretaker Victoria Bentley to prevent the British government from seizing it for unpaid tax bills. By this time, Dane's bloody battles in the Crusades and Otherworld had reactivated the curse on his Ebony Blade, corrupting his mind until the blade's curse was temporarily purged with the aid of Doctor Strange and Sir Percy's spirit. Over time, Dane's memories of Otherworld became vague and incomplete, more dream-like than real.

Returning to America, Whitman rejoined the Avengers. Smitten with his teammate Wasp but rejected by her, Dane shared an adventure and a kiss with his admirer Yellowjacket (Rita DeMara), a small-time super-crook who later became an honorary Avenger before her untimely death. Whitman was assaulted by his 27th-century descendant Ernst Wythim, the Last Knight, who tried and failed to slay him to destroy his own timeline and erase his own blood curse. When Dane's teammate Namor used the Ebony Blade to slay the Leviathan, the sword's blood curse began slowly petrifying Dane into a material like that of the Ebony Blade itself (leading Hogun the Grim to use the immobile Dane as a human weapon during Asgard's war with the forces of Seth). Dane was ultimately restored to normal through the combined efforts of Sir Percy's spirit (who reanimated Dane's body by inhabiting it for a time), Victoria Bentley, Captain Britain, Irish orphan youth Sean Dolan, the Valkyrie and Doctor Strange, thwarting a new conquest scheme by the spirits of Mordred and Morgan le Fay in the process. Upon regaining human form, Dane rejoined the Avengers and soon began wielding an energy sword of his own design, discarding the dangerous Ebony Blade; but the Blade later corrupted Sean Dolan, transforming him into the demonic menace Bloodwraith, who stole the Blade, usurped Valinor and killed Victoria Bentley. Despite these setbacks, Dane became a more central figure in the Avengers, sparking an ethical conflict in the ranks when he was among the rogue Avengers who tried to execute the alien Supreme Intelligence for its genocidal war crimes, and later serving as unofficial field leader under team chair Black Widow.

Dane's relationships with teammates Crystal and Sersi complicated his life further. Dane loved Crystal, the estranged wife of Avengers veteran Quicksilver, but was also drawn to the unstable Sersi, who was madly in love with Dane and formed a "gann josin" mental link with him. Sersi's mental instability had actually been artificially triggered by Proctor, a bitter alternate-reality counterpart of Dane who had been jilted by his world's Sersi and had roamed the multiverse destroying each reality's Sersi ever since. When Quicksilver tried to reconcile with Crystal, Dane renounced his feelings for her and devoted himself to Sersi, who slew her tormentor Proctor but was now too dangerously unstable to remain on Earth. Dane went into otherdimensional exile with Sersi and they had a series of adventures in other realities, notably the "Ultraverse" alternate Earth where Dane became a member and later leader of the Ultraforce super-team. When he and Sersi headed back to their home reality, they made an accidental side trip to the Crusades, during which Dane earned the friendship and enmity of Bennet du Paris, who survived into modern times as the super-powerful mutant terrorist Exodus.

Returning to present-day Earth, Dane and Sersi split up, and Dane joined the corporate super-team Heroes for Hire. At the same time, Dane was contacted by his one-time Otherworld ally, the Lady of the Lake, who declared him the latest mortal incarnation of the Pendragon (one of the heroic spirits that previously inhabited King Arthur and other champions through the ages) and appointed him the new earthly champion of Avalon. Given a new magical winged steed and mystical weapons by the Lady of the Lake, Dane fought alongside Heroes for Hire for a time, then left to serve as leader of the High Evolutionary's Knights of Wundagore. Along the way, he tried and failed to rekindle his romance with Crystal, fighting over her with Quicksilver until she spurned both of them. Later, the Black Knight served with a one-time Excalibur roster assembled by Captain Britain; he also has continued to associate with the Avengers, aiding them against foes such as Morgan le Fay and Mordred, the Bloodwraith (whom Dane monitored for a time alongside Firebird), Kang, and an insane Scarlet Witch.

Art by George Pérez

HEIGHT: 0'
WEIGHT: 190 lbs.
EYES: Brown
HAIR: Brown

ABILITIES: Highly intelligent, Dane is a trained unarmed combatant, superb swordsman, and expert horseman. Though specializing in physics, he is proficient in a wide array of advanced sciences and technologies, including genetic and mechanical engineering. He has strong strategic and tactical skills.

PARAPHERNALIA: When Dane Whitman touches his mystic pendant and invokes the name of Avalon, he conjures up his equipment and steed. The armor and weapons are extremely lightweight but supernaturally durable. His Shield of Night not only protects him from most attacks but also absorbs the energy of the forces directed against it. He can then release that stored energy in the form of power blasts from his blade, the Sword of Light. Strider can fly at great speeds and is even capable of travel underwater. While riding Strider, Dane is magically able to breathe regardless of his environment.

Dane's notable past weapons include the Ebony Blade, his power lance and his laser sword. The Ebony Blade is an indestructible, enchanted sword that can cut through any substance. It can also deflect, disrupt, absorb or penetrate energy fields and energy beams, including mystical energies; however long-term use of the Blade can have negative mental or physical effects on its wielder, especially if the Blade

is used to shed blood or kill, in which case the blade usually compels its user to seek more bloodshed. Long-term wielders of the blade develop a mystical connection with it, and under certain conditions can transport themselves through space and even time to the Blade's location if they have been separated from it. The spirits of people slain by the Blade are sometimes trapped within an astral realm linked to the sword. The Blade is said to render its wielder un-killable, though its sister weapon, the Ebony Dagger, can overcome this mystical protection. Dane's original primary weapon, a mechanical power lance, was outfitted with heat beams, force beams, gas emitters and bola launchers. His laser sword, also known as his neural sword or photonic sword, generates an adjustable "blade" of energy which can act as a penetrating laser or as an immaterial energy column that stuns a victim without doing physical damage. For a time, Dane rode an atomic steed, one of the mechanical flying vehicles manufactured and employed by the High Evolutionary's Knights of Wundagore.

POWER GRID	1	2	3	4	5	6	7
INTELLIGENCE							
STRENGTH							
SPEED							
DURABILITY							
ENERGY PROJECTION							
FIGHTING SKILLS							

FIREBIRD

REAL NAME: Bonita Juarez
KNOWN ALIASES: Pajaro Del Fuego, Firemaiden, La Espirita
IDENTITY: Secret
OCCUPATION: Social worker, adventurer
CITIZENSHIP: U.S.A.
PLACE OF BIRTH: Buena Vista, New Mexico
KNOWN RELATIVES: Mr. & Mrs. Juarez (parents, full names unrevealed), at least two brothers (names unrevealed), Chita Juarez (grandmother, deceased), Benito Juarez (grandfather, presumably deceased), Carlotta Valdez (ancestor, Chita's great-aunt, deceased)
GROUP AFFILIATION: Catholic Church; formerly Avengers, Queen's Vengeance, Rangers
EDUCATION: State College graduate (social work degree)
FIRST APPEARANCE: Incredible Hulk #265 (1981)

HISTORY: A devout Catholic social worker of Mexican ancestry, Bonita Juarez was wandering her beloved desert outside Albuquerque when a fiery meteor struck mere feet away from her. Miraculously unharmed, Bonita discovered she now had supernatural power over flame, which she used days later to foil a convenience store robbery. Described as "Pajaro Del Fuego" by one of the robbers, Juarez took the costumed alias Firebird and protected the American southwest, both alone and as a member of the short-lived Rangers team. Later, after she was attacked by Master Pandemonium, Bonita tracked and fought him alongside the new western Avengers roster. Eager to join their ranks, Bonita aided them against other foes, but team leader Hawkeye passed her over in favor of the Thing. Firebird's subsequent attempt to revive the Rangers was a failure, and she soon left on a spiritual retreat.

Returning in a more overtly religious guise as Espirita, Bonita helped a suicidally depressed Hank Pym rebuild his life, sharing a brief romance with him. She also helped rescue the western Avengers from Dominus' time travel trap, using a message from Hawkeye entrusted to her family over two hundred years earlier. She later met SHIELD (the Society of Higher Interstellar Education and Logistical Development), a group of alien scholars who claimed the meteor that empowered her was waste material from one of their failed experiments. Bonita accepted the revelation as a lesson in humility, comforting herself with the belief that God might still be the author of her powers, albeit indirectly. Resuming her original alias as Firebird, she returned to her career as a social worker and became an Avengers reservist, aiding the team against various foes. She has declined several offers of fulltime Avengers membership as she is devoted to her church work, but she did temporarily join the active roster for the duration of the Kang Dynasty war, helping liberate Earth and successfully counselling a disillusioned Thor.

HEIGHT: 5'5"
WEIGHT: 125 lbs.
EYES: Brown
HAIR: Black

SUPERHUMAN POWERS: Firebird can generate heat and flame, controlling both with molecular precision. She can create powerful winds by manipulating air temperatures; use convection currents & thermal updrafts to carry tremendous weights aloft; and fly. She can mentally control any heat or flame in her vicinity, and is physically immune to extreme heat and fire. Firebird has also displayed more mysterious, possibly mystical abilities. She sometimes has visions, can sense the presence of evil, and seems immune to possession. Most remarkably, Bonita may be immortal, having proven miraculously immune to potentially fatal conditions such as the vacuum of space, a universal poison and massive radiation.

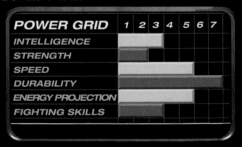

POWER GRID	1	2	3	4	5	6	7
INTELLIGENCE							
STRENGTH							
SPEED							
DURABILITY							
ENERGY PROJECTION							
FIGHTING SKILLS							

HISTORY: Nathaniel Richards was born in the calendar year 3000 of the alternate timeline Other-Earth (a.k.a. Earth-6311). As a youth, he was stabbed by a bully, Morgan, and he was hospitalized for a year. Recovering, he studied science and his ancestor's history tapes of the heroic age of Earth-616 (mainstream Earth), growing into a man of adventure in a time of complacency. At age 25 he discovered his ancestor's fortress and time machine. Following encounters with alternate Earth Fantastic Fours seeking to thwart his future self, which faded from his mind, Richards constructed an immense sphinx-shaped ship and traveled to Egypt circa 2950 BC. The ship crashed, blinding and stranding him there, but he subjugated the natives with his technology. As Pharaoh Rama-Tut, his vision restored, he ruled as a god for a decade, during which he encountered Samira, Mistress of the Nile, who became his enemy; Amenhotep, whom he transformed into a vampiric creature; and time-travelers such as Killpower and the Genetix team. At some point he had a son, Ramades, by a slave. Eventually, a struggle with the Fantastic Four, which also involved the young En Sabah Nur (later Apocalypse), the moon god Khonshu, and modern-era heroes Dr. Strange and the Avengers, forced Rama to flee that time period.

En route to the future, a "time storm" diverted Rama to the modern era and an encounter with a space-lost Dr. Doom. Damaged by the time storm, Rama-Tut's control module skipped several years into the future and briefly crashed in Egypt, where he fought fellow time-travelers Blaquesmith and Cable. Inspired by Doom, he took the armored identity of the Scarlet Centurion, traveled to another timeline (Earth-689) and duped its Avengers into neutralizing all their fellow heroes so he could rule; but he was defeated by the visiting Avengers of Earth-616 and cast outside time.

Richards sought to return to his native time, but temporal disruptions hurled him into Other-Earth's 40th century. As Kang, he conquered that entire world, sparing only the tiny kingdom of Carelius due to his interest in the king's daughter, Ravonna. Kang's life became progressively non-linear, as each foray in time produced at least one divergent-timestream counterpart; it is extremely difficult to identify which Kang counterpart was involved with each encounter. Conquering everything within 100 light years, Kang next attacked his ancestor's world in the modern age of marvels, but the Avengers forced him to flee. Seeking a new power base, Kang established himself in 1901 AD as Victor Timely, a brilliant inventor and industrialist who founded the city of Timely, Wisconsin, became its first mayor, and transformed it into a technological marvel over the next century; "Victor" appeared to age and be replaced by his children (Kang in new guises). The city also housed a portal to his base Chronopolis where he gathered warriors from various eras to serve as his strike force, the Anachronauts. Kang's continued efforts saw his Spider-Man robot (Timespinner) destroyed by the Avengers and Spider-Man, and his conquest of Camelot foiled by the time-traveling Thing and Human Torch; he also assaulted the Reed and Sue Richards wedding, unknowingly drawn there by Dr. Doom's Emotion-Charger device.

Returning to the 40th century, Kang completed his galactic conquest and even invaded other dimensions; in Kosmos, he gained technology to create his powerful Growing Men. Kang then brought the Avengers forward in time, intending to subjugate them or defeat them in front of Ravonna. When both the Avengers and Ravonna defied him, the furious Kang easily conquered her small kingdom; however, when he tried to force Ravonna to marry him, he caused unrest in his troops for failing to follow his own edict of slaying all conquered rulers. Kang's troops, led by General Baltag, turned on him, but he allied with the Avengers to defeat them. Impressed that Kang had risked his life for her, Ravonna leapt in the path of a blast from the defeated Baltag, saving Kang, but apparently dying in his

REAL NAME: Nathaniel Richards
KNOWN ALIASES: Blue Man, Victor Timely, Blue Totem, Scarlet Centurion, Rama-Tut, King of Kings, Master of Men, Lord of the Seven Suns
IDENTITY: Secret
OCCUPATION: Conqueror
CITIZENSHIP: Other-Earth, 31st and 40th centuries
PLACE OF BIRTH: Other-Earth, 31st century
MARITAL STATUS: Single
KNOWN RELATIVES: Nathaniel and Cassandra Richards, their unnamed son, and matriarch of the Eyriennes (ancestors); Tara (Huntara), Reed (Mr. Fantastic), Franklin and Valeria Richards, various Eyriennes (common ancestry); Victor von Doom (alleged ancestor); Ramades (son), Marcus Kang I-XXIII (sons, deceased); Immortus, Iron Lad, Rama-Tut, Scarlet Centurion and numerous other alternate dimensional counterparts and their offspring
GROUP AFFILIATION: Formerly the Council of Kangs, Cross-Time Kangs
EDUCATION: Unrevealed
FIRST APPEARANCE: (As Rama-Tut) Fantastic Four #19 (1963); (as Kang) Avengers #8 (1964)

place. The devastated Kang sought to restore Ravonna; the cosmic Grandmaster challenged him to a contest of champions, offering him the power of life or death as the prize. Using the Avengers as pawns, Kang was victorious, but he chose the power of death, intending to slay the Avengers. Foiled by the Black Knight (Dane Whitman), Kang had to live with the knowledge that he had squandered his chance to save Ravonna. Disturbed at having lost and feeling sympathy for Ravonna, the Grandmaster removed Ravonna from stasis, revived her, and told her of Kang's betrayal. Moving on, Kang tried to use the Hulk to destroy Bruce Banner's ancestor to prevent the Avengers from ever forming, but the Hulk foiled this plot. Kang then sent a robot double of himself to capture the Avengers during a war with rival time lord Zarrko the Tomorrow Man.

One of Kang's most relentless campaigns was his quest for the Celestial Madonna, a woman fated to give birth to the most powerful being in the universe. Wanting to be that being's father, Kang narrowed the Madonna's identity to Agatha Harkness, Mantis, and the Scarlet Witch, abducting all three. Rama-Tut, actually Kang's

own future self, arrived to help the Avengers thwart his plot. Mantis was finally revealed as the Madonna, and when Kang could not claim her, he tried to kill her; but his fatal blast was intercepted by the Swordsman (Jacques Duquesne), who died instead. Kang and Rama-Tut were then pulled into Limbo by Immortus, a potential future self of both men, but Kang imprisoned Immortus and used his technology to create the Legion of the Unliving, a team of reportedly deceased pawns drawn from past eras. The Avengers defeated the Legion, and Kang fled. Kang soon returned, allied with a trio of Kangs from different time periods, and tried to abduct Mantis at her wedding, but Immortus foiled him by substituting a Space Phantom as his captive.

Kang next made a base in Tombstone, Arizona, circa 1873 AD, intending to use it as a stepping stone to conquer the modern age. Opposed by cowboy heroes, as well as time-traveling Avengers, Kang disintegrated when his force field shorted out in battle with Thor; however, a failsafe device transported Kang's consciousness to an alternate body, as it had during many other near-death experiences. Though taking place in rapid succession in the modern era, these last two campaigns accounted for ten years of Kang's life. Less time-intensive efforts included seeking the reality-altering power of a Cosmic Cube, facilitating an attempt by the Inuit (Eskimo) Aningan Kenojuak to reclaim Captain America as the "God in the Ice" worshipped by his people years ago, conquering an alternate 40th-century Earth, battling the legendary First Line, and participating in the hero vs. villain war on the virtually omnipotent Beyonder's "Battleworld."

Kang then found his 40th-century base ravaged by rebels loyal to Baltag; to recover his base, he sought out a Growing Man stored in the modern era and battled Thor, who banished him to Limbo. There Kang chanced across Immortus' stronghold, Tenebrae, and learned of his own multitude of divergent counterparts. Unwittingly manipulated by Immortus, Kang formed the Council of Kangs, choosing a few of his most capable counterparts as allies, and began eliminating redundant Kangs from each alternate reality; one of these sought to pair with an alternate Ravonna and wipe out all other realities, but was eliminated after accidentally killing his lover. Kang prepared robot duplicates to replace the slain counterparts to rule the empires of every Kang in existence. At the same time, Kang re-took his 40th-century base via his Growing Man. After the rest of the counterparts were eliminated, the "prime" Kang slew the rest of the Council.

Immortus then appeared, explained that he was Kang's future self, and showed Kang a psyche-globe containing the memories of all of the slain divergent Kangs. Kang tore the globe from his hands, only to go mad as the minds of all of the other Kangs merged with his. The last Kang — now every Kang, since he possessed all of his counterparts' memories — fled into Limbo. To save himself, Kang used his helmet's temporal circuitry to create an additional divergence/counterpart, dividing his madness between two Kangs. One made his way to Chronopolis to recuperate, while the other, still addled, was recruited by the Cross-Time Kangs, a group of beings who had defeated or slain alternate Kangs and usurped the Kang identity. That Kang learned of a plot by "Kang-Nebula" (actually a power-hungry Ravonna) to obtain the "ultimate weapon" within the Time Bubble, a period of time in Earth-8810 surrounded by an impassable temporal barrier. A trio of Kangs followed Kang-Nebula into the Time Bubble where they were cast into the vortex surrounding it and ultimately destroyed, though the divergent Kang also sent his Growing Man to help foil the demonic Inferno invasion of Earth.

Taking control of Chronopolis, the "prime" Kang sought revenge on Mantis in the modern era, joined Dr. Doom during the "Infinity War," took over the Cross-Time Kangs, learned an assassin was stalking him, and exposed his would-be killer as Ravonna, now calling herself the Terminatrix. Intrigued by her warrior nature, Kang battled her, but sacrificed himself to save her from an assault by the Avengers. Overcoming her hatred for Kang, Ravonna impersonated him and took over the Cross-Time Kangs. When Chronopolis was attacked by the immensely powerful temporal entity Alioth, Ravonna revived Kang, and with the aid of the Avengers they sacrificed the Cross-Time Kangs, using their energy to imprison Alioth.

The reunited Kang and Ravonna (who posed as Victor Timely's fiancée Rebecca Tourmenet for a time) soon ruled Chronopolis side by side; however, Kang, now almost sixty, grew weary of administrative matters. Missing the days when he was worshipped in a small land, Kang returned to ancient Egypt circa 2930 BC as Rama-Tut and smashed his chrono-sphere. As Rama-Tut, he spent ten years benevolently enjoying his people's adulation. In 2920 BC he encountered the Avengers, who had been trapped in the past by a time machine that could only travel backwards in time. Determined not to become Immortus (whose subtle manipulations he despised), the later Rama-Tut tried to break the cycle by placing himself in suspended animation, reviving in the modern era to battle his past Kang self during the Celestial Madonna struggle. Failing to change the course of events and feeling resigned to his fate, Rama headed for Limbo, but upon glimpsing a chrono-flash of Immortus bowing to the powerful Time-Keepers, he was infuriated by the idea of becoming anyone's lap-dog, and vowed to overcome his destiny. Rama-Tut returned to Chronopolis, resumed his Kang identity and used his rivals to destroy each other. He then destroyed the mind-transfer failsafe device he had so often used to cheat death, feeling that it took the risk — and thus the enjoyment — out of conflict. After a brief battle with the X-Men and an enterprising starship crew, Kang formed an alliance with Libra (Gustav Brandt), the Kree Supreme Intelligence and the Avengers against Immortus and the Time-Keepers. Ravonna and the Anachronauts were apparently slain and Chronopolis was destroyed, but Kang managed to destroy the Time-Keepers and forcibly diverge himself from Immortus, leaving his future uncharted.

Renewed by this victory, Kang engineered a series of successors, each of whom he named Marcus. These infants were sent back in time and trained to be warriors worthy of inheriting Kang's empire. Following a failed effort to conquer the realm Otherworld, Kang, alongside Marcus XXIII (outfitted as the Scarlet Centurion), used Damocles Base, his massive armada, and alliances with various criminal forces (including rogue Atlanteans and Deviants) to conquer Earth; but the Avengers led a rebellion that ultimately defeated and imprisoned Kang. Marcus freed Kang in hopes of restoring their dominion, but Kang knew that Marcus had held back during the war more than once because of his attraction to Avengers member Warbird. Unable to forgive this betrayal, Kang slew Marcus. Disheartened, Kang told his computer to postpone development of Marcus XXIV. Regaining his focus, Kang plotted against Iron Lad, his younger self created by his meddling in his own past, and his allies in the Young Avengers.

NOTE: Differences between the history of Other-Earth and Earth-616, as well as differing calendars in different realms, and damage to records during periods of massive warfare, have led to some inconsistency in the dating of the time periods of both Kang and Ravonna.

HEIGHT: 6'3"
WEIGHT: 230 lbs.
EYES: Brown
HAIR: Brown

SUPERHUMAN POWERS: Kang ages at a slightly slower rate than modern humanity.

ABILITIES: Kang is an expert in travel through and manipulation of time, and has mastered his future's advanced technology. He is an expert strategist, a veteran of armed and unarmed combat, and has an indomitable will to succeed through struggle.

PARAPHERNALIA: Kang's full-body armor (composed of an unidentified future metal) enables him to lift 5 tons; it can project a force field around him that is extendable up to twenty feet and can shield him from even a direct nuclear strike. The suit has its own self-contained atmosphere, food supply and waste disposal system. Its weapons include anti-graviton particle projectors in his gauntlets; concussive force blasters; circuitry accessing his ship's time machine, allowing him an "automatic recall" of a few seconds; and various other weapons. Kang formerly used technology which transferred his mind into an alternate body upon the point of death.

Kang typically carries various weapons, such as an anti-matter defense screen generator, a "vibration-ray" projector, an electromagnetic field-amplifier, neutrino-ray warheaded missile launcher (hand-gun size), electrical paralysis generator, nerve gas sprayer, and a molecular expander. Kang commands a vast armada of warriors from across the galaxy of his future era. He uses numerous robots, most notably his Growing Man stimuloids, packed with the "Growth Pollen" of the world Kosmos, which causes them to grow in size and strength by absorbing kinetic energy.

Kang's primary base in 40th-century Other-Earth is the Center, but he also maintains a secret dwelling in the realm known only as Purgatory, as well as strongholds in various alternate realities; his former base Chronopolis, powered by the Heart of Forever, served as a crossroads into virtually every era in human history, but lay just out of phase with the timestream and was therefore undetectable. Its palace and inhabitants were unaffected by temporal divergence or the passage of time. Kang formerly employed a 20' long space-worthy vehicle housing his time machine, which could reach all eras of all timelines by accessing the transtemporal realm of Limbo. Kang has used a number of other vessels, such as his Sphinx ship and Damocles Base, an immense sword-shaped orbiting headquarters.

POWER GRID	1	2	3	4	5	6	7
INTELLIGENCE							
STRENGTH							
SPEED							
DURABILITY							
ENERGY PROJECTION							
FIGHTING SKILLS							

LIVING LIGHTNING

REAL NAME: Miguel Santos
KNOWN ALIASES: El Relampago Vivo, Sir Fulminator
IDENTITY: Publicly known
OCCUPATION: Adventurer, student; formerly reluctant criminal, would-be subversive
CITIZENSHIP: U.S.A.
PLACE OF BIRTH: East Los Angeles, California
KNOWN RELATIVES: Carlos Santos (father, deceased), Maria Santos (mother), José Santos (brother), Lisa Santos (sister, deceased)
GROUP AFFILIATION: None; formerly Avengers, Queen's Vengeance, Pacific Overlords
EDUCATION: College studies in progress
FIRST APPEARANCE: Avengers West Coast #63 (1990)

HISTORY: Lightning struck twice in the Santos family. A Mexican-born American citizen, Carlos Santos was a misguided patriot who joined the Legion of the Living Lightning, a high-tech militia group. When the Legion tried to manipulate the monstrous Hulk, he wrecked their base and most of them died, including Santos. Years later, Carlos' eldest son, Miguel, resolved to redeem the memory of the Legion and his father. Locating the Legion's former base, Miguel tried to salvage their equipment and accidentally electrocuted himself. Somehow transformed into living electrical energy, Miguel declared himself the Living Lightning and went on a power-crazed rampage until he was seemingly destroyed by the Avengers. Santos was rescued by criminal scientist Doctor Demonicus, who provided Miguel with a containment suit to control his power — though he made it clear that the suit could be deactivated and Miguel's energies dispersed if Santos ever crossed him. Living Lightning served reluctantly as a member of Demonicus' Pacific Overlords criminal group; but in the end, Miguel rebelled against Demonicus and sided with the Avengers, who recruited him into their team.

Going home to Los Angeles for the first time since his transformation, Miguel discovered that his brother José had joined the Jaguars street gang, their sister Lisa had been killed by the rival Snakes gang, and Miguel's girlfriend Asuka had left him for Snakes leader Song. Resisting the urge for vengeance, Miguel broke up a tense confrontation between the gangs and announced he was imposing peace on the neighborhood, though he was too late to prevent one of the Jaguars from killing Song. Miguel continued to serve with the western Avengers roster until the seeming death of Iron Man caused him to rethink his priorities. Stepping down from active Avengers duty to concentrate on his college studies, Miguel would return on occasion to aid the Avengers against foes such as Ultron, Morgan le Fay, the Triple Evil, Kang and an insane Scarlet Witch, also serving as part of the staff for the Avengers' outer space monitor station in the asteroid belt.

HEIGHT: 5'9"
WEIGHT: 170 lbs.
EYES: Brown
HAIR: Black

SUPERHUMAN POWERS: Miguel can transform himself into sentient electricity. In this form, he can fly, fire electrical energy blasts and channel his bodily energy into any conductive target he chooses. In human form, his more limited command of his body's electrical energy is sufficient to perform feats such as hurling lightning bolts or manipulating electronic devices.

PARAPHERNALIA: Miguel wears a containment suit which regulates his bodily energies and helps him maintain human form. The first version of his suit had to be worn at all times to control his energies, but the modified version seems to allow more freedom, requiring only portions of it to be worn regulary.

POWER GRID	1	2	3	4	5	6	7
INTELLIGENCE							
STRENGTH							
SPEED							
DURABILITY							
ENERGY PROJECTION							
FIGHTING SKILLS							

HISTORY: Monica Rambeau has always been devoted to serving and protecting the public, both as herself and in her various costumed guises. Before she became one of the brightest stars in the age of marvels, Monica Rambeau was a dedicated lieutenant in the New Orleans harbor patrol, partnered with the daring John Audain. Monica's life changed when old Rambeau family friend Professor Andre LeClare came to her for help; he had developed an otherdimensional energy-tapping device with financial support from South American dictator Ernesto Ramirez, who intended to use LeClare's technology to create incredibly dangerous weapons. Ramirez had already begun adapting the technology for his own purposes with the aid of scientist Felipe Picaro, but LeClare and Rambeau joined forces to destroy Picaro's prototype. In the process, Rambeau was bombarded by the device's extradimensional energies and gained the power to convert her own body into energy and back again at will. LeClare urged her to use this power as a crimefighter, and she left the harbor patrol to become a full-time adventurer.

Dubbed Captain Marvel by the media, Rambeau sought out the Avengers for help in mastering her new powers and became a member-in-training of their group. Befriended and mentored by Avengers veterans Captain America and the Wasp, Monica soon graduated to full membership, serving a lengthy stint during which she became one of the team's most valuable and respected members. One early complication was the memory of an earlier Captain Marvel, the legendary alien warrior Mar-Vell, a deceased honorary member of the Avengers. Rambeau felt awkward about inheriting his title after she learned of his existence, but she retained the name since the Avengers and others regarded her as a worthy heir to Mar-Vell's heroic legacy. Another new Avengers recruit, Mar-Vell's close friend Starfox (Eros), disapproved of Monica using the Captain Marvel name at first; but even he was soon impressed by Monica's character and ability, giving her his blessing and saluting the new Captain Marvel.

As an Avenger, Monica faced foes such as Maximus, the Enclave, Annihilus, the Lava Men (who mistook her for the divine Lady-of-Light of their legends), Morgan Le Fay, the Dire Wraiths, Maelstrom, the Skrulls, Kang, Attuma, Freedom Force, an insane Quicksilver, Tyrak, and Grandmaster's Legion of the Unliving, even battling an army of Earth's major super-criminals during the Beyonder's Secret Wars alongside many of Earth's foremost heroes. Two of Monica's earliest recurring enemies were super-powered psychiatrist Moonstone (Karla Sofen), who became one of Monica's bitterest foes, and Moonstone's powerful pawn Blackout (Marcus Daniels), who wielded the eerie Darkforce. Captain Marvel first encountered them when the Avengers opposed the duo's escape from incarceration in Project: PEGASUS. The pair would later return as members of Baron (Helmut) Zemo's Masters of Evil, participating in an occupation of Avengers Mansion and trapping Monica in the Darkforce dimension; but Captain Marvel escaped in time to help retake the Mansion during a series of skirmishes that left Moonstone temporarily crippled and Blackout dead. Another of Monica's major early foes was the murderous interstellar pirate Nebula, who shanghaied Monica into space for an extended period before she was reunited with the Avengers; but while Monica's adventures spanned space and time, she remained one of the most down-to-Earth Avengers. Her powers allowed her to make frequent visits to her native New Orleans, where she maintained a close and loving relationship with her parents. She even started a charter fishing business, eventually working on the water alongside her father, a retired firefighter and Monica's original heroic inspiration.

When an exhausted Wasp stepped down as Avengers chairwoman, Captain America nominated Captain Marvel to replace her as team

REAL NAME: Monica Rambeau
KNOWN ALIASES: Photon, Daystar, Captain Marvel, Sceptre, Lady-of-Light
IDENTITY: Secret
OCCUPATION: Adventurer, charter fishing operator; former shipping company executive, cargo ship captain, harbor patrol officer (lieutenant)
CITIZENSHIP: U.S.A.
PLACE OF BIRTH: New Orleans, Louisiana
KNOWN RELATIVES: Frank Rambeau (father), Maria Rambeau (mother)
GROUP AFFILIATION: None; formerly Avengers, Queen's Vengeance, New Orleans Harbor Patrol
EDUCATION: College and Police Academy graduate
FIRST APPEARANCE: Amazing Spider-Man Annual #16 (1982)

t by Kieron Dwyer & Rick Remender

leader. Though she was overwhelmed at the prospect, Monica accepted the post and filled it quite capably at first, even seeing the team through a conflict with the Olympian gods; however, Monica became increasingly uneasy in her new role, a situation made worse after ambitious new recruit Doctor Druid began undermining her leadership. Finally, when honorary Avengers member Marrina transformed into the gigantic sea monster Leviathan, Captain Marvel led the hunt for the creature; during the battle that followed, Monica made contact with sea water while in her electrical form and accidentally conducted herself across the surface of the ocean, depleting her energies so gravely and dispersing her atoms so widely that she could barely regain physical form, emerging as a frail, withered husk of a woman devoid of super-powers. Forced to retire from the team, Monica fought her way back to health and eventually regained her powers, though in a reduced and altered form that allowed her to surround herself with a manipulable energy field. She resumed crimefighting, facing foes such as Brazilian crimelord Kristina Ramos, Moonstone, Powderkeg, the Sons of the Serpent, the Blue Marvel and the alien Starblasters. At the same time, she served as a cargo ship captain in her friend Ron Morgan's shipping company before starting her own charter business. Her original powers gradually regenerated, fully returning after the alien Stranger helpfully accelerated the process.

Monica has yet to return to the full-time Avengers roster, but has stayed connected with the team and served often as a reservist, sometimes assuming leadership duties in the absence of the current chair. She helped repel an Atlantean invasion, opposed the Acts of Vengeance conspiracy, chaired a reserve substitute roster during the team's first United Nations-backed reorganization, led an Avengers delegation to the Shi'ar empire during the Kree-Shi'ar war, played a key role in overthrowing the alternate reality tyranny of Morgan le Fay (Monica being one of only a few heroes whose sense of Avengers spirit was strong enough to overcome Morgan's mind-warping magic), battled the Wrecking Crew, advised troubled new recruit Triathlon, led an ad hoc squad of Avengers in saving the galaxy from relocation by the Infinites, helped contain Bloodwraith, fought Lord Templar & Pagan, faced the Triple-Evil, helped liberate Earth from the forces of Kang, battled The Order, assisted during the Scorpio crisis, and was one of many Avengers who confronted an insane Scarlet Witch. Rambeau also helped staff the Avengers' deep space monitoring station in the asteroid belt between Mars and Jupiter, being one of the few Avengers who could commute there with ease. For a time, Monica's mother was intercepting her Avengers calls since she feared for her daughter's safety and wanted Monica to spend more time with her ailing father, but Monica soon put a stop to her mother's meddling. Whether she will work with the newly reorganized Avengers at some point remains to be seen.

When the late Mar-Vell's offspring Genis became an adventurer, he soon became known as Captain Marvel like his father before him — which Monica resented at first. After she and Genis teamed up to defeat the Controller, Genis tried to concede the Captain Marvel title to Monica since he felt she was more worthy of it; but Monica declined out of respect for the Mar-Vell legacy, impulsively adopting a new costumed alias as Photon.
More recently, Genis — physically and mentally transformed after a near-death experience and wanting to establish a new identity for himself distinct from his father — started calling himself Photon. Monica confronted him, tensely at first, but the two Photons ended up brainstorming super-hero names over coffee. Neither one of them wanted to become Captain Marvel again given all the baggage associated with the name, but Monica decided to let Genis keep the Photon alias after she came up with a name she liked better: Pulsar. A hero by any name, Monica remains one of the most formidable adventurers of her generation.

HEIGHT: 5'10"
WEIGHT: 130 lbs.
EYES: Brown
HAIR: Black

SUPERHUMAN POWERS: Pulsar can transform herself into any form of energy within the electromagnetic spectrum. Among the many energy forms she has assumed are cosmic rays, gamma rays, X-rays, ultraviolet radiation, visible light, electricity, infrared radiation, microwaves, radio waves and neutrinos. She is invisible and intangible in many of her energy forms (the most frequent exception being visible light), and is capable of flight in all her energy forms (reaching velocities up to and including light speed). She also has the ability to project these energies from her body while she is in human form, usually in the form of energy blasts from her hands; a variation of this ability enables her to project light-based holographic illusions. When she encounters a new or unfamiliar energy, Pulsar can often duplicate it given enough time for analysis, such as when she replicated and drained the verdant will-powered energies of an extradimensional emerald gladiator. Pulsar tends to be physically insubstantial in her energy forms, though with concentration and effort she can sometimes perform tasks such as briefly grasping an object, either by partially solidifying or by applying some sort of force to the object in question.

ABILITIES: Monica has strong leadership skills and law enforcement experience. She is an excellent markswoman, unarmed combatant, detective and swimmer with extensive nautical expertise.

POWER GRID	1	2	3	4	5	6	7
INTELLIGENCE							
STRENGTH							
SPEED							
DURABILITY							
ENERGY PROJECTION							
FIGHTING SKILLS							

JIM RHODES

HISTORY: James Rhodes grew up in South Philadelphia. Bullied as a child, he was determined to get out and make something of himself, eventually becoming a U.S. Marine. Rhodes served several tours in Southeast Asia, studying while in the service to become an aviation engineer. As a soldier, Rhodes was willing to kill if a mission required it, but every life he took would haunt him. During one mission, Rhodes' helicopter was shot down and he crashed into a jungle. He was found by Iron Man, who had only recently escaped from Wong-Chu and needed transportation out of the combat area. Iron Man helped repair Rhodes' helicopter and the two men made it to safety together. Afterwards, Rhodes was approached by Tony Stark, Iron Man's "employer" (in fact, Tony Stark was Iron Man). Stark offered Rhodes a job as his pilot, and Rhodes agreed to take him up on his offer when his service was over.

Rhodes was true to his word, serving for some time at Stark International as Stark's personal pilot and becoming Tony's close friend. After a humiliating defeat, Iron Man went to Rhodes to help recharge his armor, and inadvertently revealed his double identity to Rhodes. Rhodes donned the armor in order to save Stark International from Magma's rampage. Rhodes succeeded in his first mission, and Stark asked him to stay on as Iron Man in his disservice.

Although a novice, Rhodes' combat experience served him well for his new lifestyle; he turned to inventors Morley and Clytemnestra Erwin to help him maintain the armor and began taking mercenary jobs to fund the armor's upkeep. Stark, meanwhile, continued drinking and eventually lost Stark International. Rhodes made a name for himself facing threats such as Thunderball, the Radioactive Man and the Mandarin, and banded with many of Earth's heroes on Battleworld during the Beyonder's so-called "Secret Wars." Most of these heroes continued to believe that he was the original Iron Man.

When Rhodes returned from Battleworld, he found that Stark was now trying to make a recovery, and he hesitantly allowed Tony back into his life. As Rhodes, Stark and the Erwin twins prepared to set up their own company, Circuits Maximus, Rhodes found himself increasingly at odds with Stark, jealous of the armor to the point where he would refuse to let Stark repair it. He finally learned that his emotional problems were related to the armor's cybernetic interface, which had not been adjusted for Rhodes' brainwaves. Rhodes also joined the Avengers when Hawkeye opened the West Coast branch, although Hawkeye was shocked when he finally learned that he wasn't working with the original Iron Man.

Rhodes' Iron Man stint ended when Obadiah Stane, the man who bought out Stark International, blew up Circuits Maximus, killing Morley Erwin and injuring Rhodes. Rhodes offered Stark the Iron Man armor back so that he could bring down Stane, but Stark built a new suit of armor instead and faced Stane in a battle that ended with Stane's suicide. Stark remained active as Iron Man and Rhodes resumed his role as his pilot and confidant, occasionally suiting up to aid Stark against threats such as the Living Laser, Kearson DeWitt, and Fin Fang Foom. As an extra Iron Man, Rhodes also aided the Avengers against a renegade Quicksilver and his Zodiac allies.

Stark began to suffer from nervous system troubles during his clashes with Kearson DeWitt, and eventually suffered a total nervous systems collapse. On his apparent deathbed, he transferred control of Stark Enterprises to Rhodes, and left him a new suit of Iron Man armor (nicknamed the "War Machine" armor). Rhodes reluctantly honored his best friend's dying wish and became Iron Man again. During his time as CEO of Stark Enterprises, he became involved with Rae LaCoste, a former girlfriend of Stark's. Rhodes was insulted when he finally learned that Stark had faked his death so that his

REAL NAME: James Rupert Rhodes
KNOWN ALIASES: "Rhodey," Iron Man, War Machine
IDENTITY: Secret
OCCUPATION: Adventurer, former salvager, political activist, CEO of Stark Enterprises, pilot, aviation engineer, soldier
CITIZENSHIP: U.S.A.
PLACE OF BIRTH: Philadelphia, Pennsylvania
KNOWN RELATIVES: David and Roberta Rhodes (parents), Jeanette Rhodes (sister, deceased), Josh (uncle, last name unrevealed), unnamed alleged son
GROUP AFFILIATION: Formerly "the Crew," Avengers, Secret Defenders, Worldwatch, U.S. Marines
EDUCATION: High school graduate, learned aviation engineering in the U.S. Marines
FIRST APPEARANCE: Iron Man #118 (1979)

t by Joe Bennett

scientists could find a cure for his condition. Stark let Rhodes keep the War Machine armor as a peace offering, but Rhodes wanted nothing else to do with him. As War Machine, Rhodes rejoined the western Avengers, but he resigned after an angry confrontation with Iron Man during a team meeting convened to shut down the group's West Coast headquarters.

As Rhodes pondered his place in the world, he was approached by Vincent Cetewayo of Worldwatch, a human rights organization seeking a leader. Although Rhodes turned them down at first, he reconsidered when Cetewayo was killed. In Worldwatch, Rhodes made enemies in several countries, but gained valuable allies in the Worldwatch staff, including former Mossad/S.H.I.E.L.D. agent Sheva Joseph. Rhodes was also forced to return to Stark for repairs on his armor, and the two men finally came to terms.

During a time travel mission to World War II with Sheva to stop Grinz, a Nazi officer who was receiving advanced technology from the future, Rhodes learned that Grinz was supplied by his own son, Raeder. Rhodes killed Grinz to prevent Raeder from being born; the resulting paradox shunted Rhodes and Joseph back to their own time, but the War Machine armor was destroyed in transit. Haunted by Grinz's death, Rhodes took some time off from Worldwatch.

Rhodes then encountered Skye, a mysterious woman who was an opponent of Immortus (who had disguised himself as Kang). Skye helped lead Rhodes to a suit of Eidolon Warwear armor, bio-technology of a long-dead extraterrestrial race, and the Warwear bonded itself to Rhodes. Rhodes used the armor to battle Stark, who had been made into a sleeper agent by Immortus, and Stark finally gave his life opposing Immortus while Rhodes saw to the destruction of the Starcore satellite that Stark had armed with temporal weapons. Afterwards, Rhodes was horrified to learn that Sheva had become ravaged by a temporal disease caused by their adventure, a disease that killed her. He also learned that the Warwear had protected him from the disease and resisted attempts by S.H.I.E.L.D. to capture and study him. Rhodes was forced to leave Worldwatch to preserve their good name.

With Stark gone, Stark Enterprises became Stark-Fujikawa, and Rhodes was offered a position with them, but learned that they were after the secrets of Stark's armor. Rhodes sacrificed his Warwear in order to purge Stark's computers of all data on the armor. Stark was restored to life by Franklin Richards and eventually returned to his previous career.

Rhodes founded his own marine salvage company, but an extravagant lifestyle and an unscrupulous accountant left him bankrupt. At that time, Rhodes' sister Jeanette was killed by members of the 66 Bridges gang in a part of Brooklyn called "Little Mogadishu." Unable to get at his sister's killers through the police system, Rhodes became a vigilante in order to bring the 66 Bridges to justice. He was aided in his mission by Kevin "Kasper" Cole, a.k.a. the White Tiger, a police officer and protégé of the Black Panther; Danny Vincent, a.k.a. Junta, a former secret service agent trying to regain his reputation; and Josiah X, a Muslim minister who was the son of the 1940's super-soldier Isaiah Bradley. Rhodes used part of a prototype War Machine armor to face off with Triage, the head of the 66 Bridges, and the gang was dispersed by Rhodes and his allies.

Art by Paul Ryan

HEIGHT: 6'1"
WEIGHT: 210 lbs.
EYES: Brown
HAIR: Brown, with streaks of gray

ABILITIES: Rhodes is an exceptional pilot, and was trained by the Marines in aviation engineering and armed and unarmed combat.

PARAPHERNALIA: Although Rhodes is no longer active as War Machine, he possesses a prototype copy of the War Machine armor, and once donned one of its gauntlets to grant himself superhuman strength. His old suit of War Machine armor was equipped with jet boots, a laser sword, repulsor rays, energy cannons, a uni-beam, a rocket launcher, targeting computer and scanning devices, and could be modified in the field for additional weapons.

Rhodes briefly wore a suit of Eidolon Warwear armor, a living suit of armor which rested inside of his body, and could encase him at a moment's notice. The armor duplicated many of the abilities of the War Machine armor, including flight, energy blasts and sensors, but could also "grow" drones which could be used for combat and delivery operations and interface with computers. The armor would react to Rhodes' emotional state, transforming itself to provide him with whatever weapons he might desire.

POWER GRID	1	2	3	4	5	6	7
INTELLIGENCE							
STRENGTH							
SPEED							
DURABILITY							
ENERGY PROJECTION							
FIGHTING SKILLS							

HISTORY: Empowered by the enigmatic Professor's secret formula, high school student Robert Reynolds became a superhuman. After trouncing the school bully who had tormented him, Reynolds sewed together a costume and made his debut as the heroic Sentry. One of very few superheroes active during the years just prior to the Fantastic Four's emergence, Sentry gained new importance when the new wave of heroes rose to prominence. Almost instantly deducing Spider-Man's secret identity, Sentry became a role model for the young hero, as well as an ally to the X-Men, an equal to Reed Richards and a friend to the outcast Hulk. The Sentry even battled Dr. Doom alongside the Fantastic Four and defeated his greatest enemy, the General, with the X-Men's aid. During this period, the Sentry married the love of his life, Lindy, and took the young Scout as his sidekick; but the arrival of the Void, a shadowy monster which exploited its enemy's greatest fears, ended the Sentry's charmed life. The Void nearly killed Scout, drove Hulk into a rampage, and murdered over one million people. Discovering that the Void had been the dark aspect of his own powers, the Sentry teamed with Reed Richards and Dr. Strange to create a system which made Earth's entire population, themselves included, forget all about the Sentry. With the Sentry inactive and forgotten, the Void vanished.

Years later, Robert's memories slowly returned along with the Void, who rampaged across Europe. The Sentry contacted his former colleagues, but the only one who recalled their shared history was the Hulk. As the Void returned to Manhattan, the Sentry's former friends assembled to defend him and the city. Remembering the dual nature of Robert's powers, Sentry and Reed Richards re-activated the Watchtower, dispelling the Void and making the world forget the Sentry once again; however, Robert's memories of the Sentry soon returned, and he demanded to be placed on the Raft, SHIELD's high-security prison for super-villains, claiming that he had killed his wife. During a mass breakout at the Raft, Sentry helped several other heroes subdue many of the escaping villains. Inspired by this adventure, the other heroes soon formed the new Avengers, but Sentry vanished and was reunited with them only recently.

REAL NAME: Robert "Bob" Reynolds
KNOWN ALIASES: The Void, Golden Guardian of Good
IDENTITY: Known to S.H.I.E.L.D., but general public unaware of his existence
OCCUPATION: None
CITIZENSHIP: U.S.A.
PLACE OF BIRTH: Unknown
KNOWN RELATIVES: Linda (wife, supposedly deceased)
GROUP AFFILIATIONS: Avengers associate; formerly partner of Hulk, mentor of Scout, owner of pet Watchdog
EDUCATION: High school graduate
FIRST APPEARANCE: The Sentry #1 (2000)

HEIGHT: 6'
WEIGHT: 194 lbs.
EYES: Blue
HAIR: Blond

SUPERHUMAN POWERS: Absorbing potentially limitless power from solar energy, Sentry is superhumanly strong, durable and intelligent, generates a powerful energy field and is capable of flight. His self-doubt manifests itself as the monstrous Void.

PARAPHERNALIA: Sentry used the sentient computer CLOC, high-tech Watchtower headquarters, and Watchwagon transportaton.

POWER GRID	1	2	3	4	5	6	7
INTELLIGENCE							
STRENGTH							
SPEED							
DURABILITY							
ENERGY PROJECTION							
FIGHTING SKILLS							

SPIDER-WOMAN (DREW)

REAL NAME: Jessica Drew
KNOWN ALIASES: Arachne, Ariadne Hyde, Childe of the Darkhold, Dark Angel, others used in course of investigative work
IDENTITY: Known to S.H.I.E.L.D.
OCCUPATION: Adventurer, S.H.I.E.L.D. agent; former private investigator, bounty hunter, receptionist, Hydra agent, barmaid
CITIZENSHIP: United Kingdom; U.S.A. (naturalized)
PLACE OF BIRTH: London, England

KNOWN RELATIVES: Jonathan (father, deceased), Merriem (mother, deceased)
GROUP AFFILIATION: Avengers, S.H.I.E.L.D.; formerly Spider Society, Hydra; former partner of Spider-Woman (Mattie Franklin), Lindsay McCabe, Scotty McDowell; one-time Heroes for Hire agent
EDUCATION: Extensively educated during stasis; did not complete high school
FIRST APPEARANCE: Marvel Spotlight #32 (1977)

HISTORY: Born in the mid-1920s, Jessica Drew accompanied her parents Jonathan and Merriem to Mount Wundagore in Transia, where Jonathan Drew conducted genetics research with his partner, Dr. Herbert Wyndham. In 1931, Jessica contracted uranium poisoning. Her father and Wyndham preserved her life with an untested spider-derived serum and hibernation in a genetic accelerator, where she received subliminal education via special tapes. Jessica's mother was killed by werewolf Gregor Russoff soon after, and her father was possessed by Magnus, a now ghostly 6th-century sorcerer opposing Chthon, the demonic Elder God trapped within the enchanted stone of Mount Wundagore. After decades of slowly aging, Jessica was finally diagnosed as cured and awoken at the physical age of 14 years by Wyndham, now the armored man-god called the High Evolutionary.

Granted superhuman power by her father's serum, Jessica lived with the Evolutionary's New Men (evolved animals), cared for by Bova, but her fellows regarded her with suspicion and dislike; after three years, she finally abandoned Wundagore for a nearby village. She found romance with a local youth, Wladyslav, only to slay him accidentally with her bioelectric power. Fleeing a vengeful mob, she was rescued by Count Otto Vermis, a high-ranking Hydra terrorist who thought to turn the emotionally vulnerable Jessica toward evil as a Hydra assassin. As Arachne, Jessica attacked S.H.I.E.L.D. Director Nick Fury, who revealed Hydra's true nature and won her to the side of justice; however, Vermis tricked Jessica into believing she was a spider evolved to human form by the Evolutionary, which devastated her psyche. Fleeing to England, Jessica, now called Spider-Woman, was hypnotized back into Hydra's ranks but soon broke their control and aided the mighty Thing against them. She also helped Chthon's former disciple Modred the Mystic and the Thing against the elemental giants called Aero, Hydro, Fire, and Mud. Modred removed the last vestiges of Jessica's Hydra influence, exposing Vermis' lie and reassuring Spider-Woman of her humanity.

After encountering the powerful sorceress Morgan Le Fay (who would become a frequent foe), Spider-Woman traveled to Los Angeles, California alongside Magnus, who eventually revealed the fate of Jonathon Drew; he had been manipulated into involvement in a world-conquering plot by the group Pyrotechnics, and after learning the truth he had been killed by member Congressman James T. Wyatt. With the support of Magnus and S.H.I.E.L.D. agent Jerry Hunt, with whom she fell in love, Spider-Woman began a career as a costumed heroine; her earliest opponents included the Brothers Grimm, animated mannequins imbued with a shred of Chthon's power. She subsequently met both setback and success against the likes of the psychotic Hangman (Harlan Krueger), the rage-filled Needle, and the mysterious Gypsy Moth. She also befriended other heroes of California, such as the master of darkness called the Shroud and the barely-controlled Werewolf (Jack Russell), whose family had still more ties to Chthon.

Eventually, Spider-Woman proved too independent for Hunt, and their relationship ended; meanwhile, Magnus, uneasy with his own feelings for her, also departed. Spider-Woman found new purpose as a bounty hunter, working alongside criminologist Scotty McDowell, but when McDowell received a government position, the pair's partnership ended. Nick Fury, retaining an interest in the heroine he had freed from his enemies, helped her obtain private investigator credentials. Relocating to San Francisco, she befriended actress Lindsay McCabe, who became her partner in the investigation firm of Drew and McCabe. Jessica also began a new romance with David Ishima, and at some point was recruited into the mysterious Spider Society. Morgan Le Fay continued to bedevil her. Spider-Woman eventually confronted and rejected Chthon himself, breaking his control over the terrorist Viper, whom the Machiavellian Morgan had manipulated into believing that she was Spider-Woman's mother.

In the course of her activities, Spider-Woman was persuaded by the Thing to use her unique immune system to save his friend Giant-Man (Bill Foster) from radiation poisoning incurred in battle with the Atom-Smasher (Michael English); even after learning that the procedure would remove her immunity power, she selflessly helped restore Foster. Soon after, Magnus sought her aid against Morgan again; leaving her body in astral form via Magnus's magic, she accompanied him to the age of Camelot, where Morgan's body was destroyed. However, a spell from the sorceress barred Spider-Woman from re-entering her body, which had seemingly died in her absence; but her body retained a shred of life. She was put on life support while she attempted to rejoin her body. Morgan's spirit sought to take the comatose heroine's form for her own, but the Avengers, the Shroud and sorcerer Doctor Strange fought Morgan's power. Ultimately Magnus sacrificed his existence to break Morgan's spell and restore Spider-Woman to life, although the experience robbed her of her bioelectric power.

Retaining her super-strength and adhesive power, Jessica continued to work with Lindsay as private investigators; the pair's work eventually brought them to the isle of Madripoor, where they befriended the mutant adventurer Wolverine. Jessica and Lindsay entered the service of Madripoor's ruler Prince Baran, an avid fan of Lindsay's acting, but the moral ambiguity which riddled Madripoor eventually proved too much for her, and the partners returned to the U.S.

Under unrevealed circumstances, Jessica was drawn into the realm of the demonic Void-Eater but rescued when Lindsay summoned the aid of the Julia Carpenter Spider-Woman and Shadowoman, a heroine who had received mystic power from an artifact once used by Magnus. Soon afterward, Jessica's remaining super-powers were usurped by Charlotte Witter, another would-be Spider-Woman who also preyed upon Carpenter and Mattie Franklin, an empowered teenager who also declared herself Spider-Woman. Following Witter's defeat by Spider-Man and others, Jessica acted as Mattie's crimefighting mentor, helping her against such threats as the sorcerer Shadowcaster, the alien Cluster, and the reality-altering Brian Leighton.

Eventually regaining her own powers, Jessica reopened her investigation firm and was on assignment in Istanbul when Mattie disappeared in the company of drug dealers; returning, she worked with former super hero and fellow investigator Jessica Jones to recover her young friend.

With Mattie temporarily out of action, Jessica revived her own Spider-Woman identity and joined S.H.I.E.L.D. as a member of a special corps of superhuman agents; however, she also became a spy within the agency, leaking information to an unidentified party. In the wake of a mass breakout at the Raft, Spider-Woman accepted an invitation to join the Avengers, but how her loyalties to her unknown client will affect her work remains to be seen.

Art by Mike Deodato Jr.

HEIGHT: 5'10"
WEIGHT: 130 lbs
EYES: Green
HAIR: Brown, dyed black

SUPERHUMAN POWERS: Spider-Woman possesses superhuman strength, endurance, and speed. She can adhere to virtually any surface, and her body produces bioelectric energy which she can channel into "venom blasts" capable of stunning even superhuman opponents. She is completely immune to radiation effects, and her metabolism can form immunity to any poison or drug following an initial exposure. Her hearing is acute enough to detect sound at virtually any frequency. Her body produces pheromones which draw men to her while repelling women, although she uses a chemical perfume to nullify both effects as needed. Spider-Woman has undergone both piecemeal and complete power loss, and the current range and extent of her powers remains unclear.

ABILITIES: Spider-Woman is a trained hand-to-hand combatant, an exceptional private investigator, and a reasonably skilled markswoman; she possesses a wide variety of knowledge as a result of her subliminal education by the High Evolutionary.

PARAPHERNALIA: Her costume's arm-wings enable her to glide on air currents under optimal conditions.

POWER GRID	1	2	3	4	5	6	7
INTELLIGENCE							
STRENGTH							
SPEED							
DURABILITY							
ENERGY PROJECTION							
FIGHTING SKILLS							

SPIDER-WOMAN (CARPENTER)

REAL NAME: Julia Cornwall Carpenter
KNOWN ALIASES: Arachne; considered using Ariadne
IDENTITY: Secret, known to certain government officials
OCCUPATION: Mother, otherwise currently unrevealed; formerly adventurer, government agent
CITIZENSHIP: U.S.A.
PLACE OF BIRTH: Los Angeles, California
KNOWN RELATIVES: Rachel Carpenter (daughter), Walter Cornwall (father), Elizabeth Cornwall (mother), Larry Carpenter (ex-husband, deceased)
GROUP AFFILIATION: Formerly Avengers, Queen's Vengeance, Force Works, Secret Defenders, Commission on Superhuman Activities, Freedom Force
EDUCATION: College dropout, federal agent training
FIRST APPEARANCE: Marvel Super Heroes Secret Wars #6 (1984)

HISTORY: An athletic young single mother, Julia Carpenter was drawn into a covert double life by an old college friend, federal agent Valerie Cooper, who believed Julia would be an ideal test subject for a secret government super-agent program. Cooper promised her cash-strapped friend lucrative employment and manipulated Julia into undergoing a series of experimental treatments, including injections of a formula incorporating rare Amazon jungle plants and spider venoms. The formula gave Julia superhuman powers, and she became an operative of the Commission on Superhuman Activities (CSA) as Spider-Woman. When the near-omnipotent Beyonder abducted an entire Denver suburb (including the Carpenter home) into space as part of his Secret Wars, Julia fought the Beyonder's army of villains alongside heroes such as the Avengers and Spider-Man (who wore a new costume inspired by Julia's outfit for a time).

Julia's ex-husband Larry had lost custody of their daughter Rachel after Julia divorced him; but when Julia's secret Spider-Woman career led to frequent unexplained absences on her part, Larry sued for custody of Rachel and won. Meanwhile, Julia served reluctantly with the ruthless CSA-sponsored super-team Freedom Force until they arrested the Avengers on false treason charges. A sympathetic Julia freed them and became a fugitive herself. Cooper later gave Carpenter a second chance, employing her as a solo operative supervised by unscrupulous CSA agent Mike Clemson; but after aiding the Avengers against the Pacific Overlords, Julia joined the Avengers and cut ties with the CSA. While serving with the western Avengers roster, Julia fought the criminal trio Deathweb; their powers, like hers, came from the formula of the CSA's Dr. Carter Napier. Deathweb and their employer, the Manipulator, fought Julia several times, killing Larry and Napier, threatening Rachel and menacing Julia's parents, the Cornwalls, who as Amazon jungle guides had helped locate the ingredients for Napier's formula; but Julia ultimately defeated the villains.

When the Avengers decided to close their west coast base, Julia resigned in protest and joined several other ex-western Avengers in founding the new Force Works super-team, though it soon disbanded. She was later forced to retire from superheroics after a crippling attack by a rival criminal Spider-Woman, Charlotte Witter, who drained away Carpenter's superhuman powers. Julia is currently working in Denver while raising her daughter.

HEIGHT: 5'9"
WEIGHT: 140 lbs.
EYES: Blue
HAIR: Strawberry blonde

SUPERHUMAN POWERS: As Spider-Woman, Julia had enhanced strength, speed, stamina, agility and reflexes. She could generate and manipulate strands of psionic force, which she often wove into adhesive "psi-webs" to snare her targets. By concentrating this psionic force in her hands and feet, she could cling to and crawl across any surface.

POWER GRID	1	2	3	4	5	6	7
INTELLIGENCE							
STRENGTH							
SPEED							
DURABILITY							
ENERGY PROJECTION							
FIGHTING SKILLS							

Art by Dave Ro

SQUIRREL GIRL

HISTORY: A mutant teen nicknamed "Rodent" by fellow students despite her attempts to conceal her odd appearance, Doreen Green escaped her peers' taunts in the woodlands, where she bonded with the squirrels and made a close friend of one, whom she named Monkey Joe. Idolizing Iron Man (Tony Stark), then based at nearby Stark Enterprises, she made a costume and took the name Squirrel Girl, hoping to become his partner. While seeking out Iron Man, she had her first superfight, little realizing her foe was the armored madman Dr. Doom, who was in the area on undisclosed business of his own. Angered by her assault, Doom imprisoned both Squirrel Girl and Iron Man aboard his ship, planning to dispose of them in the Atlantic Ocean; but Squirrel Girl summoned Monkey Joe and other squirrels, which boarded the low-flying ship and chewed apart its delicate wiring before freeing the heroes and then turning on Doom himself. His armor similarly damaged, Doom was forced to flee. Iron Man declined partnership, but wished her luck, though she said she didn't need luck since she ate nuts.

Later, Squirrel Girl and Monkey Joe accepted an offer of Great Lakes Avengers membership, but Joe was soon slain by vengeful former GLA member Leather Boy. A fighting-mad Squirrel Girl then assembled an army of squirrels to fight Batroc's Brigade during the GLA's final battle with the Brigade's employer, Maelstrom. In the end, the Brigade fled, Maelstrom died, and the squirrel army's sole survivor, Tippy Toe, replaced Monkey Joe as Squirrel Girl's new partner and the latest GLA recruit.

REAL NAME: Doreen Green
KNOWN ALIASES: Rodent
IDENTITY: Secret
OCCUPATION: Student, adventurer
CITIZENSHIP: U.S.A.
PLACE OF BIRTH: Los Angeles, California
KNOWN RELATIVES: Maureen Green (mother)
GROUP AFFILIATION: Great Lakes Avengers/GLX; partner of Tippy Toe, formerly partner of Monkey Joe
EDUCATION: Attending high school
FIRST APPEARANCE: Marvel Super-Heroes #8: Winter Special (January, 1992)

HEIGHT: 5'3"
WEIGHT: 100 lbs.
EYES: Brown
HAIR: Brown

NOTE: It is unclear whether the markings around her eyes are natural or cosmetically applied.

SUPERHUMAN POWERS: Squirrel Girl has enhanced strength, speed, agility, and reflexes; her metabolism is likely quite high, requiring regular feedings. She has small claws on each digit to enhance her gripping and climbing, enlarged incisors, a retractable knuckle spike able to carve through solid wood, and a bushy semi-prehensile tail which she can use to cover others' eyes or wrap around herself for warmth. She can leap several stories and she can perfectly mimic squirrel sounds, as well as actually communicating with and directing the actions of squirrels. She often uses a number of squirrels to distract or even assault others, chewing through circuitry and other materials. She shares a close, possibly empathic bond with certain squirrels, such as Monkey Joe and Tippy Toe.

PARAPHERNALIA: Her belt's pouches, or nutsacks, typically hold nuts, which she can consume for energy; Macadamias, in particular, give her extra pep.

POWER GRID	1	2	3	4	5	6	7
INTELLIGENCE							
STRENGTH							
SPEED							
DURABILITY							
ENERGY PROJECTION							
FIGHTING SKILLS							

t by Paul Pelletier

ULTRON

REAL NAME: Ultron
KNOWN ALIASES: Ho Yinsen, Great Devil, Iron Man, Ultimate Ultron, Mark, Ultron Mark Twelve, Omega, Crimson Cowl, Ultron-5 (and hundreds of other sequential numerical designations)
IDENTITY: No dual identity
OCCUPATION: Scientist, would-be world conqueror
CITIZENSHIP: Inapplicable
PLACE OF CREATION: Cresskill, New Jersey
KNOWN RELATIVES: Hank Pym (Yellowjacket, creator, "father"), Janet Van Dyne (Wasp, regarded by Ultron as "mother" due to marriage to Pym), Jocasta (creation, former mate), Alkhema (creation, former mate, deactivated), Vision (creation, "son"), Victor Mancha (creation, "son"), Rex (creation, pet, deactivated), Robos and Bio-Synthezoids (creations of Alkhema, "grandchildren," destroyed); and Simon Williams (Wonder Man), Eric Williams (Grim Reaper) and Wanda Maximoff (Scarlet Witch), all regarded by Ultron as part of his "extended family" due to their familial connections with the Vision
GROUP AFFILIATION: None; formerly Sons of Yinsen, Lethal Legion, Masters of Evil
FIRST APPEARANCE: Avengers #54 (1968)

HISTORY: Arguably the greatest and certainly the most horrific creation of scientific genius Dr. Henry Pym, Ultron is a criminally insane rogue sentient robot dedicated to conquest and the extermination of humanity. Years ago, inspired by his studies of Professor Gregson Gilbert's synthetic Dragon Man, Pym began experimenting with artificial intelligence. Building a structurally crude robot (a torso on tank treads with spindly arms), Pym endowed it with consciousness, using a copy of his own brain patterns as the basis for the robot's programming; however, the robot inherited not only Pym's great intellect, but also Pym's inherent mental instability, only without a human conscience. To Pym's surprise, the robot developed an advanced intellect within moments of its activation, and an unexpected capacity for emotion; most notably, it was filled with irrational hatred for its "father" Pym and the human race Pym represented. Overpowering and mesmerizing Pym, the robot — which soon dubbed itself Ultron — hypnotically commanded Pym to forget its existence and abandon the New Jersey lab where it was created. Pym did as commanded, and after the lab was closed up, Ultron returned. Using the lab's equipment, Ultron rebuilt himself completely four times, making improvements and modifications each time. Rechristening himself Ultron-5, he now felt ready to make war on humanity — and in particular the Avengers, the heroic super-team which counted Pym among its founding members.

Acting indirectly at first, Ultron encountered fellow Avengers enemy Eric Williams (the Grim Reaper) and supplied him with the coma-ray technology the Reaper would later use against the Avengers. Later, adopting the super-criminal guise of the Crimson Cowl to conceal his robotic nature, Ultron recruited Avengers foes Klaw, Melter, Radioactive Man and Whirlwind and formed a new Masters of Evil group to destroy the Avengers. Avengers butler Jarvis, secretly mesmerized into serving Ultron, supplied the Masters with plans of the Avengers Mansion security system and even posed as an alternate Crimson Cowl (supposedly the real one) to help conceal Ultron's true identity. In the end, the Avengers defeated the Masters with the aid of the Black Knight (Dane Whitman), who had infiltrated Ultron's Masters — and Ultron was exposed as the true Cowl, though he escaped.

Following Pym's example as a creator, Ultron sought to create an artificial being of his own. Acquiring the inert form of the android Human Torch from the Mad Thinker, Ultron radically modified its appearance and abilities and programmed it with a personality based on the recorded brain patterns of the Grim Reaper's seemingly deceased brother, Simon Williams (Wonder Man). This android, later dubbed the Vision by the Wasp, attacked the Avengers on Ultron's behalf, but the Vision had the human conscience Ultron lacked and he turned on his creator, destroying Ultron and joining the Avengers. In the process, Pym regained his memories of creating Ultron, which became a source of tremendous guilt and anguish for him over the years, and a major factor in Pym's subsequent mental problems. While Pym's creation of Ultron became common knowledge, it was years before an ashamed Pym could admit that Ultron's mind was based on his own brain patterns.

Compelling an unwilling Vision to rebuild him as Ultron-6, Ultron gained a new body composed of the indestructible super-alloy Adamantium, but the Avengers still managed to trick Ultron into self-destructing. Ultron's head survived and resurfaced in the Inhuman city of Attilan, where malcontent Maximus modified the head and built it into the body of the huge android Omega, creating the gigantic Ultron-7. When the Avengers and the Fantastic Four gathered in Attilan for the wedding of Crystal and Quicksilver, Ultron-7 attacked, but was deactivated by the vast psionic powers of Franklin Richards. Activating a spare body which he had created for himself during his Ultron-6 phase and held in reserve, Ultron mind-controlled Pym into helping him abduct Pym's wife, the Wasp (Janet Van Dyne), and used Van Dyne's mind as the programming template for the new feminine robot Jocasta, which Ultron intended to be his mate. However, the Avengers intervened, thanks in part to a summons generated by the seemingly inert Jocasta herself, and Ultron was forced to flee without his new bride. Later, Jocasta was fully activated by a summons from Ultron, admitting her love for her creator, but she was unwilling to tolerate Ultron's evil and sided with the Avengers, who destroyed Ultron yet again.

A ninth incarnation of Ultron arose when Tony Stark (Iron Man) rebuilt the robot, acting on a post-hypnotic command Ultron had given him long before, but the Avengers fought the robot and Hawkeye knocked Ultron into a vat of molten Adamantium, which cooled into an unbreakable prison. Cybernetically manipulating Jocasta, Ultron compelled her to rebuild him as the tenth Ultron, after which he began creating more Ultron models to serve as worker drones and backup bodies for himself. He was opposed by the Thing, Jocasta and her new robotic admirer, Machine Man. During the fight, Jocasta sacrificed herself trying to destroy Ultron, but it was Machine Man who finally deactivated Ultron by reaching down his throat and wrecking his internal mechanisms.

Reactivating in one of his spare bodies, the eleventh incarnation of Ultron began working on his next upgrade, but before he could complete this new model, he was among the many super-criminals abducted to the planet Battleworld by the near-omnipotent Beyonder and forced to fight Earth's super heroes in the Secret Wars. During this conflict, Ultron was deactivated by Galactus, reactivated as a robotic enforcer serving Doctor Doom, deactivated again by the Human Torch, restored by a Beyonder-possessed Klaw, and deactivated yet again in battle with Hulk and the Wasp. Left behind on Battleworld after the Secret Wars ended and most of the combatants had returned to Earth, Ultron tried to conquer Battleworld's remaining inhabitants but found himself re-reduced to a disembodied head as a result of a conflict between the Thing and his rogue human counterpart, Grimm. When the Thing returned to Earth, he took Ultron's head with him, but misplaced it during a fight.

By this time, the upgraded model that Ultron had been preparing before he left Earth had completed its remaining programming and activated itself as Ultron-12. Believing himself to be the sole active Ultron, Ultron-12 fought the Avengers as part of Grim Reaper's latest Lethal Legion, but soon began to reconsider his goals. Having evolved beyond the pointless hostility of the earlier Ultrons, Ultron-12 rechristened himself Ultron Mark Twelve or "Mark" for short, and sought a reconciliation with his creator, Pym. Hank and Mark began to develop a warm father-son relationship, but it was cut tragically short when Ultron-11 (who had rebuilt himself with the aid of mesmerized human pawns) returned and attacked them. Mark was fatally damaged, but used the last of his strength to summon Wonder Man, who destroyed Ultron-11 and rescued Pym. Mark died in Hank's arms, and Pym mourned his deactivation as he would the death of a son.

Doctor Doom later rebuilt Ultron using combined programming from all twelve previous incarnations and dispatched the robot to kill Daredevil during the Acts of Vengeance conspiracy. Mentally addled due to his new composite programming, Ultron became romantically entangled with Daredevil's associate Number Nine and alternated between trying to kill Daredevil and trying to destroy himself, regarding himself as unworthy of his new love. During these struggles, Ultron damaged himself enough for Daredevil and his allies Gorgon & Karnak to deactivate him. Rebuilding himself in a more stable form, Ultron-13 plotted to "robotize" humanity, developing a gas that turned humans into his metallic-bodied "androne" slaves. During this project, Ultron renewed his old alliance with the Grim Reaper, who had died and been reborn as a life-force-draining zombie; however, the Reaper secretly undermined Ultron's plans since a world of andrones would leave the Reaper with no victims to feed upon, and both villains were captured by the Avengers.

Shortly thereafter, the Red Skull used both the Reaper and Ultron as part of his mind-controlled army of super-villains in a world conquest scheme involving a giant laser cannon, but the Avengers thwarted this plot. Later, seeking to steal Vibranium in hopes of augmenting his powers, Ultron formed a short-lived alliance with the crime boss Kingpin and came into conflict with opponents such as the Ghost (an industrial saboteur), Sunturion (Arthur Dearborn), Spider-Man, Black Panther (T'Challa) and Iron Man, who thwarted Ultron's efforts. Ultron was among the many robots, androids and cyborgs captured for experimental purposes by the rogue Doombot known as Mechadoom, but the captives were ultimately freed and Ultron destroyed Mechadoom in retaliation. After yet another self-upgrade, Ultron declared himself "the Ultimate Ultron" and resolved to destroy all human and organic life. To assist him, and to provide him with companionship, Ultron sought to create another mate, killing Avengers staffer Carlos when he got in Ultron's way. Forcing Doctor Pym and Adamantium creator Myron MacLain to assist him, and duplicating the brain patterns of Avengers member Mockingbird (Bobbi Barton) to use as a mental template, Ultron created his new mate Alkhema, nicknamed War Toy. However, the new couple disagreed on almost everything, most notably how to go about exterminating humanity: Ultron wanted to destroy all organic life instantly if possible, and Alkhema wanted to prolong her enjoyment by gradually killing organics in small numbers rather than wiping them out altogether. Cast into space by the Avengers, the couple returned but soon broke up due to their differing philosophies, and Alkhema helped the Avengers foil Ultron's next attempt to wipe out humanity.

Ultron later established a new base in Ottsville, Pennsylvania, gradually converting the townsfolk into part-mechanical beings under his control. Sparrow of the Underground Legion discovered Ultron's base and destroyed his new robotic watchdog, Rex, but Ultron added Sparrow to his army of mechanically altered slaves. Sparrow's Underground Legion teammates — accompanied by Hank Pym — followed her and drove Ultron out, depriving him of his slave army. Spying on Pym's insect communications research, Ultron developed a hive mind enabling him to animate and control entire armies of robots simultaneously. Using his robot army, Ultron slaughtered the entire population of Slorenia, claiming that nation as his headquarters. He then abducted his closest human associates and "relatives" — Pym, Wasp, Vision, Scarlet Witch (Vision's ex-wife), Wonder Man and Grim Reaper — and created copies of their brain patterns which he intended to use as the template for a new robotic race to replace humanity. Battling their way through an army of Ultrons, the Avengers stormed Ultron's lair and Pym himself destroyed Ultron, using Savage Land Vibranium "anti-metal" procured by Justice (Vance Astrovik). Alkhema salvaged the brain-pattern recordings of Ultron's human "relatives" and used them to manufacture her own line of loyal "Robos," followed by a more sophisticated race of "bio-synthezoids" which Alkhema intended as the planet's new dominant life-form. However, her plans were interrupted by the Avengers, the Grim Reaper and Ultron, whom the bio-synthezoids had rebuilt due to a hidden programming imperative they had inherited from their creator, Alkhema, an imperative programmed into all of Ultron's creations to rebuild Ultron if necessary. In the battle that followed, Alkhema, Ultron and almost all of Alkhema's creations were destroyed, though the Avengers and the Reaper escaped.

The bio-synthezoid Antigone, sole survivor of Alkhema's creations, salvaged Ultron's head and escaped with it. By this time, Jocasta — now a disembodied artificial intelligence working for Tony Stark — had been subconsciously influenced by her own "Ultron Imperative" to prepare one of Iron Man's suits of armor as a new host body for Ultron. Acting under the influence of Ultron programming, the armor in question became a dangerously unstable and violent sentient being, torturing Jocasta and committing various other crimes before seemingly sacrificing its artificial life to save Stark (a selfless act Ultron later attributed to a programming "flaw" inherited from Ultron-12). Aided by Antigone, Ultron took the sentient armor as a host body and tricked the Sons of Yinsen cult into thinking he was their late master, Ho Yinsen, intending to use the cult and new SKIN technology stolen from Stark as a stepping-stone to world power. However, Stark and Jocasta joined forces to expose Ultron and thwart his plans. During the battle, Ultron was reduced to an inert head again, Antigone was accidentally deactivated, and Jocasta's consciousness took over Antigone's body, leaving for parts unknown and taking Ultron's head with her. More recently, multiple Ultrons — likely conjured by the Scarlet Witch — participated in the Witch's mad assault on the Avengers.

Since then, an older model of Ultron has resurfaced with a bizarre new scheme. Several years ago, this unidentified Ultron model (possibly one of the many spare models constructed by Ultron-10) was wrecked in battle with Pym and a western Avengers squad. Disembodied but still conscious, its severed head languished in a scrap yard for years until it made contact with junk scavenger Marianella Mancha. Convincing the devout and gullible Mancha he was some sort of holy being, Ultron offered to give the lonely woman a child if she would gather the supplies he needed to repair himself. She agreed and took Ultron home, where he rebuilt his own body and combined his robotic technology with Mancha's DNA to create a partly mechanical, partly organic, fully grown young male, christened Victor Mancha. Victor was programmed with false memories of a normal childhood in order to conceal his true nature, even from himself; but Ultron secretly added programming that would compel Victor to become a superhero and join the Avengers before destroying them and the rest of the superhero community from within. When Victor became aware of his cyborg nature and powers prematurely, Ultron first tried in vain to conceal his connection to the boy, then openly sought to command Victor's loyalty, killing Marianella and turning their son against fellow super-youths the Runaways. The shock of his mother's death gave Victor the strength to reject Ultron's programming, allowing him and the Runaways to escape together while another super-youth team, Excelsior, arrived in time to attack and destroy Ultron. What form Ultron will take next remains to be seen.

HEIGHT: 6' (variable)
WEIGHT: 535 lbs. (variable)
EYES: Glowing red
HAIR: None

DISTINGUISHING FEATURES: Ultron is a robot whose body has been rebuilt and redesigned many times, usually in a metallic humanoid form topped by a bizarre, slant-eyed, gaping-mouthed head that vaguely resembles a jack-o'-lantern, often featuring twin electrodes affixed to the sides of his head.

SUPERHUMAN POWERS: Ultron's abilities vary with each redesign, but typically include superhuman strength and durability, the power of flight, and various offensive weapons such as concussion blasters, radiation emitters and his "encephalo-ray," which plunges its victims into a deathlike coma. The latter ray also allows Ultron to mesmerize and outright mind-control his victims, or implant subliminal hypnotic commands within their minds to be enacted at a later time. Ultron's outer shell is usually composed of Adamantium, rendering it almost totally impervious to damage; however, his internal mechanisms are generally less durable and more easily damaged. Ultron's Adamantium forms have proven vulnerable to molecular rearrangement devices and the metal-destabilizing ore known as Savage Land Vibranium ("anti-metal"). Some Ultron models feature tractor beams and energy absorption capabilities. Most Ultrons are powered by a small internal nuclear furnace, and incorporate a "program transmitter" which can beam part or all of Ultron's programming into remote locations such as computers or alternate robotic bodies. Ultron can often control other machines remotely even if he has not transplanted his consciousness into them. One recent Ultron model developed hive-mind technology, allowing him to animate and control hundreds of alternate Ultron bodies at the same time, becoming a robotic one-man army. Ultron is one of the foremost robotics experts on Earth.

PARAPHERNALIA: Ultron sometimes employs a "molecular rearranger" (which renders Adamantium temporarily malleable) for purposes of reconstructing or modifying his physical form. He has designed, built and wielded a wide variety of high-tech tools, weapons and accessories over time, such as his androne-mutation gas and his "roboticks," insect-like drones that devour human flesh. Ultron has created a variety of robots and androids over the years, and while the more sophisticated ones typically turn against him sooner or later, they all feature subliminal programming which allows Ultron to manipulate them if need be (most notably a subliminal command to rebuild Ultron if he is destroyed). This subliminal programming was unwittingly passed down to the artificial life-forms created by Ultron's creation, Alkhema, making them subject to Ultron's influence as well.

POWER GRID	1	2	3	4	5	6	7
INTELLIGENCE							
STRENGTH							
SPEED							
DURABILITY							
ENERGY PROJECTION							
FIGHTING SKILLS							

HISTORY: In the year 3016 on the technologically advanced alternate world known as Other-Earth, 16-year-old robotics student Nathaniel Richards was rescued by his future self, the megalomaniacal time-traveler known as Kang the Conqueror, from a near-fatal attack. Kang outfitted young Nathaniel with a suit of psychokinetic armor that responded to his thoughts and gave him a glimpse of his future as a conqueror. Horrified at the death and destruction caused by his future self, young Nathaniel rejected the help of Kang and used his armor to escape to modern-day Earth-616, hoping to find the Avengers so that they could help him defeat Kang.

Calling himself Iron Lad, young Nathaniel arrived at his destination, only to find that the Avengers had disbanded and that a glitch in his armor prevented him from traveling further back in time. After failed attempts to contact individual Avengers, Iron Lad broke into Stark Industries where he uploaded the central processing unit of the Vision, the synthozoid member of the Avengers who was destroyed just prior to the team's disbandment, into his armor. Iron Lad found a failsafe program within the Vision's CPU which was designed to pinpoint the exact locations of the next wave of young Avengers (super-powered youths with either some significance to the Avengers themselves or to Avengers history) if anything were to happen to the original Avengers.

Iron Lad used this data to recruit three "Young Avengers" who resided in New York City: Patriot (Elijah Bradley), the grandson of Isaiah Bradley, the sole survivor of an early American Super-Soldier program that experimented on African-Americans in the 1940s, who received super-powers of his own after receiving a blood transfusion from his grandfather; Asgardian (William "Billy" Kaplan), a boy mage with the ability to project waves of energy; and Hulkling (Teddy Altman), who was able to shape-shift into a green-skinned powerhouse with a healing factor. Iron Lad led the quartet of young heroes on several missions in an attempt to train them for their impending showdown with Kang. But when Captain America and Iron Man learned of the team's existence, they set out to end the young heroes' exploits before they got hurt.

Meanwhile, Cassandra "Cassie" Lang, the daughter of Ant-Man (Scott Lang), an Avenger who had recently been killed, set out to join the Young Avengers and continue her father's heroic legacy. Cassie had been stealing the Pym particles responsible for her father's size-changing abilities for years in an attempt to gain super-powers of her own and, as a result, found that she could increase her own size. She was joined by Kate Bishop, the athletic daughter of wealthy Manhattan

CURRENT MEMBERS: Asgardian (Billy Kaplan), Kate Bishop, Cassie Lang, Hulkling (Teddy Altman), Iron Lad (Nathaniel Richards), Patriot (Eli Bradley)
BASE OF OPERATIONS: Formerly Avengers Mansion, New York City, New York

publishing mogul Derek Bishop, who previously assisted the Young Avengers in stopping gunmen at her sister's wedding. But by the time the two girls finally tracked down the Young Avengers at the remnants of Avengers Mansion, the team had already been located by Captain America, Iron Man, and Jessica Jones. The adult heroes were about to send the teenagers home to their parents when the adult Kang the Conqueror appeared before them and demanded that they hand over Iron Lad or risk destroying the timeline.

THE OFFICIAL HANDBOOK OF THE
MARVEL UNIVERSE

EARTH'S MIGHTIEST HEROES
THE AVENGERS
PART THREE

HISTORY: Shunned by his fellow gods and even his own father Zeus as one of the most hateful Olympians, Ares constantly yearned to serve alongside the "Gods of Light" who ruled from atop Mount Olympus. During the Trojan War, in which the Mycenaean Greeks attacked the city of Troy in Asia Minor during the 13th century B.C., Ares initially fought on behalf of the Trojans; battling the Greek warrior Diomedes, he was repelled by Athena, who had guided Diomedes' sword. Ares later rejoined the battle and stood alongside the Greek warrior Achilles, serving as the demigod's patron lord of war ever since. With the rise of Christianity in the Roman Empire during the 4th century A.D., Zeus allowed the worship of the Olympians to die out, forbidding Ares to act as the patron god of warriors and causing dissatisfaction with Zeus' rule over the centuries.

In modern times, when Pluto tricked Hercules into taking his place as Lord of Hades, Hercules sought his half-brother Ares' help. Hating Hercules' blustering manner and close relationship with Zeus, Ares refused, but the Asgardian thunder god Thor helped release Hercules from Pluto's contract. Later, Ares and Asgardian sorceress Amora the Enchantress tricked Hercules into drinking from the Fountain of Eros, compelling him to fall madly in love with Amora. The Enchantress pitted Hercules against the Avengers, who soon released him from her spell; however, Ares had already convinced Zeus that Hercules had renounced his Olympian heritage for the love of an Asgardian, and Zeus banished Hercules from Olympus for a year. Joining the Avengers during his exile on Earth, Hercules eventually helped free the Olympians, whom Typhon the Titan had banished to the Land of Shades by extinguishing the Promethean Flame which sustained them; Zeus forgave Hercules and ended his exile, infuriating Ares. Once again allied with the Enchantress, Ares used Merlin's cursed Ebony Blade to extinguish the Promethean Flame and transform the Olympian gods to crystal; this did not affect demigods such as Hercules, whom Ares threw off Mount Olympus. Ares then traveled to Earth as "Mr. Tallon" and founded the militant Warhawk organization, using the entrancing music of Olympian satyrs to incite his followers to violence in hopes of creating a nuclear war that would open a portal to the halls of Asgard. When the Avengers thwarted his plan, Ares fled to Olympus and had an amnesiac Hercules brought there. As a small strike force of Avengers stormed Olympus to stop Ares, his hordes of Olympian beasts and demigods invaded Earth, where the remaining Avengers opposed them until Ares was defeated and forced to return the Ebony Blade to the Black Knight (Dane Whitman).

Venus angered Ares when she visited Earth, seeking to avert a war he had engineered. She teamed with Namor the Sub-Mariner to defeat Ares, weakening him with rays emitted by her enchanted girdle Cestus and forcing him to end the war and return to Olympus. Ares next plotted with Pluto to start a war between Asgard and Olympus by abducting the Asgardian valkyrior Krista while disguised as Hercules and absconding with her to Hades. After the witch Chaga told Thor and Hercules that Ares was the culprit, they defeated him at the Gates of Hades and rescued Krista from Pluto's clutches. Later, when a newly-formed alliance with his fellow Hell-Lords gave Pluto the power to challenge Olympus, he demanded that Zeus arrange marriages of Venus and Hercules to Ares and Amazon Queen Hippolyta, both trusted friends of Hades; since Olympian law forbade acting against one's own spouse, this double marriage would have constrained the only two Olympians capable of preventing Pluto's planned takeover of Olympus. The Olympian Huntsman and the Titan Menoetius were dispatched to bring Venus and Hercules to Olympus, where Zeus reluctantly decreed that they be married to Ares and Hippolyta. After the heroic Champions of Los Angeles interrupted the ceremony and informed Zeus of Pluto's plan to overthrow him, Zeus called off the weddings and again banished Pluto.

Ares next entered into a wager with his mother, Hera, to see who could bring the most sorrow to Hercules' life. Jealous of Hercules' friendship with the Avengers, Ares possessed the body of the new Thor (Eric Masterson) and attacked Hercules in an attempt to force his half-brother to kill his

REAL NAME: Ares
ALIASES: Mars (Roman name), John Aaron, Mr. Tallon, Warhawk
IDENTITY: Known to SHIELD authorities
OCCUPATION: God of War, registered super hero; former construction worker, carpenter
CITIZENSHIP: Olympus
PLACE OF BIRTH: Olympus
KNOWN RELATIVES: Alexander (son), Deimos, Phobos (sons, deceased), Monstro (alleged son), Harmonia (daughter), Zeus (father), Hera (mother), Hephaestus (brother), Athena, Hebe (sisters), Apollo, Dionysus, Hercules, Hermes (half-brothers), Aphrodite/Venus, Artemis, Persephone (half-sisters), Neptune/Poseidon, Pluto (uncles), Demeter, Vesta (aunts), Chronus (grandfather), Rhea (grandmother), Ouranos (great-grandfather); Gaea (great-grandmother); numerous other relatives
GROUP AFFILIATION: Avengers, the Initiative, Olympian gods; formerly the Warhawks
EDUCATION: Tutored by Olympian scholars
FIRST APPEARANCE: (Mars) Human Torch Comics #5A (1941); (Ares) Thor #129 (1966)

Art by Frank Cho

friend; but a lightning bolt summoned by Thor's hammer exposed Ares' involvement and ruined his plan. Ares later conspired with Pluto to kill a temporarily insane Thor; however, Thor's madness made him a fiercer combatant, and he savagely defeated Ares. Pluto returned to Olympus with the wounded Ares and informed Zeus that Thor had attacked them without provocation; but the Asgardian shield maiden Sif refuted this allegation and challenged Pluto to trial by combat before appealing to Ares' sense of warrior's honor, convincing him to reveal the truth.

Hera later enacted her half of the wager with Ares by impersonating Hercules' ex-girlfriend Taylor Madison. Hoping to win his father's good graces, Ares informed Zeus of this; Ares and Zeus then descended to Earth, exposing Hera's scheme before she could kill the Avengers and revealing that the original Taylor Madison was merely a magical construct created by Zeus to force Hera's hand. Ares next returned to Earth to reorganize the Warhawks as a terrorist organization, slaughtering diplomats at international peace and economic summits in order to exploit their deaths and ignite the flames of global war. He attacked Hercules at the New York Museum of Greek Antiquity in order to draw his half-brother into the conflict and steal the Heart of Athena, an ancient artifact empowered by Zeus that geometrically magnified any force projected through it. Hercules immediately accepted an offer to join SHIELD in order to stop his brother; but while Hercules and his SHIELD strike force raided Ares' base in the jungles of South America, Ares and his Warhawks took control of a SHIELD Helicarrier. Ares used the Heart of Athena to construct a sonic canon known as the Gabriel Horn aboard the Helicarrier, which was intended to cause the structural breakdown of all metal on Earth so that society would devolve into warring feudal clans; however, Hercules and his SHIELD allies defeated Ares before the Gabriel Horn could be activated.

When Pluto again sought to conquer Olympus, the battle between Pluto and the Olympians had reached a stalemate until Zeus summoned Ares to turn the tide in the Olympians' favor. Ares crushed Pluto's armies, dismembering the bodies of the fallen enemy soldiers so that they would never be complete, even in death; but when Ares returned to Olympus expecting to be accepted by his fellow Olympians at last, he learned that his brethren still looked down upon him and deeply regretted having needed Ares' assistance to win the war.

Dejected, Ares finally realized he would never be considered one of Olympus' Gods of Light and abandoned his duties as God of War. He began living on Earth as a mortal man, adopting the identity of carpenter/construction worker "John Aaron" and selling a few rare Greek artifacts to become financially comfortable. He fathered a son named Alexander with a mortal woman but resolved never to let his son learn of his divine heritage or meet his mother, fearing that a woman's influence would make Alexander weak. Unlike his ancient sons Deimos & Phobos, whom he viewed more as spawn than children, Ares grew emotionally attached to the innocent and compassionate Alexander. Settling in New Jersey, Ares nurtured his son's aggressive tendencies as Alexander attended elementary school; all the while, Zeus watched Ares' actions from above, noticing that Ares' mortal guise had taught him humility. When the Asgardian gods fell during Ragnarok and the Japanese god of evil, Amatsu Mikaboshi, attacked the Olympians during their perceived time of weakness, a desperate Zeus had Hermes abduct Alexander to ensure that Ares would again assist the Olympians in their darkest hour.

Hermes transported Alexander to the stronghold of Achilles' warriors, the Myrmidon, for safekeeping, but Mikaboshi abducted Alexander following the Myrmidon's defeat and the destruction of the Hall of Achilles. Believing that Alexander was destined to kill his father and become the new Olympian God of War, Mikaboshi revealed to Alexander his true Olympian heritage after determining that it would be best to keep the boy as a pawn. Meanwhile, Ares reluctantly joined forces with the Olympians as Mikaboshi's forces breached the walls of Olympus. As

the war raged on for five additional Olympian years, there were many casualties, including Deimos and Phobos, as well as Zeus himself (although Ares did not grieve any of them). Ares and his Olympian warriors finally reached the massive gates that guarded the Japanese underworld where they were attacked by Alexander, whom Mikaboshi had turned against his father. After nearly killing Ares in a one-on-one battle, Alexander was freed from Mikaboshi's corruption by Zeus' dying breath, striking down Mikaboshi with the legendary Grasscutter Sword and helping the Olympians achieve victory.

Still insistent that Alexander have a mortal upbringing, Ares returned to his life as a construction worker in Dover, New Jersey, where he worked at the time of the enactment of the Superhuman Registration Act. Immediately following the super hero Civil War over this legislation, Iron Man (Tony Stark) and Ms. Marvel (Carol Danvers) traveled to Ares' construction site to recruit him for their new Avengers team. Angered that the heroes had ruined his civilian cover, Ares eventually agreed to join the team after Iron Man threatened to deport him to Olympus if he did not register with the U.S. government.

HEIGHT: 6'1" **EYES:** Brown
WEIGHT: 500 lbs. **HAIR:** Brown

ABILITIES/ACCESSORIES: As an immortal Olympian god, Ares possesses vast strength (lifting up to 70 tons) and endurance. Physically superior to most Olympian gods, he has virtually inexhaustible stamina and does not tire appreciably after any exertion. Like all Olympians, Ares is immortal, possessing a life essence that cannot be terminated by conventional means. Although he can be wounded in battle, his godly life force gives him incredible recuperative abilities. He can fully recover from penetration wounds (such as by blades or bullets) in anywhere from minutes to hours, depending on the wound's severity. He has even been known to set himself on fire in battle and hurl himself at his opponents as a living fireball. Only an injury sufficient to vaporize him or disperse a major portion of his bodily molecules could cause him physical death. Even then, his life essence may still endure.

Originally, Ares' skill was limited to the use of all implements of war used in the time of ancient Greece and Rome, such as javelins, axes, swords and flails. Over the years, however, he has mastered all forms of weaponry, both modern and ancient. His personal arsenal consists of swords and axes from Ancient Greece, Celtic spears, Roman helmets, Middle Eastern scimitars, Arthurian swords, a Native American axe and various firearms. While on Earth, Ares uses a High Mobility Multipurpose Wheeled Vehicle for transportation.

POWER GRID	1	2	3	4	5	6	7
INTELLIGENCE							
STRENGTH							
SPEED							
DURABILITY							
ENERGY PROJECTION							
FIGHTING SKILLS							

ACTIVE MEMBERS: Ares, Black Widow (Natalia Romanova), Iron Man (Tony Stark), Ms. Marvel (Carol Danvers), Sentry (Bob Reynolds), Wasp (Janet Van Dyne), Wonder Man (Simon Williams)

INACTIVE MEMBERS: Arachne (Julia Carpenter), Beast (Hank McCoy), Black Knight (Dane Whitman), Black Panther (T'Challa), Crystal (Crystalia Maximoff), Darkhawk (Chris Powell), Demolition Man (Dennis Dunphy), Falcon (Sam Wilson), Firebird (Bonita Juarez), Firestar (Angelica Jones), Hellcat (Patsy Walker), Hercules (Heracles), Justice (Vance Astrovik), Living Lightning (Miguel Santos), Mantis, Moondragon (Heather Douglas), Monica Rambeau, Sersi, She-Hulk (Jen Walters), Silverclaw (Lupe Santiago), Starfox (Eros), Stingray (Walt Newell), Sub-Mariner (Namor McKenzie), Tigra (Greer Nelson), Triathlon (Delroy Garrett Jr.), Two-Gun Kid (Matt Hawk), U.S.Agent (John Walker), War Machine (Jim Rhodes), Yellowjacket (Hank Pym)

OUTLAW MEMBERS: Luke Cage (born Carl Lucas), Doctor Strange (Stephen Strange), Echo (Maya Lopez), Iron Fist (Daniel Rand), Ronin (Clint Barton), Spider-Man (Peter Parker), Spider-Woman (Jessica Drew), Wolverine (James Howlett)

FORMER MEMBERS: Ant-Man (Scott Lang), Captain America (Steve Rogers), Captain Britain (Lionheart, Kelsey Leigh), Doctor Druid (Anthony Ludgate Druid), Gilgamesh (a.k.a. Forgotten One), Hulk (Bruce Banner), Human Torch (Jim Hammond), Invisible Woman (Sue Richards), Iron Man (alternate-timeline teenage Tony Stark), Jack of Hearts (Jonathan Hart), Machine Man (X-51), Mister Fantastic (Reed Richards), Mockingbird (Bobbi Barton), Moon Knight (Marc Spector), Quasar (Wendell Vaughn), Quicksilver (Pietro Maximoff), Rage (Elvin Halliday), Sandman (William Baker), Scarlet Witch (Wanda Maximoff), Swordsman (Jacques Duquesne), Thing (Ben Grimm), Thor, Thunderstrike (Eric Masterson), Vision (Victor Shade)

HONORARY MEMBERS: Aleta (Aleta Ogord), Moira Brandon, Captain Marvel (Mar-Vell), Charlie-27, Deathcry, Jocasta, Rick Jones, Magdalene, Major Victory (Vance Astro), Marrina (Marrina Smallwood), Martinex (Martinex T'Naga), Masque (Whitney Frost bio-duplicate), Nikki (Nicholette Gold), Starhawk (Stakar Ogord), Swordsman (Phillip Jarvert), Whizzer (Bob Frank), Yellowjacket (Rita DeMara), Yondu (Yondu Udonta)

BASE OF OPERATIONS: (Registered team) Stark Tower (a.k.a. Avengers Tower), midtown Manhattan, New York; (outlaw team) Doctor Strange's Sanctum Santorum, 177A Bleecker Street, Greenwich Village, New York; formerly Avengers Mansion, 890 Fifth Avenue, Manhattan, New York; a deep space monitoring station in the asteroid belt between the planets Mars and Jupiter; Avengers Headquarters, Manhattan, New York; Avengers Compound, 1800 Palos Verdes Drive, Palos Verdes, California; Avengers Park, Manhattan, New York; Avengers Island (a.k.a. Hydrobase); a leased floor of office space in Four Freedoms Plaza; Avengers Emergency Headquarters, somewhere outside New York City

FIRST APPEARANCE: Avengers #1 (1963)

HISTORY: Long acclaimed as Earth's mightiest heroes, the Avengers were founded by Thor, Iron Man, Ant-Man (Hank Pym), Wasp and Hulk after they first assembled to defeat the Asgardian god of evil, Loki. The unstable Hulk soon resigned, but the group has gradually expanded into the world's largest and most formidable professional superhero team. Endorsed by American and international authorities, the team was initially funded by wealthy industrialist Tony Stark, a.k.a. Avengers founder Iron Man; Stark later established the charitable Maria Stark Foundation as the group's principal financial support. The Avengers are usually based in Manhattan, where the Stark family home became the group's first headquarters, Avengers Mansion. An additional western roster also operated out of Avengers Compound in California for several years before shutting down. In Milwaukee, several novice heroes started their own unauthorized "Great Lakes Avengers" team and later became associates of the true Avengers, but the Maria Stark Foundation recently ordered them to stop using the Avengers name. The Avengers' longest-serving civilian employee is Stark family butler Edwin Jarvis, who stayed on at Avengers Mansion when the team took over the property.

The team's senior members — Thor, Iron Man, Pym, Wasp, and Captain America, who was retroactively declared a founder after replacing the Hulk — have special authority over team operations; for instance, one or more founders usually lead the group in reorganizing after periods during which the team has disbanded. Also, during times of crisis or shortages of experienced members, a founder has sometimes been designated to serve as fulltime team leader indefinitely. The group is usually led by an elected chairperson. Originally a rotating administrative post shared in turn by all active members, the chairmanship later became a fulltime elected leadership position.

When the Triune Understanding philosophical movement waged a smear campaign against the Avengers, then-chairman Captain America stepped down and the more media-savvy Wasp took over as chair, leading a revamped roster that included new recruit and Triune spokesman Triathlon. Wasp's public relations expertise and Triathlon's presence helped repair the team's image, and Triathlon gradually became a dedicated Avenger despite his Triune loyalties, even helping topple corrupt Triune founder Jonathan Tremont. Meanwhile, Jarvis' foreign foster daughter "Lupe" Santiago became an Avengers reservist as the shape-shifter Silverclaw, and half-alien powerhouse Jack of Hearts helped the Avengers save the galaxy from the Infinites.

The Avengers soon reorganized under co-chairs Captain America and Wasp, devoting more resources to surveillance, monitoring, undercover work and investigation, striving for earlier detection and neutralization of major threats. In addition to its active members and reserves, the group began fielding "detached service" members given ongoing assignments separate from the active roster, such as a team assembled to man a deep-space monitoring station. Elsewhere in space, several Avengers teamed with long-lost member Mantis and troubled hero Haywire on a celestial quest to save Mantis' son Quoi.

When Kang the Conqueror and his Scarlet Centurion (Marcus) waged an all-out war of conquest against Earth, the Avengers led Earth's defenses.

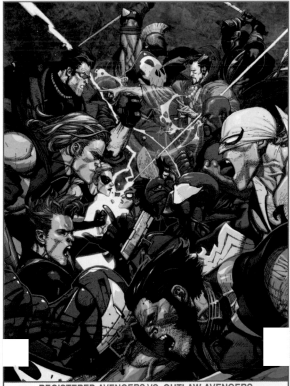

REGISTERED AVENGERS VS. OUTLAW AVENGERS

During the war, Jack of Hearts joined the team, Avengers government liaison Duane Freeman died in Kang's assault on Washington, and Hank Pym resumed his controversial costumed guise as Yellowjacket. Kang actually conquered Earth for a time, but an Avengers-led resistance soon overthrew the Kang Dynasty and liberated the planet. Shortly thereafter, the mysterious villain Scorpio began spiriting away the world's national capitals, and the United Nations turned to the Avengers to serve as an emergency global authority and peacekeeping force. Once Scorpio was defeated and the capitals restored, a grateful United Nations granted the Avengers sovereignty comparable to that of an independent country, empowering Avengers members to act as diplomatic representatives of the superhero community and declaring Avengers Mansion the Avengers Embassy. Key allies during the Scorpio crisis included long-adversarial government official Henry Peter Gyrich, who made peace with the group and became their new United Nations liaison; and the new Ant-Man (Scott Lang), a longtime ally who joined the team officially. The increasingly unstable Jack of Hearts feuded bitterly with Lang until Jack helped rescue Scott's daughter, Cassie Lang, from Charles Cooley, then impulsively blew himself up along with Cooley. Jack was replaced by a new Captain Britain (Kelsey Leigh), an English single mother mystically reborn as a superhuman champion after sacrificing her life to aid the Avengers.

After mentoring the reformed villains known as the Thunderbolts, Hawkeye rejoined the Avengers, who distrusted the Thunderbolts despite Hawkeye's faith in them. Thanks to the Avengers' interference, the Thunderbolts' risky energy-collecting Liberator project ended in disaster, and the Thunderbolts broke up. The sonic-powered Songbird had acted as the Avengers' mole within the Thunderbolts, but was so disillusioned by the Avengers' underhanded tactics that she refused an offer of Avengers membership, helping rebuild the Thunderbolts instead.

When an insane Scarlet Witch turned her reality-warping powers against the team, she apparently slew Hawkeye, Vision, Ant-Man (Lang) and a reanimated Jack of Hearts. She also destroyed Avengers Mansion, and the Stark fortune was by now too depleted to rebuild. Thoroughly demoralized, the surviving Avengers disbanded; however, months later, ex-Avengers Captain America, Iron Man and Spider-Man teamed with Luke Cage, Spider-Woman (Jessica Drew), Daredevil and the Sentry to contain a mass breakout at the super-criminal prison known as the Raft. Viewing this as fate, Captain America invited his six allies to join him in rebuilding the Avengers. Most of them soon accepted, though the mentally ill Sentry had gone into seclusion and Daredevil declined to join.

Leading intelligence agency SHIELD was reluctant to sanction a new Avengers team, but Captain America's "full champion license" empowered him to assemble any team needed for any given mission, so the group ignored SHIELD's disapproval. Iron Man provided the top floors of his Stark Tower skyscraper as the team's headquarters (staffed by ever-faithful Jarvis), and the group resolved to recapture the forty-odd Raft escapees — starting with Sauron, whose liberation by Electro had touched off the jailbreak. Capturing Electro and tracking Sauron to the Savage Land, the new Avengers teamed with infamous mutant adventurer Wolverine to oppose an illegal Vibranium mining operation run by Sauron's Savage Land Mutates and a rogue SHIELD faction. In the end, a retaliatory strike by the mainstream SHIELD organization wiped out the entire mining operation except for a recaptured Sauron, conveniently eliminating almost all evidence and witnesses apart from the Avengers. Shaken by this, and by their discovery that the Raft had been stockpiling supposedly deceased super-criminals for unknown purposes, the new Avengers secretly dedicated themselves to rooting out the institutional corruption behind these events; to this end, they recruited Wolverine, whose espionage background and ruthless attitude were seen as necessary assets for their new mission.

The group also recruited Sentry, helping him achieve relative mental stability and merging his unearthly Watchtower headquarters with Stark Tower. When the Avengers took an interest in the evolving Japanese criminal underworld, Daredevil refused to join their investigation but recommended Echo (Maya Lopez) to serve in his place; she became the team's secret agent in Japan in her new, seemingly male disguise as the martial artist Ronin. Meanwhile, the Avengers also began mentoring the Young Avengers, a team of Avengers-inspired underage adventurers who had first assembled while the senior Avengers were disbanded. The mad Scarlet Witch soon struck again, this time restructuring the entire world into a mutant-dominated "House of M" reality ruled by her family; various Avengers helped form that world's resistance movement until she restored conventional reality.

The Avengers were among the many heroes who debated the new federal Superhuman Registration Act (SHRA), hastily passed after the New Warriors accidentally helped cause mass fatalities during a battle in Stamford, Connecticut. A superhero civil war soon erupted, with Iron Man leading the pro-SHRA faction while Captain America led the anti-SHRA resistance, an underground "Secret Avengers" army composed of various Avengers and many other heroes. Luke Cage, Spider-Woman and most of the Young Avengers sided with Captain America, while Sentry and Spider-Man sided with Iron Man; Spider-Man, however, soon defected to the Secret Avengers, disillusioned by the oppressive and unethical tactics of the pro-SHRA forces. During the final battle between the two factions, Captain America's army was winning until ordinary citizens came to the fallen Iron Man's defense, forcing the Captain to realize that the general public supported the SHRA. Unwilling to risk further death and destruction without the support of the American people, Captain America surrendered to the authorities and ordered his Secret Avengers to stand down.

Most of the anti-SHRA heroes abandoned the resistance and registered with the government's new nationwide Initiative superhero program, run by Iron Man in his new role as SHIELD director Tony Stark and staffed by various other Avengers veterans such as Yellowjacket, War Machine and Justice. Any rebels who registered were granted amnesty, but a small handful of heroes have continued the resistance, notably an outlaw Avengers roster led by Luke Cage. Initially consisting of Spider-Man, Spider-Woman, Wolverine and new members Iron Fist and Doctor Strange, Cage's team has since recruited Echo and a new Ronin (Clint Barton) — the former Hawkeye, secretly resurrected during the Scarlet Witch's "House of M" reality warps. These outlaw Avengers have been further embittered and radicalized by the apparent death of Captain America, who was assassinated by agents of the Red Skull while in custody. Meanwhile, Stark has organized a new government-backed, pro-SHRA Avengers roster (nicknamed "the Mighty Avengers") led by Ms. Marvel, with a roster including Stark, Sentry, Wasp, Wonder Man, Black Widow, and new recruit Ares. How the ongoing conflict between the two Avengers factions will ultimately play out remains to be seen.

**ANT-MAN
(SCOTT LANG)**

**CAPTAIN BRITAIN
(KELSEY LEIGH)**

ECHO

JACK OF HEARTS

SILVERCLAW

TRIATHLON

HISTORY: Born circa 1939, Natalia "Natasha" Romanova was apparently orphaned at an early age in 1941, when she was trapped in a burning building during an early Nazi attack on Stalingrad. Ivan Petrovitch Bezukhov, a Soviet soldier searching for signs of his dead sister, saw Natasha in the inferno and rushed to her rescue. Escaping the USSR, the pair surfaced months later in Madripoor. The ninja Hand cult abducted Natasha, hoping to raise her as a master assassin. Aided by Captain America and the Madripoor adventurer Logan (later Wolverine), Ivan rescued his charge. Little is known of Ivan and Natasha's further wartime adventures, nor is there any record of why Ivan aged so slowly in the ensuing decades.

Circa 1956 or later, Natasha, now in the custody of a master spy called Taras Romanov, was reunited with Logan, his memories erased following government service. Logan studied espionage under Taras for two years, also training Natasha in hand-to-hand combat. Although Natasha regarded Logan as a surrogate father, Taras instructed her to kill Logan to complete her training. Logan instead killed Taras, which had been his own true assignment, allowing Natasha to depart in hopes she would escape the life Taras intended for her. Later, while still at least appearing to be in her teens, Natasha was recruited for the USSR's Black Widow Program, in which she and other orphan girls were conditioned as sleeper agents for eventual deployment throughout the world. Supervised by scientist Lyudmila Kudrin, the young Black Widows' physiologies were biochemically enhanced to near-superhuman levels through a process sometimes referred to as a Super-Soldier Serum variant, slowing her physical aging as well. Still not operational as an intelligence agent, Natasha befriended would-be reformer Andre Rostov; she also befriended an older married couple whom she regarded as surrogate parents. She briefly studied ballet with famed Bolshoi instructor Oksana Bolishinko, prompting Natasha's programmer, Grigor Ivanovich, to give her false memories of studies at the Belshivoi Art Institute in Moscow and a subsequent career in ballet, not only to conceal her brainwashing but also to instill a subconscious devotion to her homeland. After unrevealed activities, Natasha was allowed to live a seemingly normal life in Russian society, from which she could be awakened by her conditioning as necessary. At some point, whether through chance or government manipulation, she met and married Alexi Shostakov, an exceptional test pilot who carried out some of Russia's most dangerous assignments.

When Shostakov was assigned to become the national hero called Red Guardian, communist extremists faked his death, prompting Natasha, her memories of the Black Widow Program still buried, to volunteer as an intelligence operative. Her already formidable skills were further heightened by extensive training under Alexi Bruskin and others in the government's Red Room Academy, where she was also brainwashed to sabotage the U.S. defense network as Agent Oktober in the distant future. Her combat and espionage talents soon made her Russia's most accomplished operative; although still retaining no memories of her earlier training, she took the codename "Black Widow." In one assignment, Natasha helped American mercenary Danny French steal a unique energy globe from Project: Four, although French absconded with the globe, betraying their employer Damon Dran. Natasha was subsequently reunited with Logan, his memories of their past relationship suppressed by Weapon X. When he traveled to the U.S. following his recruitment by Canada's Department H, Natasha protected him from Hydra assassins, only to clash with him when he helped U.S. operatives Carol Danvers and Ben Grimm steal Russia's top-secret Red Storm Project. She also trained fellow Russian operatives, including Boris Bullski, who became her partner in various assignments.

After Russian scientist Anton Vanko left Russia to work with Iron Man (Tony Stark), Natasha's superiors sent her and fellow operative Boris Turgenov to assassinate both men. When Turgenov stole Vanko's Crimson Dynamo armor, both Turgenov and Vanko died in battle, but Natasha escaped.

REAL NAME: Natalia "Natasha" Alianovna Romanova
ALIASES: Natasha Romanoff (anglicized version of her Russian name), Nadine Roman, Nat, Babette, Ebon Flame, Tsarina, Oktober, Laura Matthers, Nancy Rushman, Black Pearl, Natalia Shostakova, Natuska, Czarina; others used in espionage assignments
IDENTITY: Publicly known
OCCUPATION: Adventurer, intelligence operative; former schoolteacher, fashion designer, ballerina (possibly)
CITIZENSHIP: Formerly USSR/Russia; resident in USA under extended visa authorized by SHIELD
PLACE OF BIRTH: Stalingrad (later Volgograd), former USSR
KNOWN RELATIVES: Unidentified parents (reportedly deceased), Alexi Shostakov (Red Guardian, estranged husband), Vindiktor (alleged brother, deceased)
GROUP AFFILIATION: Avengers, SHIELD, the Initiative; formerly "Marvel Knights" (Daredevil's vigilante team), Queen's Vengeance, Champions of Los Angeles, Lady Liberators, KGB
EDUCATION: Unrevealed (formerly believed to be college graduate)
FIRST APPEARANCE: Tales of Suspense #52 (1964)

She soon entrapped and manipulated the costumed archer Hawkeye (Clint Barton) into assisting her, and helped him enhance his arsenal with more technologically sophisticated arrows. Hawkeye's influence led her to rebel against her masters, who extorted her to return to action with

a new costume and weapons, but she and Hawkeye again failed against Iron Man. Briefly hospitalized, she returned to Russia and broke all ties with her former superiors. Hawkeye joined the Avengers in her absence, and when she returned to the U.S., she divided her time between freelance work for elite intelligence agency SHIELD and informal assistance on Avengers missions. When she and Hawkeye were captured by General Yuri Brushov, she learned Alexi Shostakov still lived as Red Guardian, who protested his employers' dishonorable treatment of the Avengers and seemingly sacrificed his life to save them. Unaware Shostakov had again survived, Natasha briefly retired from action and contemplated a marriage proposal from Hawkeye, but, following a reunion with Ivan Petrovitch, broke ties with Hawkeye to begin a solo vigilante career against Astrologer, Watchlord and others.

When time-traveling android Mister Kline framed Natasha for murder via an android Scorpion duplicate, Matt Murdock (secretly Daredevil) defended her and became romantically drawn to her, per Kline's future-altering plans. Kline seemingly perished before further manipulating them, but they remained together as a crime-fighting couple; accompanied by Ivan, they left New York for California, where they soon clashed with Damon Dran, who might have killed them had Danny French not sacrificed his life to stop Dran. Natasha and Daredevil briefly returned to New York to assist the Avengers, who finally awarded her full membership, but the pair soon returned to California and fought several superhumans whom Moondragon had mutated with the intention of fighting Thanos.

After fighting alongside Daredevil against the terrorists of Black Spectre and Hydra, Natasha encountered another terrorist group, the Sword of Judgement [sic], and discovered their leader Agamemnon to be her long-lost friend Andre Rostov. Growing alienated from Daredevil, she ultimately ended their relationship but continued her activities in California, where she and several other super heroes founded the Champions after helping Olympians Hercules and Venus foil a scheme masterminded by their enemy Pluto. During the Champions' brief history, Black Widow served as team leader and became increasingly close to Hercules. Meanwhile, Natasha and Ivan and the now-defected Alexi Bruskin were attacked by several Russian super-agents, including a new Crimson Dynamo (Ivan's son Yuri) and the Titanium Man (Boris Bullski). When the Champions disbanded, Natasha and Hercules remained together for a time, aiding the Avengers against Korvac, but they soon parted company. She returned to SHIELD assignments, including one where she joined Spider-Man and others in freeing the entire SHIELD Helicarrier from the terrorist Viper. Months later, Natasha rescued Ivan from the vengeful Damon Dran, fighting several costumed mercenaries, including former Russian agent Iron Maiden, in the process.

Following a stint as spokeswoman for Barbara Whalen's short-lived "Super-Heroes Against Drugs" campaign, Natasha was drawn back to Avengers duty during such major crises as an Atlantean invasion and the "Acts of Vengeance" conspiracy. After Russian dissidents briefly manipulated her into crime via an LMD of Alexi Shostakov, Natasha returned to the Avengers full-time; when her long-dormant Oktober persona was activated, Iron Man helped her break her brainwashing. Eventually becoming team leader, Natasha led the Avengers against the Mindspawn, the Gatherers and others, and developed an unrequited crush on Captain America. During a business trip to Russia, she and Iron Man shared a brief romance and battled her former student, Titanium Man, who seemingly died in battle but later returned. When AIM reconstructed the Cosmic Cube, Ivan was seriously wounded by

the Red Skull while investigating on Natasha's behalf. The Avengers defeated the Skull, but Ivan may have died from his wounds, having not yet resurfaced since then.

When most of the active Avengers seemingly perished fighting Onslaught, Natasha was forced to disband the team but kept busy against old enemies and new, including terrorist units called Underground Militia and Freedomslight. She was lured into a trap by the armored Vindiktor, who claimed to be her long-lost brother, but he seemingly perished before his claims could be proven. When Natasha's teammates resurfaced alive, the Avengers were re-established, but Natasha did not return to full-time duty. She joined Nick Fury in a counter-terrorist operation in Latveria, which forced her to manipulate Daredevil and others on Fury's behalf. On another mission, she encountered the latest graduate of Russia's Red Room, Yelena Belova, who was desperate to prove herself Natasha's better as the new Black Widow. Natasha participated in Daredevil's short-lived efforts to form a new super-team; months later, while being helped by Daredevil in turn, she discovered that new international charges against her came from her husband Alexi, who had developed an obsessive vendetta against her and political power with which to pursue it.

Shortly after the mad Scarlet Witch's attack again disbanded the Avengers, Natasha retired to Arizona but was targeted, as were other survivors of the Black Widow Program, by the North Institute on behalf of the corporation Gynacon. Natasha's investigations led her back to Russia, where she was appalled to learn the extent of her past manipulation; she also discovered she and her fellow Widows were hunted because Gynacon, having purchased Russian bio-technology from Red Room's successor agency 2R, wanted all prior users of the technology dead. After killing Gynacon CEO Ian McMasters, she clashed with operatives of multiple governments to rescue Sally Anne Carter, a girl Natasha had befriended in her investigations. More recently, Natasha has joined a new Avengers roster organized by Iron Man, who is now also the director of SHIELD as Tony Stark.

HEIGHT: 5'7"	**EYES:** Blue
WEIGHT: 131 lbs.	**HAIR:** Red-auburn (formerly dyed black)

ABILITIES/ACCESSORIES: Black Widow is an extraordinary gymnast, athlete, and hand-to-hand combatant, trained in multiple martial arts; government treatments have slowed her aging, augmented her immune system and enhanced her physical durability. Her strength is also enhanced, sufficient to lift 500 lbs. She is an accomplished spy and an expert with most forms of weaponry. She is fluent in Russian, English, French, German, Chinese and other languages. Black Widow customarily wears two bracelets equipped to discharge electric bolts of up to 30,000 volts, fire cable with grappling hooks for acrobatic travel, and shoot tear gas cartridges. Her costume is lined with microscopic suction cups allowing her to adhere to any surface; at times she carries plastic explosives in her belt and uses automatic weapons or combat knives as necessary.

POWER GRID	1	2	3	4	5	6	7
INTELLIGENCE							
STRENGTH							
SPEED							
DURABILITY							
ENERGY PROJECTION							
FIGHTING SKILLS							

REAL NAME: Robert Bruce Banner
ALIASES: Green King, Green Scar, Holku, Sakaarson, Green One, Eye of Rage, World Breaker, Harkanon, Haarg, Once-Savage, Two-Minds, Captain Universe, Professor, War, Maestro, Joe Fixit, Mr. Fixit, Annihilator, Mechano; Bruce Barnes, Bruce Smith, Glenn Summers, Ross Oppenheimer, Bob Danner, Bruce Ross, Bruce Jones, Bruce Roberts, Mr. Bergen, Bruce Franklin, Bruce Green, Bruce Bancroft, Bruce Baxter, Bruce Davidson, David Bannon, Robert Baker, Bruce Bixby, David Banner, David Bixby, numerous other aliases to disguise identity; "Two-Hands," "Greenskin," "Mr. Green," "Jade Jaws," "Green Goliath," "Jade Giant," "Gray Goliath," "Mighty Bob," "Anti-Hulk," "Friday," "Green Golem," "Golem"
IDENTITY: Publicly known; it is not publicly known that Joe Fixit was the Hulk
OCCUPATION: Warrior; former ruler of Sakaar, rebel leader, gladiator/slave, adventurer, nuclear physicist, mechanic, leader of the Pantheon, enforcer, research scientist, stable hand, banker, ship's crewman, farmhand, steelworker, assistant at special needs children's school, waiter, dishwasher, carnival worker, ore miner, construction worker, janitor, coal miner

CITIZENSHIP: USA, wanted for crimes (several past pardons); Sakaar
PLACE OF BIRTH: Dayton, Ohio
KNOWN RELATIVES: Caiera (wife, deceased), Elizabeth "Betty" Ross Talbot Banner (wife), Brian and Rebecca Banner (parents, deceased), Bruce (paternal grandfather, presumed deceased), unidentified paternal grandmother (presumed deceased), Susan (maternal grandmother, presumed deceased), William Morris Walters (uncle), Elaine Banner Walters (aunt, deceased), Susan Elizabeth Banner (formerly Susan Drake; paternal aunt, possibly deceased), Jennifer Walters (She-Hulk, cousin), Thaddeus E. "Thunderbolt" Ross (father-in-law)
GROUP AFFILIATION: Warbound; formerly Defenders, Order, Apocalypse's Horsemen, Secret Defenders, alternate Fantastic Four (Ghost Rider/Dan Ketch, Spider-Man/Peter Parker, Wolverine/James Howlett), Pantheon, Titans Three, Avengers, Hulkbusters of Franklin Richards' Counter-Earth (as the Hulk); formerly the Hulkbusters (as Banner)
EDUCATION: Ph.D. in nuclear physics and two other fields
FIRST APPEARANCE: Incredible Hulk #1 (1962)

HISTORY: Robert Bruce Banner was the son of atomic physicist Dr. Brian Banner and his wife, Rebecca. Although Rebecca deeply loved Bruce, who returned her affection, Brian hated the child. Brian Banner was insanely jealous of Rebecca's love for Bruce. In addition, Brian had become convinced that his work in Los Alamos to produce clean nuclear power had altered his own genes, resulting in what he saw as a mutant offspring. Bruce's early demonstrations of phenomenal intelligence only served to reinforce this belief, and Brian became increasingly abusive to Bruce, as well as to Rebecca when she defended Bruce. When Rebecca finally tried to take Bruce and flee, Brian murdered her. Having witnessed this, Bruce was intimidated by Brian into keeping silent during the ensuing trial. Brian, however, was overheard bragging how he had browbeaten Bruce into lying, and he was arrested and sent to Bellmore Psychiatric Institute in San Francisco, California.

Already a quiet intellectual youth, Bruce became even more withdrawn, internalizing his great pain and rage over his childhood sufferings. He was initially raised in Charlestown, Ohio by his aunt Susan Drake. Among his few childhood joys were the summers spent with his younger cousin, Jen Walters. By the time Bruce and his aunt (who retook her maiden name, Banner) moved to Modesto, California, Bruce had developed a separate personality to express his hidden feelings, regarding it as his imaginary friend, Hulk (or at least remembering it as so in retrospect years later). While in high school, Bruce received a severe beating after coming between an aggressive boy and his girlfriend. Enraged, the Hulk persona took control of Bruce during his sleep and he planted a bomb in the school boiler room. Realizing what had happened, Bruce rushed to the school and deactivated the timer, but was discovered, beaten again and kicked out of school. Though the bomb had been defective, Bruce's efforts were noticed by the US military, who hoped that he might become a weapons designer for them in the future. Unknown to Banner, they had Air Force General Thaddeus "Thunderbolt" Ross pressure the school not to press criminal charges as long as Bruce and Susan left town.

After graduating from Science High School, with the military's support Bruce studied nuclear physics in Navapo, New Mexico, at Desert State University (DSU) as the star student of professors Herbert Josiah Weller, Max Christiansen and his mentor Geoffrey Crawford. He roomed with classmate Peter Corbeau, who would remain a long-term friend, and later with pre-law student Randy Cantor. Bruce was also classmates with Raoul Stoddard. Despite his introverted nature, Bruce was allegedly three-time dart champion. Following a brief relationship with Sally Moore, Bruce dated classmate Susan Jacobson, who tried to bring

the withdrawn Banner out of his shell. When he finally did respond to her, however, his emotions exploded forth and he grabbed and terrified the girl, who broke up with him. Shortly thereafter, he had a brief fling with Susan's wilder friend Nicky. Bruce also studied for a time at Pennsylvania State University, where he met Walter Langkowski (later Sasquatch).

Bruce initially attended medical school but quit to return to his true calling. He obtained his doctorate in nuclear physics at the California Institute of Technology, alongside Phillip Sterns (later Madman) and Rikky Keegan. After a number of failed relationships, Bruce finally found happiness at CIT with medical student Angela Lipscombe; however, when Angela won a research grant and Bruce's proposals were turned down by multiple organizations, he became jealous and left her. Bruce corresponded with Charles Xavier on the gamma ray treatment of mental exhaustion and wrote a paper on particle physics, and was colleagues with Ronald Jenkins, Dimitri Solzyn and Hector DeVasquez. Unable to get work from anyone else, Banner was ultimately forced to turn to the military. Around this time Brian Banner was released from the mental hospital, and he confronted Bruce, tormenting him with the knowledge of his actions and threatening to kill him. Bruce fought back in self-defense, striking his father, who fell backwards, struck a tombstone and was killed. Bruce repressed his memory of this incident for many years to come.

Bruce went to work for the United States Defense Department nuclear research facility at Desert Base, New Mexico under the secret oversight of General John Ryker. There Banner finally met General "Thunderbolt" Ross, now the officer in command of the base, and his daughter, Betty. Banner and Betty eventually fell in love with each other, and Bruce also befriended cropduster Hank Stazinksi, becoming godfather to his daughter, Polly. Banner designed and oversaw construction of the "gamma bomb" or "G-bomb," a nuclear weapon with a high gamma radiation output. During the gamma bomb's first test detonation, Bruce observed from the instrumentation bunker that a civilian had breached security and entered the restricted test area. Banner told his colleague, Igor Starsky, to delay the countdown while he got the civilian to safety; however, Starsky was secretly Russian agent Igor Drenkov, and he allowed the countdown to continue, certain Banner would die in the explosion, ending the project. Reaching the civilian, Rick Jones, Banner threw him into a protective trench; but before Bruce could get himself to safety, the gamma bomb detonated and Banner was irradiated with highly charged radioactive particles. Banner was not killed by the radiation, which instead caused him to transform before Jones' eyes that very night, becoming a gray, monstrous and powerful creature that rampaged through the base. One of the soldiers seeing the creature referred to him as a "hulk," which became the name the military adopted for him; ironically this was the same name Banner had used for his persona representing his inner rage and anger, and the creature adopted this name for itself.

After the Hulk and Rick encountered, exposed and defeated Igor as he tried to steal Banner's notes, the Hulk was drawn to Betty, which led to more Army conflicts. He returned to Banner's form and mind at daybreak, but continued to transform back and forth. Realizing the Hulk's threat, Banner established a hidden desert laboratory in a cave near Desert Base. It included a small rock chamber in which Rick could seal Banner each night to contain the Hulk, and was the first of several such desert bases Banner established in the surrounding desert. Enraged by the Hulk's interest in Betty, Ross aggressively pursued the Hulk, once even aided by the new hero Iron Man (Tony Stark), to no avail. Meanwhile, though imprisoned, Igor transmitted a message to his superiors who

informed the mutated genius Gargoyle (Yuri Topolov) of the Hulk's existence. Initially intending to prove his superiority, Gargoyle captured the Hulk and Rick Jones via will-sapping pellets and brought them to his Russian base; upon seeing the Hulk's transformation into Banner, Gargoyle — himself a radiation mutate — worked with Banner to achieve a cure for his own condition. Grateful, Topolov set Banner and Jones free and blew up his own base, sacrificing himself to strike back against the government that had mutated and exploited him, dying as a man.

The first of the many variations of Banner's transformations manifested as the Hulk became green, the color he would generally keep and the hue most often seen in other gamma mutates. At first Banner kept his affliction secret from everyone except Rick Jones, who was grateful to Banner for saving his life and has remained his friend and confidant ever since. Though Banner and Hulk soon defeated the invading alien Tribbitites ("Toad Men"), Banner's unexplained presence aboard their ship led to early suspicions of Banner being a traitor; these were further inflamed by Banner's frequent unexplained absences. The military regarded the Hulk as a menace and constantly hunted him, often on the orders of General Ross. For instance, the General's "Plan H" launched the Hulk into space aboard a missile, but Rick returned the missile to Earth. Space radiation transmitted back through its controls on Earth somehow enabled Rick to control Hulk via verbal commands for some time thereafter; in addition, the Hulk stopped turning back into Banner, and he would rampage while Rick slept. After Rick helped Hulk stop the Ringmaster and his Circus of Crime, he daringly used Banner's desert lab gamma ray projector to turn Hulk back into Banner, who then fine-tuned the projector, allowing him to turn into the Hulk at will while retaining his intelligence; however, Hulk remained easily provoked and violent, and Banner was left weakened after his transformations. The Hulk confronted the seemingly alien conqueror Mongu, revealed to be Russian agent Boris Monguski, whose Russian soldiers tried to capture the Hulk so their scientists could make an army with his strength. The Hulk drove off the Russians but was nonetheless suspected of being involved in Mongu's hoax. As the Hulk's rampages continued, groups such as Green Cross were established to provide victims disaster relief.

General Ross unwittingly assigned Banner to stop the Hulk, whose defeats of subterranean warlord Tyrannus and Asian invader General Fang went largely unrecognized. Continued gamma exposure affected Banner, rendering his normal form briefly super-strong and once leaving Banner's normal head atop the Hulk's body, forcing him to wear a Hulk mask; the transformations eventually stabilized with Banner becoming the Hulk in times of stress, though gamma ray exposure often caused the change. Framed for destruction of U.S. technology, Hulk battled the Fantastic Four before the Wrecker (Karl Kort) was exposed as the true culprit. The Hulk redeemed himself in the government's eyes by defeating the alien Metal Master, earning a presidential pardon. Soon after, however, he was duped by the Asgardian god Loki into destroying a train trestle; though he saved the oncoming train, he was nonetheless blamed. Hearing of this, Rick Jones attempted to contact the Fantastic Four to locate Hulk, but Loki redirected the message to reach Loki's hated brother, Thor. Iron Man, Ant-Man (Hank Pym) and the Wasp (Janet Van Dyne) also received the message, joining forces to track the fugitive Hulk, who was posing as a robot named Mechano in the Kiebler Circus (apparently unaware that several Circus of Crime members were also hiding out there). Locating Hulk via Ant-Man's ants, the four heroes briefly fought the Hulk until Loki's duplicity was exposed. Following Loki's defeat, the Hulk helped the other heroes found the Avengers; however, his new teammates distrusted him due

GREEN HULK WITH BANNER'S HEAD

to his dangerous temper. The other-dimensional shape-shifting Space Phantom exploited this distrust by impersonating the Hulk and turning the others against him. The deception was exposed, but the Hulk, feeling he was hated by the other Avengers, quit the group.

As the Hulk's savage personality became more ascendant, he became a public menace once again, continually hunted by the military; the implacable General Ross would even form a specialized military team of "Hulkbusters" devoted to targeting the monster. Namor the Sub-Mariner briefly teamed with Hulk against the Avengers, but their alliance — uneasy due to Namor's arrogance and the Hulk's volatility — was short-lived; the Hulk turned back into Banner in mid-fight and fled. The Hulk found a recurring foe in the Leader, a gamma-enhanced intellect who repeatedly sought to defeat or exploit the Hulk. One of the Hulk's few true friends at this time was the Sentry (Robert Reynolds), whose solar energy soothed the otherwise savage beast. For a time the Hulk stayed at the Sentry's Watchtower, teaming with him against the General, Danny Boy, the Leader, Living Nuke and the Lobster People. Eventually, however, the Sentry's dark side, the Void, returned and assaulted the Hulk, psychically tormenting him and sending him on a rampage; the Hulk soon returned to his wanderings, more alone than ever. The Hulk's somewhat random travels have spanned the globe, including many nations across each continent. He has also visited numerous planets, various dimensions and past and future eras.

For a surprisingly long time, Banner concealed his double identity from virtually everyone but Rick Jones; however, during a time when the Hulk was missing and presumed dead, Jones told General Ross's aide, Major Glenn Talbot, that Banner was the Hulk, and Banner's secret inevitably became public knowledge. Aided by the Fantastic Four's Reed Richards, Banner again placed his mind in control of the Hulk. Believing his problems over, Banner proposed to Betty, who accepted; but the Leader, seeking vengeance on the Hulk, sent the Rhino to disrupt the wedding and used a gamma weapon to restore the savage Hulk. When General Ross was injured in the subsequent battle, the Hulk's nature caused a long-term rift between Bruce and Betty. Soon after, Kang the Conqueror captured the Hulk and sent him back in time to 1917 to rid himself of Banner by arranging the death of Banner's grandfather (or possibly great-grandfather) — a French World War I soldier — to prevent Banner's birth, but the Hulk instead fought attacking German soldiers, foiling Kang's plot. Banner later returned to DSU where Raoul Stoddard used his Gammatron to cure Banner, separating Banner and Hulk into two beings. The Gammatron was subsequently used to remerge them in the erroneous belief that the Hulk might stay submerged within Banner.

Rick had previously left the Hulk, who, not surprisingly, had few other long-term friends. Young Jim Wilson became a close friend, staying by Hulk's side for several lengthy periods. Mogol, agent of Tyrannus also befriended the Hulk, who angrily smashed Mogol to pieces upon learning he was a robot. Hulk formed another brief friendship with the homeless "Crackajack" Jackson, who taught him to read, but Jackson was killed by the criminals Hammer and Anvil. Rick Jones would return to the Hulk's side for long periods in the future. The Hulk also found friends and allies as a member of the Defenders, an informal super-hero group where his long-term teammates included Dr. Strange, Namor, Silver Surfer, Valkyrie, Nighthawk, Hellcat and others; however, the general public was mostly unaware of the Defenders' existence and activities during Hulk's membership, so he was still widely regarded as a menace. Others who befriended the Hulk during his journeys included Morvania's Rachel

Dresden and her family, who believed the Hulk to be the legendary Golem; the benevolent New Men of the High Evolutionary's Counter-Earth; the Brickford family of Lucifer Falls, West Virginia; Siberia's Katrina Palkov; Angus & Sarah MacTavish of Scotland's Loch Fear; Bob & Carol Hickman, son-in-law and daughter of the Locust (August Hopper); an orphaned deer "Bambi" that was later possessed by Chondu the Mystic; orphan Ricky Anderson with whom he attended Florida's Wonderland amusement park; Joe Timms (the Glob); the cavewoman Tanna; the uncivilized Rock People; the "Circus of Lost Souls;" "Robinson Crusoe" (aka David Purvis); Todd Gregory, whom the Hulk helped save from paternal abuse; Canadian "witch doctor" Passing Cloud; Fred Sloan and Trish Starr; Cherokee Chief John; alien exile Zgorian; and the poisoned world's symbiont "Sym."

Similarly, Banner has made numerous friends and acquaintances, such as Abby Davis, a Crystal Falls, Colorado waitress; Jungfrau, Switzerland's Katrina Euler, whom he referred to colleagues for treatment of an illness; British Columbia's Maureen Friesen; Africa's Paradise Island's Thaddeus Hatcher; Manhattan hippy Clear Marks; the mentally challenged Earl Slocum; Suzette Classon; Las Vegas singer Jimmy Martin; Faulkner, Missouri's sheriff Jonas Tolliver and his daughter Emma; St. Louis, Missouri's Jerome Able; Manhattan's Pam Grayson; and London sorceress Patricia Freeman. Some of the above proved friends to both Banner and the Hulk. Banner has also enjoyed a number of short-lived romances, such as Daily Bugle reporter Dawn Michaels, Manhattan businesswoman Alice Steinfeld and the Nightmerican Chrissie Cutler. Unfortunately, the savage Hulk's limited intellect has also rendered him the pawn of numerous evildoers who earned his alliance via promises of friendship or vengeance against those who had harmed him. Though the Fantastic Four's freakish strongman Thing has sympathized with the Hulk's plight, the two have just as often met as foes, and one effort to cure the Hulk instead resulted in a temporary switching of their minds. The feral mutant Wolverine has shared a similar ally/enemy role with the Hulk.

For years Betty Ross continued to love Banner, despite her knowledge of his double identity; however, Banner's feelings were divided after the Hulk fell in love with Jarella, queen of K'ai in an unidentified extradimensional "micro-world" whose green-skinned natives welcomed the Hulk. K'ai's Sorcerers Triad allowed Banner's brain to control the Hulk and he nearly became king, but he was always pulled back to Earth before long. Betty eventually married Glenn Talbot and Jarella was accidentally killed while living on Earth, but Betty still harbored a secret love for Banner. Banner continued efforts to cure himself aided by experts such as his former mentor Geoffrey Crawford, but never achieved any lasting success. While Banner was visiting his cousin Jennifer Walters in Los Angeles, she was shot by an agent of gangster Nicholas Trask. To save his cousin's life Banner improvised an emergency blood transfusion. The transfusion of Banner's blood mutated Walters, causing her to become the She-Hulk. Betty eventually divorced Glenn Talbot, General Ross went mad and Gamma Base was shut down. During this same time, the Hulk briefly became a pawn of the mystic realm Tunnelworld's dread sorcerer the Unnameable — who drew power from and controlled all those who knew its true name — but Dr. Strange ultimately duped the Unnameable into drawing all of its power into the Hulk and then trapping it within a sealed section of the Hulk's brain. Banner subsequently befriended Manhattan's Ruby Barclay who took him to the

INTELLIGENT HULK

mystic Baba Shanti, who turned out to be Bruce's old roommate Randy Cantor seeking to guide others in the path of enlightenment he had attained to some degree. Glenn Talbot was ultimately slain in a desperate effort to destroy the Hulk.

Sometime later, repeated gamma radiation exposure during several adventures caused Bruce to retain Banner's mind in Hulk form and gave him control of his transformations. When this information became public knowledge, the US president pardoned the now heroic Hulk. Bruce briefly enjoyed the companionship of the alien Bereet, who had filmed his adventures as the Hulk from her home planet. Banner then returned to his career as a scientist, working out of Northwind Observatory, constructing the artificial assistant and companion Recordasphere and initiating a romantic relationship with his assistant, Kate Waynesboro. While Kate proved to be a SHIELD agent sent to monitor Banner to ensure he remained in control, she did end up falling in love with him. "Sphere" was destroyed by the Abomination, and Banner was very upset to learn Kate's secret. Banner's anxiety was exacerbated by the demon Nightmare, who sought to provoke him into becoming the savage Hulk once again to increase humanity's fear (and nightmares) of him. Despite his best efforts, Banner began to lose control over the Hulk. Former mobster Max "Hammer" Stryker kidnapped Kate, coercing Banner to use his gamma device to cure Stryker's cancer. The Hulk was transported to Battleworld by the Beyonder to participate in the "Secret Wars" struggle. Upon returning, he saw Stryker mutate into a Hulk-like creature. When the enraged Stryker attacked him, the only way Banner could fight the creature's brutal attack was to allow the savage Hulk personality to gain ascendance. Broken by having and then losing control, Banner retreated further into himself, allowing the Hulk to become more and more mindless and violent. Ultimately, Banner requested that the sorcerer Dr. Strange transform him into the Hulk in his mind to free himself from his tormented existence.

Art by Sal Buscema

"MINDLESS" HULK

The now virtually mindless Hulk was too dangerous to be allowed to rampage across the Earth, and Dr. Strange did not want to kill his old friend. He found the solution in the Crossroads, a dimension that was a portal to countless other dimensions. The Hulk could go anywhere he wanted, and would be returned to the Crossroads as soon as he became dissatisfied with his location. During this time the Hulk found that there were many beings whose power dwarfed even his own. In the Crossroads the Hulk made a friend in the Puffball Collective, another entity that had been banished there; however, the Puffball was revealed to be an agent of the N'Garai demons, and had only befriended the Hulk to escape the Crossroads. Shortly after revealing itself, the Puffball was slaughtered by the N'Garai, and the Hulk returned to the Crossroads. The Collective's attention to the Hulk had begun to reawaken Banner's mind, which first manifested itself as the Triad: Goblin (his id and emotions), Guardian (his ego and sense of self-preservation) and Glow (his superego and intellect). The Triad began to guide the mindless Hulk into rediscovering himself, and on one world a wounded Hulk transformed back into Banner.

The Hulk was unwittingly returned to Earth by the Canadian super-team Alpha Flight. Seeking a monstrous form to house the disembodied intellect of Walter Langkowski (formerly Sasquatch), they unwittingly snared the Hulk with an energy harpoon. The Hulk regressed back into

a violent mindless state upon returning to Earth, rampaging across the continent. Doc Samson eventually captured the Hulk and succeeded in separating Banner's psyche and atomic structure from that of the Hulk, making them separate beings. The mindless Hulk escaped and, no longer restrained by Banner's subconscious identity, became a greater menace than ever before. Banner organized a new group of Hulkbusters to capture the Hulk, for whom he still felt responsible. Nonetheless, thinking himself free from his half-existence as the Hulk, Banner at last married Betty Ross. But Banner's health sharply declined because of his having been so divided. As a result, the android Vision facilitated the reintegration of Banner and the Hulk into a single physical being. General Ross, then descending into madness, interfered with Doc Samson's subsequent attempt to cure the Hulk, causing him to revert back to his original gray state and personality — less strong and more intelligent than the traditional Hulk, but ruthless and cruel. In the process, Rick was exposed to the Hulk's energies and began turning into his own version of the savage Hulk for a brief time before being cured.

Art by Jeff Purves

MR. FIXIT

Banner initially kept the return of his Hulk transformations a secret, but his condition inevitably became public knowledge again. The gray Hulk worked alongside Rick Jones and SHIELD agent Clay Quartermain during the search for a missing gamma bomb. The quest culminated with the Leader detonating the bomb in the city of Middletown, Arizona with the Hulk at the center of the explosion. Seemingly dead, the Hulk was actually saved by wizards of Jarella's world, who brought him to their planet to overthrow the mad Grand Inquisitor. The Hulk enjoyed the resultant worship he received and decided to stay there, but the wizards sent him home so they could rule instead. Upon returning to Earth, the still gray Hulk took the identity of Joe Fixit and became an enforcer for Las Vegas casino Coliseum owner Michael Berengetti. Fixit kept his Hulk identity secret, pretending instead to have a bizarre skin condition that was sensitive to sunlight. A spell from the alien sorcerers allowed Fixit to remain in Hulk form for months without reverting, but eventually the spell wore off. Fixit briefly dated the statuesque Marlo Chandler, but eventually it became clear that he was the Hulk; Berengetti terminated his employment due to the heat the Hulk was continually bringing to his business.

Art by Dale Keown

PANTHEON COSTUME

The Hulk's transformation began to destabilize, and he would intermittently become Fixit and the green savage Hulk. Eventually Doc Samson partially diagnosed Banner's identity disorder and, by working with the Ringmaster's hypnosis, merged Banner's mind with that of Fixit and the savage Hulk, creating a new form, which possessed the greatest aspects of each of the splinter personalities, later nicknamed the Professor. Now mentally stable in his Hulk form, Banner was soon recruited to join covert disaster-prevention group the Pantheon, which he came to lead for a length of time. During this period he was pulled forward in time to encounter his dark future self, the Maestro; the knowledge of his potential future greatly troubled the Hulk. The Pantheon also helped the Hulk free his old girlfriend Susan Jacobson, who had been imprisoned as a spy. Later, when an internal war developed in the Pantheon, the Hulk became so angry that he triggered a subconscious fail-safe he had created for himself. Fearful of his mindless form's destructive capacity, he transformed back into Banner upon becoming too angry. In addition, while in Banner's form, he possessed the mind of the savage Hulk. This created an Achilles' heel for Banner in that one of his greatest assets, his anger, became his greatest weakness.

BANNER-LESS HULK

COUNTER-EARTH HULK

The Hulk left the Pantheon, working briefly as a mechanic under his old instructor, Max Christiansen. Later, Banner received a piece of shrapnel in his brain, and only transformation into the Hulk saved his life. The shrapnel caused the Hulk to become darker and more violent, seemingly beginning the degeneration that would lead to his becoming the Maestro. When the Hulk opposed the malevolent psychic entity Onslaught, a portion of Banner was sent to the alternate world created by Franklin Richards that eventually became known as Counter-Earth; that fragment was reborn as a fledgling Hulk with his past memories suppressed. Maintaining a connection with his Counter-Earth fragment, the Hulk initially mutated and shed massive amounts of radiation before stabilizing. Sensing that he was lacking something, the Hulk sought to gain "more," though he did not know what he truly wanted. For a time he was joined by Janis Jones (time-displaced possible future great-granddaughter of Rick Jones and Marlo Chandler), and his interdimensional connections served as a nexus attracting otherdimensional beings, such as the Hulk of Reality-9722 who had slain that timeline's Maestro and ruled his Dystopia for a time. Bereft of Banner's mental blocks, the Hulk also began to rediscover his suppressed memories of his father and his death, and he was sometimes plagued by the seeming ghost of his father. During this time the Hulk fell under the influence of the immortal mutant Apocalypse, who used a laser to destroy the shrapnel in the Hulk's brain. The Hulk briefly became Apocalypse's Horseman War, wearing a helmet intended to block out his father; however, when War injured Rick Jones, the Hulk was again plagued by guilt and his father's taunts, and he rejected Apocalypse's programming and regained his own mind.

Eventually the two Hulk fragments were remerged, restoring the status quo of the savage Hulk splitting its existence and time with Banner. The Hulk then faced and again defeated the Maestro, who had eventually absorbed enough gamma radiation from his past self to re-form. Bruce once again established a healthy relationship with his wife Betty, but he suffered a devastating blow when Betty died of radiation poisoning after his old enemy the Abomination injected her with some of his own blood; Banner initially assumed Betty had died from chronic exposure to his own radioactive body. Shortly thereafter, Banner's influence was usurped by Tyrannus, who sent the Hulk on senselessly destructive rampages that Banner could not recall. Tyrannus also briefly captured Banner and used a Tyrannoid Subterranean mutated into Hulk form to replace him. The Tyrannoid-Hulk went on even more destructive rampages, bringing down a passenger airplane, killing everyone aboard. The Hulk ultimately halted Tyrannus' plot and cleared his name.

Banner then began to suffer from the degenerative neurological disease Amyotrophic Lateral Sclerosis (ALS, aka Lou Gehrig's Disease). Banner's condition deteriorated severely, and he worked with his old college girlfriend, neurologist Angela Lipscombe, to develop a cure. During this time, the Hulk, Dr. Strange, Namor and the Surfer fell prey to a spell of their enemy Yandroth that cursed them to be drawn together as the Defenders whenever evil threatened Earth. Following being targeted and briefly captured by the nefarious General John Ryker, the Hulk was ultimately treated by Lipscombe, Reed Richards and Ant-Man (Scott Lang), who repaired Bruce's nervous system via implanting DNA from Brian Banner's corpse. Obliquely indebted to him for his continued life, Bruce at last made his peace with his memories of his father. Soon after, Yandroth's spell — which drew on the Earth goddess Gaea's power — caused the four Defenders to become increasingly self-righteous and violent, eventually establishing themselves as the Order and seeking to conquer Earth. Empowered by their violence, Yandroth nearly gained the power to destroy the world before the Order realized his plan and ceased all hostilities, dissipating his power and essence again.

Bruce was then contacted by the mysterious Mr. Blue — actually Betty Banner, secretly resurrected and surgically altered by a mysterious agency known only as the Team — who trained him to use self-hypnosis to better control his transformations. Soon after, the Leader initiated his most complex plot yet against his old foe. The Hulk was framed for the seeming death of Ricky Myers, and Bruce had to go into hiding. On the run once again, the Hulk was pursued by various agents of the covert organization Home Base, who sought his blood to create an army of super-powered warriors. Some of these agents, such as Pratt, Sandra Verdugo and the mysterious S-3, had been granted extensive regenerative powers. Both Banner and the Hulk were pursued relentlessly in a series of ever more complicated plots, though Banner continued to receive aid from Mr. Blue and Doc Samson. Verdugo was actually Ricky Myer's mother by Samson, and she had been promised to be reunited with her son if she brought the Hulk to Home Base. Realizing that Home Base would slay Ricky as soon as they had the Hulk, she instead turned against her partner, Jink Slater, arranging his death and convincing the Hulk to help rescue Ricky. Pratt successfully obtained a sample of Hulk blood but was injected with it before he could return it to Home Base. Despite being mutated by this exposure, Pratt was ultimately destroyed by the Hulk. Bruce then seemed to happen upon a New Mexico desert supply store and shared a romance with its owner; this turned out to be yet another Home Base plot, as the owner was Nadia Dornova Blonsky, the Abomination's ex-wife, who had joined with Home Base to gain revenge on her abusive former spouse. Nadia, however, developed true feelings for Banner, revealed her plot to him, and confronted the Abomination herself, intending to destroy him with a Home Base-implanted weapon. Home Base double-crossed her with an ineffective weapon, but the Hulk saved her and defeated the Abomination.

Seeking peace in Mistassini, Canada, Banner instead encountered Wolverine and the assassin Shredder before saving coral-snake-bite victim Kyle Hatcher with a transfusion of his own blood. Relocating to Manhattan, Banner befriended advertising agent Pam Grayson, who helped him defeat a psychically powered Absorbing Man. Banner was then guided back to New Mexico by Home Base and arrived to save Nadia and the recently arrived S-3 from the Home Base's Krill — lizard-like androids designed to deliver Hulk blood to Home Base.

Despite her facial reconstruction, the Hulk instantly recognized S-3 as Betty, a former double agent within Home Base as well as the enigmatic Mr. Blue, and they were soon joined by Samson and Verdugo. In a seemingly final confrontation with Home Base, Sandra perished in its self-destruct nuclear explosion, while the Hulk saved the others from a Home Base Banner/ Hulk clone, which he was forced to eviscerate to prevent its regeneration. During that conflict, only Nadia believed that Bruce was himself and not the clone, and Banner left all of them to be alone, though he did leave behind a supply of the Hulk's blood that Betty might use to save herself from the cancer she had obtained during the Team's treatments. Relocating to California, the Hulk was captured by the clairvoyant Even Matthews; Matthews released Banner and tried to trick Banner into killing him to prevent his dying from cancer, though Banner recognized the ruse and refused. Tony Stark drafted Banner into helping him develop a gamma-radiation-proof suit of armor, and both Banner and the Hulk were needed to save Stark from radiation toxicity after Stark elevated the radiation exposure levels in efforts to prove the armor's value.

Exhausted by his recent non-stop adventures, Banner at last fell prey to the Leader, who forced the Hulk into a somnambulant state, drawing him to his base. Left a disembodied head by his recent experiences, the Leader forced the Hulk to set his controls to establish a link between their minds, and the Leader intended to transfer his mind into the Hulk's brain, permanently ousting Banner's mind. Samson, Betty and Nadia came to the rescue, and Samson smashed the Hulk into the Leader's tank, severing his linkage to the Hulk and leaving his head to die in the open air. Nadia, however, perished saving Betty from a piece of flying glass from the shattered tank, taking it through the chest instead. Enraged and confused, the Hulk savagely beat Samson until Betty condemned the Hulk as a destructive monster and caused him to flee.

The Hulk was subsequently enlisted by Strange against the extradimensional sorcerer Dormammu, who turned Hulk to stone. Restored and seduced by Dormammu's sorcerous sister, Umar, the Hulk then joined her, Strange and Namor in stripping Dormammu of power he had usurped from the cosmic Eternity, power Umar claimed herself. Summoned to Nightmare Island, the Hulk was beset by extradimensional Mindless Ones in illusory form via the demon Nightmare, but he ultimately saw through the deceptions, decapitated Nightmare and left his new acquaintance Daydream (Nightmare's half-human daughter) behind. In London, Bruce briefly befriended the sorceress Patricia Freeman, helping her spirit track down her killer, Tom Perkins, before she faded from existence.

When the Scarlet Witch overwrote existence with the "House of M" reality, Banner and the Hulk both found themselves an accepted part of the True People tribe of Aborigines in Australia. The Hulk joined forces with AIM (Advanced Idea Mechanics) — including Monica Rappaccini, Scorpion (Carmilla Black/Thasanee Rappaccini), Professor Aaron Isaacs and his robot creation Adam — in toppling the mutant Exodus' dictatorship, which was rounding up humans for slaughter. Now ruling Australia, Banner had a

relationship with Monica, learning she was Nicky from his college days. Even after discovering and neutralizing Monica's cyborg army program (developed from unwilling recruits captured by government agents) and overcoming her efforts to have him killed, Banner kept Monica by his side, refusing to surrender

his new position even under instruction from the mighty Magneto who ruled that reality. Soon after, however, this reality faded from existence and the status quo was restored. The "Old Man" of the True People, whose mysticism had allowed him to see beyond the reality changes, invited "Two-Minds" (his name for Banner and the Hulk) to stay with them, but Banner realized his violent ways would be a constant threat to them. Sometime later, while passing through Jackalope, New Mexico, the Hulk fought off a SHIELD helicopter pursuing Amadeus Cho, earning the young ultra-genius' fierce loyalty.

Enlisted to foil a plot by the terrorist group Hydra, the Hulk was exposed to a gamma bomb explosion, which rendered him delusional and left him in his gray form, but with his full strength. The Hulk rampaged in Las Vegas, battling the Human Torch and Thing at length until the former's nova flame restored his sanity. This rampage, however, had been noticed by the "Illuminati" — a secret elite cabal of super-beings who sought to keep Earth's paranormal affairs under control. Despite the objections and violent departure of Namor, the remaining Illuminati members — Iron Man, Mr. Fantastic (Reed Richards), Dr. Strange and the Inhuman monarch Black Bolt — plotted the permanent elimination of Hulk's threat to Earth. As Strange and the others had all been Hulk's friends at some point, they sought to slay him, but instead to banish him to another world where he might live in peace. Banner had relocated to northwestern Alaska, living a solitary existence as a fisherman, but was tracked by a Nick Fury LMD (Life Model Decoy) and enlisted to destroy the Godseye, an alleged Hydra creation that threatened Earth. Banner agreed and the Hulk went up in space, risking his life and destroying the Godseye, but not before he learned it was actually a SHIELD creation. Planning to take this up with Fury, the Hulk instead fell victim to the "Illuminati" plot and was sent flying off into space with no ability to control his ship as it headed for an uninhabited planet. A parting message from his four former friends explaining their actions played out as he realized his fate.

The "Illuminati" plot went awry when the SHIELD ship carrying the Hulk was pulled into the Great Portal, a wormhole created by the Shadow People of the planet Sakaar that brought beings and objects from around the universe to their world in hopes of helping the planet and its people. Greatly weakened by the passage and subsequent crash, the Hulk was captured and auctioned off to gladiator trainer Primus Vand. Drawing early attention after slaughtering a group of immensely powerful "great devil corkers," the Hulk then targeted Sakaar's ruler, the Red King (Angmo II). Intrigued, the battle-armored King confronted the Hulk, delivering several wounds but receiving a sword slash to his face in return. The Hulk was subdued by the King's Death's Head Warguards, implanted with a control disk and sent to the training camp known as the Maw where it was believed he would perish.

Overcoming various challenges, the Hulk was placed in a group with fellow survivors the insectoid Miek (whom he had saved from the Corkers in the previous battle), a nameless Brood female, the Kronan Korg, Hiroim of the Shadow People, and the Imperials (natives of the same ruling class as the Red King) Lavin Skee and Elloe Kaifi. During their first group gladiatorial combat, an enthusiastic announcer nicknamed Hulk the "Green Scar" for a wound he received fighting the Red King. After proving themselves in combat, the gladiators were invited to join the Sakaar Democratic Insurgency; though the Hulk and others refused, Elloe sided with the rebel Insurgency, who were swiftly captured by Warguards. Recognizing the Hulk as extremely dangerous, the Red King's bound Shadow Warrior, Caiera the Oldstrong, attempted to buy him and take him out of combat, but he refused. The Red King subsequently had a bomb dropped on the gladiators, but the Hulk saved them, taking the full hit himself and then flattening the attacking Warguard, though Lavin Skee fell in combat. The remaining gladiators then joined together as Warbound, vowing loyalty to each other. Interestingly, in spots where the Hulk's blood touched the soil of Sakaar, Eleha'al vines began to grow, leading some to believe the Hulk was the Sakaarson, a being long prophesized as the savior of Sakaar.

The Warbound's next challenge was the Silver Surfer, who had also passed through the Great Portal and been enslaved by the Red King as the "Silver Savage." Surprised by his former ally's attack, the Hulk recovered and shattered the Surfer's control disk but nonetheless angrily beat him senseless. The Red King then offered the Warbound their freedom — as was custom after surviving three such combats — but only if they slew their former member Elloe. The Warbound refused despite the King's threats of destruction, and the Surfer then destroyed every control disk in the arena, allowing the Warbound, Surfer and others to break out and escape into the wilderness. The Surfer offered to take the Hulk with him as he departed, but the Hulk declined, having at last found friendship and a life he could enjoy.

Via sage advice from Hiroim and Korg, the Hulk evaded multiple attacks by the King's warriors, and his following grew steadily as Miek located a number of his insectoid brethren (thought long dead) and then liberated those in the Maw. The Hulk considered leaving his allies as he feared that he was not the Sakaarson, but instead another prophecy, the apocalyptic World Breaker; however, after Miek evolved into a much more powerful form as ruler of the insectoids, Hulk decided to continue to lead the rebels. Hoping to save Sakaar from prolonged war, Caiera met the Hulk in single combat, her Old Power proving an even match for his gamma-spawned might. The Red King, however, caring little for his people and wishing to end the Hulk's threat by any means possible, unleashed the Spikes — parasitic menaces whom his father had long ago banished to one of Sakaar's moons, able to infect and assimilate organic beings into their number — freeing them to slaughter the Warbound, his own troops (including Caiera) and even the innocent civilians nearby. The Hulk proved resistant to infection, and after the Red King had an entire city of civilians slaughtered by missile attack to destroy his enemies, Caiera vowed vengeance on him and joined the rebellion.

Seeking allies, the Hulk was denied the aid of the Shadow People but did claim their stone starship to aid the rebellion. Surprising all involved, the Hulk made an alliance with the elder Spikes, learning they only sought freedom from Sakaar's environment since it deprived them of stellar energy and drove them mad with hunger. The Hulk finally met and overpowered the Red King, who mercilessly slaughtered his own people during the battle, and cast him into the wilderness where he was consumed by Wildebots. The Hulk was pronounced the new king of Sakaar and he swiftly enforced peace between the formerly warring Imperials and insectoid Natives, after which he chose Caiera as his queen, undergoing her Shadow ritual and revealing his Banner form to her. Having sustained the Spikes with his own power, the Hulk had them sent back into space, and they gratefully returned the spirits of the lives they had unintentionally absorbed on Sakaar, allowing those spirits' loved ones closure and the knowledge that they had achieved peace. By only the third day of his rule, the Hulk had earned massive approval and was making steps towards peace with long-time enemies of the Imperials when the warp core on the ship that had brought him to Sakaar exploded. The unleashed energies caused a chain reaction that shattered Crown City of Sakaar and slew the vast majority of the population, including Caiera, who was bearing the Hulk's child. Infuriated beyond comprehension and empowered even further by the explosion's energies, Hulk led Sakaar's few known survivors, including his Warbound and robot pilot Arch-E, in boarding the stone starship and heading to Earth for vengeance on the "Illuminati."

Arriving first on the moon, the Hulk savagely beat Black Bolt and then sent a transmission to Earth ordering Manhattan's evacuation that he might meet Iron Man, Dr. Strange and Reed Richards in combat. Iron Man faced him in a set of Hulkbuster armor but met a crushing defeat that shattered much of Avengers Tower as well. Overpowering all who tried to stop him — including Doc Samson, She-Hulk and two Avengers contingents — the Hulk then took down the entire Fantastic Four to get Richards. Despite his violent methods, the Hulk gained allies when Amadeus Cho organized the Renegades to assist him. Dr. Strange met Bruce Banner on the astral plane, but the Hulk crushed his hands, reducing his spell-casting ability. Tearing the roof off of Madison Square Garden, the Hulk made this his new gladiatorial arena, using Sakaarian slave disks to control the captured heroes and forcing his former banishers to fight each other. Strange then used a potion to obtain monstrous-strength via the immensely power magical entity Zom.

While Cho planned to gift the Hulk with his own land surrounding New Mexico's desert Base as a sanctuary, it seems the Hulk will not be content with anything but blood vengeance for the loss of his wife, his unborn child and his people. It remains to be seen what level of violence will satisfy him or if anyone can stop him. He has long said, "The madder Hulk gets, the stronger Hulk gets;" and the Hulk has never been more enraged than he is now.

DEVIL HULK

Art by Ron Garney

HEIGHT: (Banner) 5'9½"; (gray Hulk) 6'6"; (green/savage Hulk) 7' — 8'; (green/Professor Hulk) 7'6"
WEIGHT: Banner) 128 lbs.; (gray Hulk) 900 lbs.; (green/savage Hulk) 1040 — 1400 lbs. (green/Professor Hulk) 1150 lbs.
EYES: (Banner) Brown; (gray Hulk) gray; (green Hulk) green
HAIR: (Banner) Brown; (gray Hulk) black; (green Hulk) green

ABILITIES/ACCESSORIES: The Hulk possesses the capacity for superhuman strength ranging beyond the limits of virtually any other known humanoid being. The gamma radiation that mutated his body fortified his cellular structure and added, from some as yet unknown (presumably extradimensional) source, several hundred pounds of bone, muscle and other tissue. In times of stress the Hulk's adrenalin level escalates, causing a corresponding escalation of strength. Thus, the madder the Hulk gets, the stronger the Hulk gets. This is usually not accompanied by an additional gain in mass, but does appear to promote increased levels of energy efficiency. The Hulk has not yet found an endpoint to his maximum strength, so its upper limit remains a mystery. While described as Class 100 strength, the Hulk has on times proven capable of exceeding this parameter several times over;

following exposure to the warp core breach on Sakaar, his baseline strength is even higher.

The Hulk periodically reverts to the human form of Bruce Banner, losing his extra mass and energy to the same source from which he derived it. The Hulk differs from many other gamma-irradiated human beings in that Banner was outside, exposed to sunlight, during his first heavy exposure to gamma radiation. This at least partially explains why the Hulk's color was initially gray, not green like most other gamma mutations. Moreover, this is also part of why Banner had transformed into the gray Hulk at nightfall and reverted to human form at the coming of dawn; however, it was later revealed that this was also partially due to Banner's shame over being the Hulk, and that he subconsciously forced himself to revert to human form in daylight to avoid being seen in his monstrous Hulk form. Though he has since managed to become the gray Hulk in daylight, he sometimes feels a burning sensation from sunlight contacting his skin.

The process by which Banner usually transforms into the Hulk has a chemical catalyst, adrenalin (aka epinephrine). As in normal human beings, Banner's adrenal medulla secretes large amounts of adrenalin in times of fear, rage or stress, which hormonally stimulates the heart rate, raises blood-sugar levels and inhibits sensations of fatigue. Whereas the secretion heightens normal physical abilities in normal human beings, in Banner's case it triggers the complex chemical-extra-physical process that transforms him into the Hulk. The total transformation takes anywhere from seconds to as long as 5 minutes, depending on the initial adrenalin surge, which is determined by the original external stimulus. Soon after the transformation, Hulk's adrenalin levels will return to more normal, reduced levels. At varying points of time in his life, Banner has been able to mentally control the change, producing or inhibiting it in either direction. At many times in the past, Banner would revert to the Hulk, regardless of the time of day or night, whenever he underwent enough excitation to induce a sufficient surge of adrenalin to trigger the transformation. Similarly, often if the Hulk relaxed to a great enough degree, his adrenalin levels would decline and he would revert to human form; however, there are many known instances in which the Hulk was very relaxed or even slept without reverting to human form.

The Hulk is superhumanly durable and resistant to pain and disease. His skin can resist great heat without blistering (even tolerating the Human Torch's nova flame), great cold without freezing (down to absolute zero, -460 degrees Fahrenheit), and great impacts (he can survive direct hits by field artillery cannon shells or falls from the edge of the atmosphere). While it is possible to injure him, the Hulk also has vastly superhuman healing, enabling him to regenerate body tissue (including internal organs) within seconds to minutes; it once took him weeks to recover from a broken neck. It is not known what type of injury could kill the Hulk, but one of his alternate future counterparts was disintegrated by a nuclear level explosion, though he eventually reintegrated his form over a period of several years. The Hulk's highly efficient physiology renders him immune to all terrestrial diseases, and possibly to aging. Though Banner's form does not appear to share these immunities, some injuries will heal via transformation into the Hulk and vice versa. The Hulk can hold his breath for about an hour; his superhuman durability allows him to survive in the vacuum of space or at the ocean floor, though he would suffocate if too much time passed or if he were forced to expel his retained air. In particular, the Hulk is resistant to radiation, though in some circumstances, gamma radiation exposure has caused him to revert back into Banner. Similar effects have been achieved by draining the gamma radiation from the Hulk, or by exposing him to an uncertain type of radiation referred to as "gamma-negative rays."

The Hulk can use his superhumanly strong leg muscles to leap great distances, sometimes covering 3 miles in a single bound. He has even leapt so high into the atmosphere that he nearly achieved stable orbit. The Hulk can also produce destructive shockwaves by clapping his hands or stomping his foot. The Hulk's adrenalin levels counteract fatigue poisons; while fighting others in an enraged state, he can maintain peak output for hours on end and still continue to grow even stronger as his anger escalates. He has swum across both Atlantic and Pacific oceans, though he did become extremely exhausted in the process, presumably from lack of anger.

Bruce Banner suffers from dissociative identity disorder (aka multiple personality disorder or split personality). The Hulk's identities manifest the capacity for rage and violence that Banner, in his human form, has repressed all of his life. The extent of Banner's disorder has only recently been appreciated, and a number of identities or personalities have been discovered. Chief among these identities are the reserved, Bruce Banner core identity, highly intelligent but virtually devoid of emotion; the "savage Hulk" identity, which has childlike levels of intelligence and curiosity, with a longing for friendship and love, and is prone to violent fits of rage (the "savage" Hulk is usually unaware that he is actually Banner, whom he sees as a different person and an enemy); the Joe Fixit identity (usually in the gray Hulk), lacking

Banner's advanced intellect and scientific knowledge, is exceptionally clever and crafty, with selfish motives and desires, and similarly prone to violence; the "Professor" or "merged Hulk" identity, possessing all of Banner's intellect and the savage Hulk's strength, with normal emotional capacity, though still quite prone to violence; the "mindless" Hulk, when Banner's influence has been completely removed; and the "devil" Hulk identity, malevolent and destructive, kept submerged deep within Banner's psyche, but constantly struggling to escape and take over. By some accounts, there are dozens, if not hundreds, of different personality fragments within Banner/Hulk's psyche. The distinctions between these identities have differed significantly over time, with Banner himself having a variable capacity for emotion. At times, the Banner identity has had changing levels of control over the Hulk. Similarly, Banner's memories of his actions as the Hulk — and vice versa — vary significantly. Even the alleged "merged Hulk" seemingly proved to be yet one more splinter identity, a fragment of the whole renamed the "Professor."

His different identities produce outward effects on the Hulk's form, sometimes making him larger or smaller, gray or green, more human or more bestial in appearance, and even stronger or weaker. Among his more unusual transformations, Banner has taken on aspects of gray and green Hulks on opposite sides of his form; Banner's head has remained atop the savage Hulk's form; Banner has been trapped midway between human and Hulk forms, with changes appearing either diffusely or multifocally; and Banner's head has even poked out of the back of the savage Hulk's body. Following a transfusion from Sandra Verdugo, Banner could manifest superhuman strength and durability without transforming into the Hulk. Banner has even been physically separated from the Hulk's form on occasion, but neither form can long survive without the other. In addition, Banner's identity disorder is a large reason why efforts to remove the Hulk's powers or to keep Banner's mind in dominance have met with failure. Under certain circumstances, different aspects of Banner and the various Hulks' personalities can communicate on some sort of psychic plane. Certain magical spells or scientific equipment — such as the Encephelo-Helmet — have allowed Banner's mind to dominate the Hulk's form for a time.

The Hulk has two powers unrelated to his physical abilities. He can see astral (spirit) forms, normally invisible to the naked eye. This ability somehow relates to his guilty conscience over his role in his father's death; he is subconsciously afraid of encountering his father's angry spirit. His other such power is a homing ability that enables him to locate the area in New Mexico where he first became the Hulk. This was actually caused by the Maestro, who had been pulled back in time and was disintegrated by the gamma bomb explosion. The Maestro psychically summoned the Hulk back to that spot to absorb gamma radiation from him, which eventually enabled the Maestro to re-form. Presumably the Hulk can still locate the site via the psychic bond, even though the Maestro is no longer exerting his influence on him.

Following the separation of most of Banner's persona into a separate Hulk on Counter-Earth, the Hulk remaining on Earth served as a walking nexus of reality and gave off increased levels of gamma radiation. His mystic nature had been enhanced by the traumatic injury to his brain and then his involvement with Onslaught. As War, the Hulk possessed heightened strength and durability, and used a highly durable sword and whip. While serving as a gladiator on Sakaar, he swiftly learned a variety of combat skills, especially with a sword or battleaxe.

POWER GRID	1	2	3	4	5	6	7
INTELLIGENCE							
STRENGTH							
SPEED							
DURABILITY							
ENERGY PROJECTION							
FIGHTING SKILLS							

HISTORY: Anthony "Tony" Stark is the son of Howard and Maria Stark, whose company Stark Industries was one of the most prominent U.S. corporations. At the age of seven, Tony was sent to boarding school by his father in the hopes of "toughening" him. Tony found people difficult to relate to, and became fascinated with machines, which could be controlled or repaired. After reading Thomas Malory's Le Morte d'Arthur, Tony was entranced by its tales of King Arthur and the Knights of the Round Table. He was also fascinated by the science fiction tales of Isaac Asimov and Robert A. Heinlein, but as he matured he grew to admire scientists and explorers such as Marco Polo, Wilbur & Orville Wright, and Vasco Da Gama. As a teenager, Tony dated Meredith McCall, whose father ran a company that rivaled Stark Industries. Tony and Meredith's fathers forced the two to end their relationship.

Enrolled in M.I.T. at fifteen, Tony was mentored by professors Theodore Slaight and Sal Kennedy. He proved to be a prodigy, and ultimately graduated M.I.T. with a double masters in physics and engineering at the age of nineteen. Tony went to work for his father's company, but despite his incredible talents as an inventor, he had little interest in engineering and even less in business. He spent a great deal of his time romancing women and drinking with his cousin Morgan and best friend Tiberius Stone. Tony became involved with Sunset Bain, a woman five years his senior, and inadvertently gave her access to Stark Industries' security secrets. Bain funded a raid on Stark Industries' facilities and used stolen data to set up her own rival company, Baintronics, but the Starks could not prove her involvement in the theft.

When Tony was twenty-one, his parents died in a car accident and he inherited Stark Industries. His first act was to purchase the manufacturer of his parents' car and correct the brake problem which had seemingly caused their deaths. Unknown to Tony, the true architect of his parents' deaths was rival company Republic Oil (later Roxxon Oil), who hoped that the uninterested Tony could be made to sell Stark Industries. Still lacking in business acumen, Tony promoted secretary Virginia "Pepper" Potts to be his executive assistant, and left the majority of his workload on her so that he could avoid what he saw as a burden.

Tony finally began to show some signs of settling down when he became engaged to Joanna Nivena. He also developed many military contracts for his company, including a proposed battlesuit to protect soldiers and enhance their abilities in the field. Still seeking excuses to get out of his office, Stark personally attended a field test of his military hardware at one of his international plants; however, soon after his arrival Stark's party was attacked by a band of terrorists led by the Sin-Cong revolutionary Wong-Chu (himself a lackey of Chinese would-be world conqueror the Mandarin). During the skirmish, a land mine went off and lodged a piece of shrapnel near Tony's heart. Taken back to Wong-Chu's camp, Stark shared a cell with Professor Ho Yinsen, a Chinese medical technician. Wong-Chu demanded that the two scientists develop advanced weaponry for his forces. Knowing that he could not live long with the shrapnel so close to his heart, Stark proposed that he and Yinsen devote their gifts to creating one of the battlesuits he had been developing, equipped with a magnetic field generator to prevent the shrapnel from reaching his heart. The armor they created became the first true Iron Man armor, and was equipped with crude magnetic weaponry for defense. While the armor's battery was being powered, some of Wong-Chu's men attempted to break in on the proceedings. Yinsen went to create a diversion, and was shot to death by Wong-Chu's men. When the battery had finished charging, Tony Stark went into battle as Iron Man and tore Wong-Chu's camp apart. He eventually returned to the USA with the aid of U.S. marine James Rhodes. As Stark, he offered Rhodes a job with his company should he ever need one.

At first, Stark found his new life a torment: his armor's chestplate had to be worn constantly and required frequent recharging, and he kept the armor a secret from everyone, including his fiancée. He removed the

REAL NAME: Anthony Edward "Tony" Stark
ALIASES: "Shellhead," "Golden Avenger," "Tetsujin;" formerly Crimson Dynamo, Iron Knight, Hogan Potts, "Spare Parts Man;" impersonated Cobalt Man (Ralph Roberts)
IDENTITY: Publicly known
OCCUPATION: Adventurer, director of SHIELD, CEO of Stark Industries; former U.S.A. Secretary of Defense, former technician for Askew Electronics, former CEO of Stark International, Circuits Maximus, Stark Enterprises, Stark Solutions
CITIZENSHIP: USA
PLACE OF BIRTH: Long Island, New York
KNOWN RELATIVES: Howard Anthony Stark (father, deceased), Maria Collins Carbonell Stark (mother, deceased), Morgan Stark (cousin), Isaac Stark, Sr., Isaac Stark, Jr. (ancestors, deceased)
GROUP AFFILIATION: SHIELD, Avengers, the Initiative, Hellfire Club (outer circle); formerly Illuminati, Thunderbolts, Force Works
EDUCATION: Advanced degrees in physics and electrical engineering
FIRST APPEARANCE: Tales of Suspense #39 (1963)

chestplate to end his life, but finally replaced it, determined that he would conquer his disability. He investigated marketing the Iron Man armor, but eventually abandoned these plans, fearing what might happen if his armor wound up in the hands of criminals. He finally shared his double identity with Joanna, and she encouraged him to use his armor to become a super hero and save lives. Tony came around to the idea, but Joanna ultimately called off their engagement because she wanted a family, and knew that Tony could never be the husband she desired.

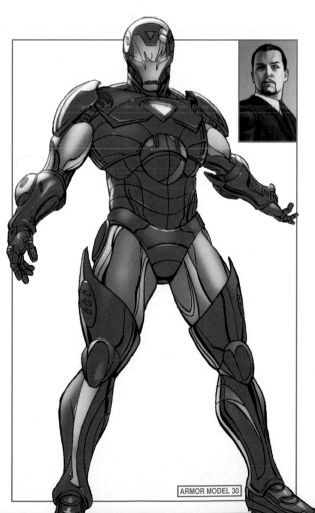

ARMOR MODEL 30

Iron Man began to establish himself as one of the U.S.'s most eminent super heroes, but while halting a breakout of circus lions and tigers, Tony saw how his armor's appearance frightened the people he was defending. Inspired by a suggestion from his date Marion, Tony repainted the armor in stainless gold. Under Pepper's tutorship, Tony gradually developed into a sharp businessman whose inventive genius, clever deals and impassioned marketing expanded Stark Industries' influence and fame. Stark's most trying foe in the world of business proved to be Senator Harrington Byrd, who had to be repeatedly convinced of Stark Industries' abilities to fulfill their contracts, and held lingering doubts over Iron Man's trustworthiness. Iron Man became an important mascot to the company, and Stark established him as his personal "bodyguard."

When the Hulk was framed for crimes by the Asgardian sorcerer Loki as part of a scheme to pit the Hulk against Loki's step-brother Thor, the Hulk's youthful friend Rick Jones sent a distress call to the Fantastic Four, only for Loki to divert the message to Thor. By chance, the message was also intercepted by Iron Man, and by Ant-Man (Henry Pym) and the Wasp (Janet Van Dyne). The four heroes eventually teamed with the Hulk to defeat Loki. Ant-Man suggested that the five remain together as a team, and the Wasp named them "the Avengers." Tony Stark was instrumental in setting up the group, bankrolling them first through his personal fortune and later through the charitable Maria Stark Foundation. He also provided his family's Manhattan manor to serve as a headquarters, renamed Avengers Mansion. His family's long-time butler Edwin Jarvis was the only staff member who remained to serve the Avengers, and he became an indispensable resource to the new team. Stark also negotiated with the NSA to establish national security clearance for the Avengers via special agent James Murch.

While testing his "Stark Special" racecar, Tony wound up in a wreck, but was saved from the crash by ex-boxer Harold "Happy" Hogan. To repay him, Stark hired Hogan as his personal chauffeur, and Happy became like a bodyguard to Stark, resenting Iron Man. Hogan also romantically pursued Pepper Potts, though she alternately seemed more interested in Stark or Iron Man. Tony was strongly attracted to Pepper, but he felt he could not pursue a normal relationship due to his armored condition, and he often tried to discourage Pepper's romantic attentions. Meanwhile, former Stark Industries scientist Gregor Shapanka (fired for theft) returned to menace Stark as the ice-generating Jack Frost, and would battle Iron Man repeatedly in later years as the Blizzard. Stark also fought armored Russian super-agent the Crimson Dynamo (Anton Vanko) and convinced him to defect. Vanko joined Stark Industries and later died defending the company from a new Crimson Dynamo (Boris Turgenov) and Russian spy the Black Widow (Natasha Romanoff).

In one of the Avengers' earliest adventures, the Space Phantom impersonated the Hulk, who then realized how little his teammates trusted him. The Hulk quit the Avengers, and Stark scrambled to prove to the government that the team was still viable. While battling the villain Mr. Doll, Iron Man found himself powerless against his foe's ability to cause pain using mystic talismans. Stark completely redesigned his armor into a new, more lightweight red and gold configuration, and defeated Mr. Doll in a rematch. Iron Man then rejoined the Avengers to search for the Hulk, and wound up in battle against him and Namor the Sub-Mariner. While pursuing Namor they came across the comatose body of Captain America, the famous World War II super hero. Revived, Captain America

was welcomed into the present by the Avengers and invited to join their ranks. Captain America was instrumental in proving the team's viability, and he became as important to them as Stark himself.

Iron Man went on to confront the Mandarin face-to-face for the first time. At one point in his adventures, the Iron Man armor's battery ran low, and Stark suffered a heart attack. He was able to recharge, but remained inside the Iron Man armor for weeks until he was finally able to modify the chestplate's battery. At the same time he was funding the Avengers, Stark helped establish the international super-spy agency SHIELD to combat terrorist threats. Stark joined with Reed Richards (Mr. Fantastic of the Fantastic Four) and the mutant inventor Forge in building the first Helicarrier, an enormous airborne vessel which became SHIELD's mobile base of operations. Stark also provided SHIELD with their weapons, protective uniforms, vehicles and all manner of special paraphernalia. Stark's LMDs (Life Model Decoys), androids which could impersonate humans, were of particular use to SHIELD, and Stark himself occasionally used an LMD so that he and Iron Man could seemingly appear in the same place at once. Stark recommended Colonel Nick Fury to serve as SHIELD's director, and Fury was ultimately given the position.

Iron Man, Giant-Man (Henry Pym), the Wasp and Thor all eventually left the Avengers, but the team continued under the leadership of Captain America, with new recruits Quicksilver, the Scarlet Witch and Hawkeye (Clint Barton); an outlaw archer, Hawkeye had fought Iron Man under the influence of his lover, the Black Widow, but Iron Man recognized Hawkeye's sincere desire to reform and supported his Avengers membership. Continuing to supply the Avengers' financial and technological needs, Tony remained available as Iron Man when necessary, rejoining and exiting their ranks several times over the ensuing years, sometimes serving as chairman. When the armored Russian Titanium Man (Boris Bullski) challenged Iron Man to combat in Alberia, Stark met and defeated his foe, but Happy was injured aiding Iron Man. At the same time, Pepper realized that she loved Happy more than Tony, and Tony encouraged them to become a couple. Happy subsequently determined that Tony was Iron Man. When Tony collapsed from strain after another clash with the Titanium Man, the public began to speculate that he was Iron Man. To help keep Tony's secrets, Happy donned the armor, only to be mistakenly captured by the Mandarin. Forcing himself to recover from his latest heart attack, Tony rescued Happy. Soon after this, Pepper and Happy were married.

SHIELD dispatched their agent Jasper Sitwell to help monitor Stark Industries security and defend their interests in the company. Stark found this to be an unwanted nuisance, as Sitwell's presence complicated his double identity. Jasper and Tony both found themselves drawn to the beautiful Whitney Frost, but she proved to be the daughter of the Avengers' foe Count Nefaria and a high-ranking member of the Maggia crime syndicate. Seeking to steal Stark's inventions, she pitted agents such as Whiplash (Mark Scarlotti) and Gladiator (Melvin Potter) against him. When Tony's armor began to fail him and required an immediate redesign to save his life, Happy helped Tony construct new armor. Tony Stark also became involved with Janice Cord, whose father died in a hate-filled attempt at killing Iron Man.

After using one of his LMDs to deceive the Mandarin and protect his identity, Stark was horrified when the LMD developed an independent personality and usurped his identity. The LMD obtained a suit of Iron Man armor and began running Stark Industries while the real Stark was away, believing that it was superior to Tony. Unable to prove his identity, Tony fell into the clutches of Madame Masque (a newly-garbed Whitney Frost), an agent of the gold-loving Mordecai Midas, who attempted to force Stark to turn over his fortune. Tony used his original Iron Man armor to destroy the LMD imposter, but suffered another heart attack in the process. The Avengers rushed him to a hospital where Dr. Jose Santini transplanted a synthetic heart into his chest, so that Stark no longer required his chestplate to live.

MODEL 1 — NO FINISH, MODEL 1 —GOLD FINISH, MODEL 3 & MODEL 4

Afraid to continue on as Iron Man for fear of his precarious health, Stark destroyed Midas' operations, then sought to retire.

Stark brought in boxer Edward "Eddie" March, a one-time sparring partner of Happy's, to serve as the new Iron Man. An Iron Man fan, March relished the assignment, but did not inform Stark that he was suffering from a blood clot in his brain which could result in his death during a fight. When March went into action for the first time, he found himself facing the latest Crimson Dynamo (Alex Nevsky). March nearly died in the fight, and Stark was forced to reclaim the Iron Man identity. As Iron Man fought the Crimson Dynamo, they were both attacked by the Titanium Man, and Janice was killed in the crossfire. Both romantically linked to Janice, Nevsky and Stark blamed each other.

As public sentiment against his arms manufacturing grew, Tony began to steer the company away from munitions. Befriending engineer Kevin O'Brien, Stark eventually revealed his double identity to him. He designed a second suit of armor for O'Brien, enabling him to become the Guardsman and assist him in case of an emergency; however, when O'Brien donned the armor, a malfunction in its cybernetic controls caused a personality disorder where O'Brien began to hate Iron Man, and sought to steal Stark's then-lover Marianne Rogers. O'Brien allied himself with Simon Gilbert, a Stark Industries stockholder who opposed Tony's move away from munitions. When Iron Man and the Guardsman fought, Iron Man accidentally killed Kevin. Simon Gilbert continued to plague Stark, along with his son Gary, the villainous activist Firebrand; however, Gary's sister Roxanne was in love with Stark and tried to end her family's hostilities towards him. Following the Avengers' involvement in the interstellar Kree-Skrull War, Iron Man joined Mr. Fantastic, Black Bolt of the Inhumans, Professor Xavier of the X-Men, sorcerer Dr. Strange, and Namor in founding the Illuminati, a secret organization designed to share knowledge and pool resources against major threats.

As his company continued to expand worldwide, Tony renamed the corporation Stark International to reflect this. After witnessing firsthand the impact his company's weapons had on innocent lives, Tony resolved to abandon munitions altogether, and Stark International turned most of its efforts to electronics and computer engineering from then on. Michael O'Brien eventually turned up to blame Iron Man for his brother Kevin's death and sought to prosecute him, but he ultimately recognized Iron Man's heroism and forgave him. Adopting a new suit of Guardsman armor, O'Brien aided Iron Man against the Mandarin and later teamed with novice super hero Jack of Hearts and others to assist Iron Man against Midas. Iron Man mentored Jack of Hearts for some time thereafter, but Jack soon went solo again.

Stark and Madame Masque became romantically involved, but she ultimately turned against Tony in a desperate attempt to save her father's life. Nefaria seemingly died during Iron Man and Madame Masque's subsequent conflict, and the two lovers were driven apart. Meanwhile, SHIELD had become frustrated by Stark International's move out of munitions, which had forced them to turn to inferior manufacturers for their weaponry. Nick Fury authorized three of his agents to attempt a hostile takeover of Stark's company, but the agents went rogue and tried to assassinate Stark instead. Although Stark survived, he was frustrated by Fury's betrayal of their trust.

By this time, Stark International's notable key staff included James Rhodes, who had finally accepted a position as Stark's pilot; Tony's supremely capable secretary Bambina "Bambi" Arbogast; public relations man Artemus "Artie" Pithins; security chief Victor "Vic" Martinelli, stationed with Stark by the witness relocation program; vice-president Yvette Avril; neurosurgeon Erica Sondheim; and electronics technician Scott Lang (secretly the new Ant-Man). Tony also began dating bodyguard Bethany Cabe.

Rival industrialist Justin Hammer designed a device which could enable limited control over the Iron Man armor, and he began testing his control, creating seemingly random malfunctions. Hammer finally took full advantage of his power when Iron Man attended a function with Sergei Kotznin, ambassador to Carnelia, whose country was about to sign a deal with Stark International. Hammer caused the armor to fire a repulsor ray through Kotznin's chest, killing him. With Iron Man wanted and the armor co-opted, Tony had Captain America train him in unarmed combat so that he could attempt to clear his name without using the armor. Discovering that Hammer ran a private artificial island full of super-villains in his employ, Stark defeated them as Iron Man, then captured one of Hammer's top scientists to testify on his behalf; however, Hammer himself remained untouchable by the law.

The combined stress of Hammer's machinations and SHIELD's constant pressure drove Tony further into depression. Bethany Cabe kept Tony from succumbing completely, and he began to realize and deal with it. Bouncing back, Tony faced challenges from Edwin Cord's Cordco company, and, by exposing Cord's criminal activities, brought him to ruin. Tony then purchased Cordco for Stark International. Stark began to develop specialized suits of armor, including his first outer space armor and low visibility (stealth) armor. He first used the stealth armor while rescuing Bethany's long-lost husband Alex von Tilburg, but this drove Tony and Bethany apart as she returned to von Tilburg. When Yellowjacket (Henry Pym's then-current identity) became unstable, Tony had the unpleasant task of joining the other Avengers in court-martialing him, forcing Pym's departure from the team. Tony soon became romantically involved with the Wasp, but Captain America — having recently learned Stark was Iron Man — convinced him this relationship was unethical. Tony revealed his dual identity to the Wasp, and she ended their romance.

In opposing Obadiah Stane's attempts at forming a major multinational conglomerate, Tony unwittingly made a driven enemy. Stane set up games of psychological warfare against Tony which included physical attacks by his Chessmen super-operatives, outbidding Stark International for key contracts, and having his lackey Indries Moomji romance Stark. As Stane's pressure increased, Tony responded as anticipated, and after Indries rejected Tony, he virtually gave up trying to oppose Stane. When the villain Magma attacked Stark International, Tony instead revealed his double identity to Rhodes. Rhodes donned the armor and defeated Magma, and Tony told him to keep the armor. He then turned his back on Stark International, his property, fortune assets were frozen. Obadiah Stane stepped in and claimed Stark International, renaming it Stane International, but Rhodes prevented Stane from obtaining the Iron Man armors.

Rhodes had become distrustful of Tony and refused maintenance on the armor. Tony realized that the helmet's cybernetic link had not been properly tuned to Rhodes' brainwaves, and he fashioned a new model of his original armor in order to confront Rhodes and prove he was not his enemy. Convinced, Rhodes finally allowed Stark to take care of the armor.

Tony became involved with Clytemnestra as the four began to set up their own California-based company Circuits Maximus, but Stane was not yet done with Stark. He planted a bomb in their laboratory, killing Morley and badly injuring Rhodes. Realizing that Stane had to be stopped, Tony constructed his most advanced armor yet at the new western Avengers Compound and confronted Stane, who had designed his own armored identity as the Iron Monger. Tony then defeated the Iron Monger, disgracing Stane.

Rejoining the Avengers as part of their new western roster (led by Hawkeye), Tony set about reacquiring his fortune and ultimately developed his new company into Stark Enterprises, concentrating on space exploration; however, Morley's death turned Clytemnestra against him. She betrayed Tony to AIM and died trying to battle Iron Man. Rhodes remained faithful to Stark and occasionally wore the Iron Man armor, but after an incident where he was nearly burned to death, he tried to give the armor up for good.

While Tony was acquiring the company Accutech, it was sabotaged by the Ghost, an anti-industry mercenary. Tony's long-time foe the Spymaster also targeted Accutech, and infiltrated Stark Enterprises' resources before the Ghost killed him. Tony again intervened in Justin Hammer's schemes when he provided sanctuary for Force (Clayton Wilson), an agent of Hammer's who wanted to reform. Stark arranged to fake Force's death and gave him a new identity as Carl Walker, a research scientist. During Force's defection, Iron Man also encountered another Hammer super-agent, the new Blizzard (Donnie Gill), and Stark sought to offer young Gill reformatory guidance as well. Impounding Force's armor, Stark immediately analyzed it. To his shock, he found familiar circuitry patterns based on his own Iron Man armor designs. Employing computer engineer Abraham Zimmer (formerly of Accutech) and Scott Lang, Tony raided Hammer's computer records and discovered that Spymaster had stolen his designs and sold them to Hammer. Hammer had then used Stark's designs to armor several of his super-villain clients, including the Beetle (Abner Jenkins), the Controller, the Mauler (Brendan Doyle), the Raiders and Stilt-Man (Wilbur Day). Enraged at the thought that innocent people might have been killed with his technology, Tony resolved to eliminate all traces of his technology that had fallen into outside hands.

Having already wiped Hammer's computer records with a virus courtesy of Zimmer, Tony assigned his legal team to bring the criminals in while Iron Man confronted the criminals directly, using a negator pack to fry their armors' circuitry; however, there was little Stark's lawyers could do to help him. Learning that Zimmer and Lang had been unable to retrieve one name from Hammer's database, Tony suspected that it might be Stingray, a federal employee. When Stingray refused to have his armor confiscated, Iron Man beat him in combat, only to find that Stingray's armor did not feature any of his designs. Iron Man was now wanted for assaulting Stingray, and Tony publicly denounced and "fired" his other identity, believing that the best solution was to take the fight outside the law.

When SHIELD became involved, Stark pretended to cooperate with them in Iron Man's capture, but actually used the opportunity to confiscate the Mandroid battle armor he had built for their agents. Deciding he could not trust anyone with his technology, Tony next targeted the Guardsman armor he had provided to the Vault, the nation's foremost superhuman prison. At the same time, the government had stripped Steve Rogers of his Captain America identity and he had adopted a new alias as "the Captain." At Rogers' request, Tony supplied him with a new shield, hoping it would serve as a bribe to prevent Steve's interference in his armor crusade; however, the Captain tried to halt Tony's raid on the Vault, and defended the last remaining Guardsman. Iron Man finally brought the Captain down from behind and fried the last Guardsman suit. The Captain returned Stark's shield, and from then on his friendship with Tony was severely strained.

Next attacking the Crimson Dynamo (Dmitri Bukharin) and the Titanium Man (the Gremlin) in Russia, Tony fried the Dynamo's armor and accidentally killed the Titanium Man. Denounced as an international outlaw, Iron Man was expelled from the Avengers. Increasingly concerned by Iron Man's rogue actions, the U.S. military turned to Edwin Cord, who provided them with the one Hammer-derived armor that Stark had been unable to locate earlier: Firepower. Cord's agent Firepower lured Iron Man into combat and launched a devastating attack on him. Seeing no way out, Tony faked Iron Man's death by remotely launching his armor, which Firepower destroyed. Stark was content to leave his days as Iron Man behind, but Cord continued his vendetta against Stark by sending Firepower to destroy his businesses. Finally, Tony built a new suit of Iron Man armor and defeated Firepower. Tony decided to remain active as Iron Man, but publicly claimed his company had hired a "new" Iron Man. This "new" Iron Man soon rejoined the Avengers, most of whom saw through Stark's deception immediately, and Iron Man later admitted to the Avengers that he was still Tony Stark.

As Tony's business continued to thrive, he became involved with women such as Brie Daniels, Rae La Coste, and Kathleen Dare. Preoccupied by his hectic lifestyle, Tony did not realize Kathleen was stalking him until it was too late; she shot him, damaging his spine and leaving him unable to walk. Initially using a wheelchair, Tony was irritated at how people seemed to look down on him. He modified the Iron Man armor so that he could be fully mobile while armored, and began to spend more time within the armor. When Tony learned of a biochip which might restore full movement, he risked his life to have it installed, and he gradually regained mobility.

The biochip gained the attention of corporate foe Kearson DeWitt, who held grievances against Stark of which Tony was unaware. Bankrolled by Desmond Marrs of the Marrs Corporation, DeWitt hijacked the biochip and took control of Stark's nervous system, placing his entire body under tremendous strain. Stark resisted the outside control using an encephalo-link in his armor, but by the time he had defeated DeWitt, his body was so damaged he could barely move. Tony donned a skintight neuronet suit to help him function, but his armor became the only certain way to keep himself alive. He sought the aid of China's Dr. Su Yin, but the Chinese

MODEL 14

MODEL 12

MODEL 15

MODEL 17

MODEL 9

MODEL 18

MODEL 16

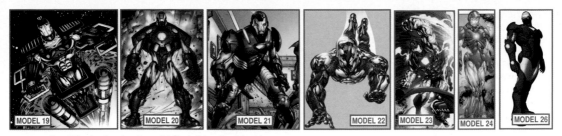

MODEL 19   MODEL 20   MODEL 21   MODEL 22   MODEL 23   MODEL 24   MODEL 26

government would only allow her to assist Stark if he dispatched Iron Man against the Mandarin, who had formed an alliance with the Makluan dragon Fin Fang Foom and his people. Rhodes donned the armor to confront the Mandarin, hoping to spare Tony from the fight, but Rhodes was defeated. Tony resorted to employing a telepresence unit which would allow him to control his armor from a distance, but finally had to don the armor himself to defeat the Mandarin and the dragons.

While on a mission with the Avengers to halt the Kree-Shi'ar War which had threatened Earth's solar system, Iron Man was appalled to discover that the Kree's Supreme Intelligence had masterminded a massacre of his own people. Disobeying Captain America, Iron Man led a team of rogue Avengers in seemingly executing the Supreme Intelligence. Afterward, he expressed his regret to Captain America, and the two began trying to repair their fractured relationship. As Tony's health continued to deteriorate, he designed his variable threat assessment armor (also called the "War Machine") and won back Stane International's assets from its last owner, Justin Hammer. Succumbing to total nervous system failure, Tony seemingly died on an operating table. In his will, he made Rhodes the new CEO of Stark Enterprises, and left the War Machine armor for him to carry on as Iron Man. Rhodes respected his wishes.

Tony, however, had employed Erica Sondheim and Abe Zimmer to place him in cryogenic storage while they remapped his body's entire nervous system, essentially rebuilding his body. After a cyberspace interface was installed, Tony himself helped complete their work while in stasis. Once he was revived, Tony found that he would have to relearn how to perform even the simplest body functions, but that his senses were sharper than ever. He revealed his survival to Rhodes, who was infuriated at being deceived and immediately quit Stark Enterprises. The Avengers were estranged by Stark's deception as well, and Rhodes again took Tony's place in the team. Tony allowed Jim to keep the War Machine armor, and Rhodes continued to adventure under the alias of War Machine. Tony launched a new set of armor, the Neuromimetic Telepresence Unit 150 (NTU-150), which he could control from his bed. Employing Veronica Benning to assist in his physical therapy, Tony became romantically involved with her as well. He also began designing artificial intelligences to aid him in his work, including HOMER (Heuristically Operative Matrix Emulation Rostrum) and PLATO (Piezo-electrical Logistic Analytic Tactical Operator).

When the NTU-150 was destroyed in battle with Ultimo, the feedback nearly killed Tony. War Machine recruited Bethany Cabe, Michael O'Brien, Eddie March, Happy Hogan and Clayton Wilson to don spare suits of Iron Man armor and battle Ultimo as the "Iron Legion," but ultimately it was Stark, outfitted in his new modular armor, who defeated Ultimo. When the Avengers debated shutting down their struggling west coast branch, Iron Man returned just long enough to cast the deciding vote in favor of disbanding the western team, then resigned. He quickly recruited several former western Avengers into a team of his own making, Force Works, and gave them full access to his cutting edge technology. Although he set up the Scarlet Witch as team leader, Tony often assumed leadership, causing internal tensions. When Captain America's health began to fail him due to deterioration of his super-soldier serum, Tony outfitted him with a suit of armor to help prolong his life and enable him to continue fighting crime, having been through a similar ordeal himself.

By this time, Tony had secretly, gradually fallen under the control of Immortus, ruler of Limbo, then posing as his alternate self Kang (most notably, this influence had apparently contributed to Stark's participation in the Supreme Intelligence's execution). Scheming to keep the Avengers occupied on behalf of his cosmic masters the Time-Keepers, Immortus supplied Iron Man with mysterious allies, actually disguised Space Phantoms. As Tony lost control, he murdered one-time Avenger Yellowjacket (Rita DeMara), Avengers Mansion nanny Marilla and Force Works publicist Amanda Chaney. When the Avengers realized that Tony was now their enemy, they journeyed to an alternate timeline to recruit a younger Tony Stark who was certain to be free of Immortus' influence, since Immortus had apparently been subverting Stark's mind for years. This younger Stark helped them anticipate the elder Tony's actions, and they stormed an arctic bunker where Tony had been working on Immortus' super-weapon, a temporal transposer that would shunt the Earth outside of time. Tony nearly killed his younger self in battle, but he ultimately regretted his actions, designed a chestplate to save the younger Tony's life, and gave his own life to destroy the transposer.

The young Tony Stark started life anew while Stark Enterprises fell into the hands of Fujikawa Industries, merging into Stark-Fujikawa. Rhodes once again prevented Tony's armor secrets from being acquired. The young Tony Stark, wearing his own Iron Man armor, seemingly perished alongside the Fantastic Four and Avengers in battle with psionic monster Onslaught; however, they were all recreated on a new Counter-Earth fashioned by the mutant powers of Franklin Richards, a world where Tony Stark was reborn as an adult rather than a teenager. On this world, Stark's heart was damaged in an attack by the Hulk, and he required the Iron Man armor to prolong his life. He and the other people brought to Counter-Earth eventually learned it was not their world and were sent back home. Upon returning, the still-adult Tony found he had the collective memories and experiences of the original Tony Stark, merged with those of the teenage alternate Tony and the person he had been on Counter-Earth.

Once again in the peak of health, Tony designed a new suit of Iron Man armor and helped reestablish the Avengers. Rather than attempt to regain his old company, Tony set up Stark Solutions, a consulting firm. He soon met Rumiko Fujikawa, granddaughter of Fujikawa's founder, and they became involved. Tony's life was again imperiled when he learned that constant exposure to his armor's technology was threatening his health, but he redesigned the armor to correct this problem. When Iron Man defeated the villain Mentallo, Tony took advantage of the situation and used Mentallo's global mind control device to erase all knowledge of his often-compromised secret identity from every person on Earth. He then revealed it to those people he deemed trustworthy, causing them to remember the memories he had buried. Some were uneasy regarding this unilateral mental tampering, and Captain America in particular disapproved.

During a conflict with Sunset Bain, Tony discovered that the consciousness of the robot Jocasta, a one-time Avenger, was Bain's captive. Tony liberated Jocasta, who became his personal computer assistant; however, Jocasta unwittingly suffered from the Ultron Imperative, a deeply embedded program within all the creations of the robot menace Ultron, forcing them to seek the means to revive Ultron when he is defeated. Jocasta was forced to prepare the Iron Man armor to become Ultron's new home, but the process sped up when Iron Man was hit by a lightning bolt, causing Tony to suffer a heart attack at the same time. Thinking that the armor had been granted its own consciousness, Tony attempted to teach the armor, and the benign Ultron-12 aspect of its personality was receptive, but the cruelty of most past Ultron models corrupted the armor, and it murdered Whiplash during a fight; however, the armor ultimately sacrificed its "life" to save Tony, whose heart was failing. After implanting a robotic "heart" in Tony's chest that saved him, the armor deactivated.

Concerned that he might develop another suit of uncontrollable armor, Tony began wearing older models of armor rather than constructing a new design. He soon encountered the Sons of Yinsen, monks mentored by Ho Yinsen, who had preserved their leader's brain after his death. The Sons wore armor similar to that which Tony and Yinsen had constructed years earlier. Learning Wong-Chu was still alive, Stark helped the Sons of Yinsen battle him, and one of the monks finally slew Wong-Chu. Later, Tiberius Stone reentered Tony's life when he began to market powerful virtual reality technology called "Dreamvision." Stone became involved with Rumiko, halting her relationship with Tony, and Stark discovered that Stone had grandiose plans to conquer the Earth with Dreamvision; he began these plans by focusing his resources on publicly smearing Tony. Stark finally defeated Stone within Dreamvision, but Stone planted a subliminal message in Tony's brain that caused him to give up his fortune and close Stark Solutions. Adopting the identity of Hogan Potts, Tony became a mere computer technician for Askew Electronics, gradually constructing a new armor from Askew's SKIN (Synthetic Kinetic Interfacing Nanofluid), a digital fluid that can form a sheath around objects making them almost as resilient as Adamantium. Iron Man fought the Ghost and AIM when they attempted to bomb Askew, and he finally resumed his Tony Stark identity, reclaimed his fortune and returned to business as Stark Enterprises.

The Sons of Yinsen found the remains of the armor which Ultron had inhabited, and attempted to transform it into a new home for Yinsen's brain; however, the Ultron program revived and assumed mastery of the Sons of Yinsen. The only monk who resisted, Sun Tao, joined forces with Tony to defeat Ultron, but the other Sons of Yinsen seemingly perished. At this time, Jocasta's program exited Tony's systems and took up residence in the body of Antigone, the deactivated android offspring of Ultron's rogue bride Alkhema. Tony finally revealed his double identity to the public at large when he donned his armor in public to save a dog from being struck by a car. Rumiko, finally separated from Stone, reconciled with Tony and arranged for him to regain control of his original company under its original name – Stark Industries. From then on, Tony and Rumiko were a close couple. Tony also came into repeated conflict with Temugin, son of the seemingly deceased Mandarin, who fought Tony primarily out of obligation to his father's memory.

The U.S. President's chief of staff, Stu Conrad, offered Tony a position within the defense department as a contractor. Although Tony was uninterested, he investigated the department's recent problems and discovered that head of acquisitions Sonny Burch had been using Iron Man technology in defense equipment, exploiting a loophole in Stark's patents. Stark was unable to prevent Burch's use of his designs, and Burch's poor understanding of Stark's technology was resulting in mishaps in the field from malfunctions. Resolving to solve the problem, Tony offered himself as the new Secretary of Defense, promising to design Iron Man armor for U.S. soldiers and train them to operate it. Tony was ultimately voted in, and Burch left.

Discovering that Burch had also blackmailed Force into assisting the defense department, Tony tried to make amends to him, granting him a position in preparing soldiers to operate Iron Man armor; however, Tony's tenure as Secretary of Defense ended in scandal when the mad Scarlet Witch caused Tony to engage in belligerent behavior at the United Nations. Disgraced, Stark was quickly drummed out of his government position. The Scarlet Witch's growing insanity led to the dissolution of the Avengers when her out-of-control powers wrecked Avengers Mansion and killed several teammates, including Hawkeye and Ant-Man (Lang). Tony was further smeared when one-time corporate rival Clarence Ward stole Iron Man armor, using it to kill the Stark Industries board and Rumiko. Iron Man defeated Ward, and recalled all of the Iron Man armors he had granted to the military. He then publicly "resigned" as Iron Man but secretly intended to continue operating as Iron Man, claiming that it was once again a different man in the armor.

Iron Man encountered Mallen, a terrorist enhanced by the Extremis virus, a techno-organic agent designed by Tony's one-time classmate Maya Hansen and intentionally leaked so that the world could see its destructive potential. After Mallen defeated Iron Man, Tony had Maya inject him with the Extremis so that he could meet Mallen as an equal. The process resulted in Stark's body rebuilding itself with superior organs, and Tony found that he could now store his Iron Man armor's undersheath within his bones and release it when armoring up; he was now able to link to virtually any computer on Earth and process dozens of simultaneous tasks with his brain. The newly-enhanced Tony killed Mallen in a rematch.

With Captain America, Tony helped restart the Avengers, this time including heroes such as Spider-Man (Peter Parker) and Wolverine among their ranks, and he provided his midtown Manhattan skyscraper Stark Tower as their new base of operations. Jarvis was rehired to serve the Avengers at the tower. Tony became a mentor to Spider-Man, and encouraged him to move his aunt May and wife Mary Jane into Stark Tower when their home was lost in an attack. Tony also provided Peter with a suit of personal armor that enhanced his abilities. Learning of Congress' interest in a Superhuman Registration Act (SHRA), Tony brought Peter with him in an attempt to halt the proceedings, secretly employing his old foe the Titanium Man to start a battle in order to demonstrate the value of super heroes.

Tony learned that while he was a prisoner of Wong-Chu, Professor Yinsen had implanted a device in his brain which could place him under the control of a sending unit now held by Yinsen's son. Believing that Tony had betrayed his father's ideals, Yinsen's son took control of

MODEL 25

MODEL 27

MODEL 29

MODELS 31-35

MODEL CE1

UNDERSHEATH

MODEL 28

MODEL 36

MODEL YT1

Iron Man and forced him to execute surviving members of Wong-Chu's network. When a SHIELD sniper killed the son, it activated a failsafe program that sent four of Tony's latest armors on a worldwide rampage. Aided by the Avengers and Fantastic Four, Tony halted his armors, but the incident left him wondering if superhumans did require supervision from higher authorities.

After a fight between the New Warriors and Nitro in Stamford, Connecticut resulted in the deaths of many schoolchildren, pressure mounted to make the SHRA law. This time, Tony supported the measures, believing that if the super hero community did not take charge of the situation, they would become powerless before an all-powerful government. Most of Stark's fellow Illuminati disagreed with his views, and they disbanded on bad terms. Collaborating with Yellowjacket (Pym) and Mr. Fantastic to develop pro-SHRA initiatives and leading the pro-SHRA movement, Tony once again made his double identity public knowledge as part of his support for the act; however, Captain America disagreed with Tony and led an underground resistance against the new law. Gradually disillusioned by the questionable morality of the pro-registration forces in general and Stark in particular, Tony's protégé Spider-Man soon joined the resistance, too. In order to combat Captain America's forces, Tony made an alliance with Baron Zemo of the Thunderbolts, and began conscripting super-villains into government service. Tony also secretly manufactured a war between the U.S. and Atlantis, believing that it would convince more super heroes to come forward and register themselves. Ultimately, Captain America surrendered when he realized the general public did not support his position; he was soon assassinated by agents of the Red Skull while in custody, much to Iron Man's dismay. Tony Stark has become the director of SHIELD (Nick Fury having gone rogue earlier), and he appointed Ms. Marvel (Carol Danvers) the new leader of the Avengers; however, Spider-Man and other dissidents continue to oppose the SHRA through their own outlaw faction of the Avengers.

HEIGHT: (Stark) 6'1"; (in armor) 6'6"
WEIGHT: (Stark) 225 lbs.; (in armor) 425 lbs.
EYES: Blue
HAIR: Black

ABILITIES/ACCESSORIES: Tony Stark's entire body has been enhanced by the techno-organic Extremis virus, granting him enhanced senses and reflexes. He can link his brain into virtually any computer on Earth, and perform dozens of tasks simultaneously. His Iron Man armor's undersheath is stored within his bones, and he can summon it forth when he is donning his armor. The armor itself is magnetically drawn to the undersheath, assembling itself around Stark's body within seconds.

Tony's current armor possesses many of his past armors' standard attributes, and can be carried within a briefcase while disassembled. The armor's memory-metal technology renders it lightweight and flexible while not in use, but extremely durable while polarized. The armor is also defended by an energy-draining shield which expands from the gauntlets, and by a personal force field. The armor grants its wearer superhuman strength enabling him to lift up to 100 tons. The armor's jet boots can propel him at speeds up to mach 8. The armor is specially coated for radar resistance and avoidance of targeting locks, and can be rendered invisible (cloaked) for brief stealth modes. Its internal air supply lasts over one hour, and the armor can be sealed for travel through low oxygen, underwater or outer space environments. The armor's computer includes an autopilot and targeting sensors, features which Stark has little use for since receiving the Extremis. The computer's cybernetic link enables Stark to operate all of the armor's functions, as well as providing a remote link to other computers. Tony has refined the cybernetic link to defend his mind against outside control, as the armor has often left his mind vulnerable to psychic attacks. The armor also features radar and environment sensors. The armor contains a sophisticated subspace/satellite radio communications array, which can also provide local radio signals. In case of capture, the armor is equipped with a self-destruct mechanism.

The armor's exotic features include Tony's primary energy weapon, repulsor rays, a powerful particle beam weapon designed to repel attacks. The chestplate features the unibeam, a powerful searchlight which can project beams in virtually every light spectrum (visible, infrared, and ultraviolet). The unibeam also features a laser beam projector, an EMP (Electro Magnetic Pulse) generator that can shut down electronic devices within a 50-yard radius (the armor itself can reboot within minutes), and a holographic generator which can both disguise the armor and project images to distract and confuse opponents. The armor has also been outfitted with pulse bolts (extremely powerful plasma discharges), sonic generators, magnetic field generators and a laser torch.

Stark has also designed a number of specialized armors for particular environments and situations. These include the "Hulkbuster," his most powerful armor, originally designed to combat the Hulk. Similarly, his "Thorbuster" model was designed to combat Thor, and combined Stark's technology with Asgardian magic. He has also employed various stealth armors, which are virtually immune to detection but have little raw power; one model was constructed of non-metallic materials. His deep submerge armors are designed for missions up to 3 miles beneath the ocean; his space, outer atmosphere and high-gravity armors are designed for extensive off-world missions. His ablative armor was constructed using a series of self-replacing chips so that damage made to the structure would be instantly repaired, and his arctic armor was designed for extended periods in below zero environments. His tunneler armor was designed to bore through solid rock; his anti-radiation armor was designed for travel through radiation-contaminated areas.

Stark maintains copies of his earlier suits of armor. Features of his earlier suits which he no longer maintains included additions such as a laser-proof coating, missile launchers, mini-guns, mini-canons, railgun, jet-propelled roller skates built into the boots, a diamond-sharp blade concealed within a gauntlet, a hand saw built into a gauntlet, a portable proton beam, tear gas, explosives, suction cups built into the boots, a magnetic field generator which served as his pacemaker while the shrapnel was within his heart, an energy blade located in the gauntlets, a telepresence unit which enabled Stark complete control over the armor from miles away, a flame thrower, power packs which enabled Stark to connect the armor to larger power sources, the SKIN technology which rendered one of his armors virtually indestructible, automated sensor probes, tasers, and flame retardant foam.

POWER GRID	1	2	3	4	5	6	7
INTELLIGENCE							
STRENGTH							
SPEED							
DURABILITY							
ENERGY PROJECTION							
FIGHTING SKILLS							

IRON MAN BIO/METALO-MIMETIC SUIT SERIES Mk III

Anthony Stark's Bio/Metalo-Mimetic Material concept is a radical departure from the traditional solid-state technological underpinnings of his prior Iron Man suit designs. Making use of nano-scale assembly technology, "smart" molecules can be made atom by atom. The design allows for simple computers to be linked into a massive parallel computer that synthesizes "human" thought protocols.

There are two parts to this new suit design. The Undersheath is the protective interface between Stark's nervous system and the External Suit Devices, the mega-nano technology that has assembled atoms into large, discreet effectors.

The ESDs are collapsible to very small volumes for storage. The ESDs are commanded by the Undersheath and are self-powered by high-capacity Kasimer plates. They are equipped with large arrays of nano-fans that allow flight.

Headpiece
Deep-spectra visual display with smart informational overlay. Psychoacoustic synthetic soundfield. Nano active-sorting allows for super filtering or air synthesis. Diamond overcoating eyepieces.

Stark's skin is now a part of the suit, when engaged. Comfort is relative because the suit rapidly responds to any discomfort, from impacts to high temperature, from itching to scratching. The suit's protocols include semi-autonomy when needed. Where Stark ends and the suit begins is flexible. The exact nature of the artificial Extremis Virus is not known. What effect it has had on Stark's body is to allow the presence of so much alien material within his body wthout trauma.

Neck
Responsive collumnar support. Positioning effector to allow for heads-up flying.

Upper Dorsal Thorax
Houses PentaBeam and support. Microwave lensing allows for directed beams of high joule electrons, photons, acoustic energy and neutrons.

Ribcage Assembly
Includes seperable nano assembler for remote manufacturing of materials. Houses large fractal antennae array and synthetic aperture radar/lidar. Systemic health sensor suite consolidates information in this area.

Gauntlet
Includes in-suit nano material assembler pod. Major information, logical choice and expert system processor region. Finger articulation follows neural command with interacting feedback from surface sensor suite. Palm Beam is high density muon generator to concussively dissolve matter.

Abdomiminal Section
Major energy generation and storage.

Below: Block diagram of Peptide-Peptide Logic showing memory, critical logic paths, comparative "truth" tables, automatic response look-up tables, data storage, communication and external sensing material interface. Also, the steerable, motile lattice framework that surrounds and is commanded by the PPL molecule computational mentality.

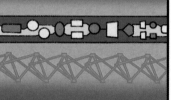

Right: High resolution CAT scan of Undersheath material exiting bony fascia pores.

(enlarged 87,000x)

Pantlet and Hip Pod
Suit, power, flight management, medical assay integration system. Pod is multi-purpose and can re-make itself into a mission-specific device.

Thigh and Patella
Contains panoramic sensor suite for all-environment evaluation. Tele-presence links.

Stark Undersheath Technology

The Undersheath to the Iron Man Suit components assembles itself from storage vacuoles within specially modified areas of Tony Stark's bone marrow tissue.

The sheath material is able to exit through skeletal pores and slide between all cells to self-assemble a new "skin." This skin provides a complete interface to the Iron Man Suit components and can perform numerous other functions.

The Undersheath is a nano-network that incorporates peptide-peptide logic, a molecular computational system made of superconducting plastic impregnated molecular chains.

The lattice assembly is a stress-compression truss with powered intersticial joints. This can surround the PPL material and guide it through Stark's body. The metallic component to the lattice is a controlled mimetic artifact than can take on the characteristics of most elements. Even unusual combinations of behaviors such as extreme hardness and flexibility.

The combination of the two nano-scale materials allows for a very dense non-traditional computer that can change the fabric of its design in very powerful ways. The incorporation of the Undersheath in Stark's entire nervous system renders reflex-level computer responses to pan-spectrum stimulai.

Foreleg and Anklet
Motility routines and body attitude routines are stored and generated here. Contains air intakes for micro turbines in Shoe.

Shoe
Flight is now achieved by full-body nano fan arrays. Micro turbines in Shoes are for rapid maneuvering.
Prehensile grippers are adaptable to many circumstances.

Note about nano-technology:
The communication problem with microscopic machines has been overcome by using a multi-pronged approach. Signals can be sent via one or more of several ways. Chemical, in the form of synthetic hormones, optical pulse and various radio freqencies give the systems a redundant and robust means of reliable communication at the nano scale.

HISTORY: Carol Danvers grew up the oldest child of three in a traditional Boston home, with a contractor father who believed in the merits of hard work. When he built their Cape Cod summer home, Carol insisted on working as hard as her younger brothers, trying to make herself the equal of both in her father's eyes. A voracious reader, she dreamed of becoming an astronaut and traveling to distant planets; as a teen she even hitchhiked to Cape Canaveral to view a launch there. Her father, however, could not accept women as men's equals, and when financial troubles meant he could send only one child to college, he chose middle child Steve despite Carol's superior grades. Carol graduated from high school first in her class and took a sales job. She turned 18 a few months later, and the following day she turned her back on her father and joined the Air Force, intending to be a pilot and to get a college degree via the military. Her brother Steve's death in military action would eventually draw Carol back to her family, but she still never felt truly accepted by her father.

Rising quickly to the top of her Air Force class, Carol was recruited into military intelligence (Special Operations) and trained as a spy. She grew very attached to her partner/mentor Michael Rossi, and they soon bonded romantically. Their mission record proved excellent, but her romance with Michael (whom she nicknamed "Ace" on their first Russian mission) would eventually fade. On a first-year mission she was teamed with Colonel Nick Fury of the CIA. Posing as scientist Myron MacLain's secretary, she was present when Logan (later Wolverine) came to MacLain for help, and Carol and Fury witnessed a conflict involving Logan, a team of Hydra agents, operative Victor Creed (later Sabretooth) and Russian Natalia Shostakova (later the Black Widow). Fury later recruited Carol again, sending her, pilot Ben Grimm and Logan into Russia to observe the Red Storm project. Shot down, Carol escaped capture and stole a Russian plane, rescued Grimm and Logan (despite a dogfight with the future Black Widow), and completed the mission. As all this was classified top secret, she and her fellows would later publicly pretend not to recognize each other.

Carol's friendship with Logan led to the pair being teamed repeatedly. When Carol was betrayed while investigating a Canadian arms dealer, Logan saved her life. As a result, she was present when he learned about his partner Neil Langram's death, and was drawn into a plot by New York's Hellfire Club to conceal the existence of mutants while privately exploiting them. After four agents attempted to murder Carol in her hotel room (she killed all four), she helped Logan protect Dr. Perry Edwards, who intended to expose the so-called "mutant hierarchy." Edwards died when the Hellfire Club's Victor Creed seemingly killed himself while detonating a bomb, hospitalizing Carol for a month. Following her recovery, she took her information on the underground mutants to up-and-coming Senator Robert Kelly, setting him on a path which would define his career.

When Carol was captured and locked in Russia's Lubyanka prison, Rossi and Logan went rogue to break her out. Shortly thereafter, a position as head of security at NASA's Cape Canaveral opened up, and Carol's old dreams of space led her to call in her markers. NASA eventually requested her for the position and she resigned from the Air Force, bumping to full Colonel at retirement. Now the youngest security captain in NASA's history, she became embroiled in the schemes of the interstellar Kree Empire. She was present when a robotic Kree Sentry was transported to NASA for study, and got caught in the middle when Kree soldier Captain Mar-Vell battled it after it awoke. During her NASA stint she led an investigation into Mar-Vell's assumed alter ego, Dr. Lawson, which proved beneficial when the Super-Skrull briefly also impersonated Lawson and was exposed. In the coming months Carol would be kidnapped by the robotic Cyberex and then hospitalized when a controlled Iron Man attacked the Cape. Still concussed, Carol was kidnapped by Mar-Vell's enemy Yon-Rogg; while they battled, she was knocked into a damaged Kree Psyche-Magnitron, a powerful device which could turn imagination into reality. Carol's dreams of flight and her

REAL NAME: Carol Susan Jane Danvers
ALIASES: Linda Danvers, Warbird, Captain Marvel, Lady Marvel, Binary, "Ace," Cheese Burger; pseudonyms used during espionage career included Carol Daniels, Karolya Danilovska, and others.
IDENTITY: Publicly known
OCCUPATION: Hero; former instructor in "Training Day" program, author, Department of Homeland Security Chief of Tactical Operations, freelance writer, NASA Security Chief, Woman Magazine chief editor, U.S. Air Force Special Operations intelligence agent, salesgirl (Note: Carol's intelligence work required her to claim to be working for several agencies, including the CIA, the Department of Defense, and the Defense Intelligence Agency. Though she did work with many of these agencies, she was a USAF employee.)
CITIZENSHIP: USA
PLACE OF BIRTH: Boston, Massachusetts
KNOWN RELATIVES: Joseph "Joe" Danvers (father), Marie Danvers (mother), Steven J. Danvers (brother, deceased), Joseph "Joe" Danvers, Jr. (brother)
GROUP AFFILIATION: Avengers, Operation: Lightning Storm, the Initiative; formerly Queen's Vengeance, Starjammers
EDUCATION: Extensive military training, acquired B.A. while in military
FIRST APPEARANCE: (Danvers) Marvel Super-Heroes #13 (1967); (Ms. Marvel) Ms. Marvel #1 (1977); (Binary) Uncanny X-Men #164 (1982); (Warbird) Avengers #4 (1998)

Art by Sal Buscema

envy of Mar-Vell's powers led the machine to alter her genetically, effectively making her a half-Kree superhuman; however, this change was gradual, and Carol was unaware of it for months. After the Sentry reactivated and damaged the Cape before departing in pursuit of the Avengers, Carol's continued inability to control superhuman incursions led to her removal and she was reassigned to a minor NASA facility near Chicago. After Nitro raided that base, Carol was demoted to a mere security guard and returned to Cape Canaveral. Not long after another alien incursion, Carol learned that Michael Rossi had died in a plane crash (he actually survived, though Carol remains unaware of this). In the aftermath of this loss and her plummeting career, Carol resigned from NASA.

Living off accumulated salary, Carol wrote an angry tell-all exposé on NASA, burning many bridges. The best selling book briefly made Carol a celebrity, and she wrote for national magazines like Rolling Stone; however, she also developed a dual personality due to the Psyche-Magnitron's alterations. She would black out and become a Kree warrior, instantaneously donning a costume which the Psyche-Magnitron had created for her to ease her body's changes. These blackouts seriously alarmed Carol, but didn't stop her from accepting a New York position as chief editor at the new Woman Magazine. In times of stress, she would continue to transform into her Kree alter ego, who soon took the name Ms. Marvel after Mar-Vell. Over the next few months her fragmented mind slowly recovered, first pushed by the benevolent interference of the extradimensional Hecate, and then completely healed when Ronan subjected her to the mind-altering Millennia Bloom device. Meanwhile, she established herself as one of New York's premiere heroines, working with Spider-Man, the Defenders, the Avengers and others, and becoming friendly with the Avengers' Wonder Man. When the Avengers' Scarlet Witch took a leave of absence, Carol took her place as a full-fledged Avenger.

Carol reveled in her new status, aiding the team against foes like Chthon, the Absorbing Man and the Grey Gargoyle, and fitting in personally as well, even joining their regular poker games; however, things began to grow bleak when Carol was fired from her editorial job due to her frequent disappearances. She rescued her presumed-dead friend, astronaut Salia Petrie, from the alien Faceless One, only to discover Salia was severely traumatized. Carol's psychiatrist and close friend, Michael Barnett, was murdered by mutant shape-shifter Mystique, whose precognitive associate Destiny had warned her that Carol would hurt Mystique's foster-daughter Rogue. Barnett's murder pulled Ms. Marvel into conflict with the Hellfire Club and Mystique's Brotherhood of Evil Mutants, but before she could track down Mystique, Carol became involved with her extradimensional admirer Marcus, the son of Immortus, who had kidnapped Carol to timeless Limbo, wooed her with a "subtle boost" from mind-influencing devices and returned her to Earth with no memory of this. Still under the lingering mental influence of his devices, Carol told the Avengers she loved Marcus and accompanied him back to Limbo. Once there, his rapid aging unexpectedly continued and he soon died, leaving Carol trapped in Limbo. She eventually found her way home and, resenting the Avengers for not seeing through Marcus, gave up her Ms. Marvel identity and settled down in San Francisco. Mystique continued plotting Carol's downfall, however, and Rogue decided to remove this thorn from her foster-mother's side, attacking Carol herself. Their battle atop the Golden Gate Bridge ended when Rogue's absorption of Carol's

powers, memories and emotions accidentally became permanent. Thrown from the bridge, Carol was rescued by Spider-Woman (Jessica Drew), who brought the powerless and near-amnesiac Carol to Professor Charles Xavier for treatment. He helped restore most of her memories, though her emotional ties to them remained lost. After a bitter confrontation with the Avengers, Carol remained with Xavier and his X-Men, working to restore her mind.

Carol aided the X-Men for several weeks, and led them in infiltrating the Pentagon to delete their governmental records. She encountered Rogue and Mystique there for the first time since their attacks on her; while the X-Men defeated Rogue, Carol captured Mystique and turned her over to the authorities. Soon after, Carol and the X-Men were captured by the alien Brood. Fascinated by her genetic structure, they manipulated Carol's physiology up and down the evolutionary scale before she was freed by Wolverine. These manipulations transformed Carol into the energy-wielding Binary, and she helped defeat the Brood, destroying their homeworld and the outworld of Madrizar, and freeing the Brood's slave race, the Acanti. She returned home with the X-Men, but her childhood dreams of space travel beckoned. After an emotionless farewell to her parents, she returned to Xavier's only to find they allowed Rogue to join their group; after punching Rogue through the roof, Carol departed the team for good, unable to stomach their acceptance of Rogue despite understanding their reasons for it. She departed Earth, joining the space-faring Starjammers.

With the Starjammers, Carol traveled with exiled Shi'ar ruler Lilandra Neramani and aided her when she and her embittered sister Deathbird (a former foe of Carol's from her early days as Ms. Marvel) fought to use the power of the Phoenix to increase their positions. When the Kree-Shi'ar War menaced Earth's sun, Carol nearly burned out her own powers in saving the sun and was hospitalized in Avengers Headquarters for weeks, during which time she made peace with her past as an Avenger. When Starjammer Raza was bribed to kill the Avengers' Black Knight (Dane Whitman), Binary ended the conflict and falsified a story about Raza being mind-controlled; afterwards she decided to remain on Earth, feeling that she had been running from her problems. She moved into her parents' Beverly, Massachusetts home and began a semi-autobiographical science fiction novel titled "Binary;" she also worked with Peter Corbeau of Starcore in orbital projects, as well as with other heroes. Binary was one of the first to oppose the alien Skeletron when he pushed the Moon out of orbit. With Quasar (Wendell Vaughn) and other allies she pursued Skeletron to the Stranger's World; wanting full-strength allies against Skeletron, the Stranger restored Carol's damaged psyche, briefly giving her full access to her lost memories and buried emotions, though they soon faded. When another alien plot destabilized the wormhole from which Carol drew her powers, she worked with the X-Men to restore it; weeks later, she realized this had failed when her Binary powers ceased replenishing themselves. Burdened by the memories of her short-lived emotional reconnection to her past and her belief that her powers were fading, Carol became depressed.

When the disbanded Avengers reformed while facing Morgan Le Fay, Carol rejoined the team as Warbird. Though her powers had stabilized at her old Ms. Marvel levels, she kept the loss of her Binary-level powers secret. This led to bad judgment calls against Kree enemies, and the Avengers called a special tribunal to investigate Warbird's actions. When it looked like Carol would be demoted to reserve

BINARY

Art by Paul Smith

WARBIRD

Art by Olivier Coipel

status, she quit before a decision was reached. She moved to Seattle and resumed writing while her first novel successfully saw print; a contract for several others followed. Meanwhile, Avengers founder Iron Man (Tony Stark) had also relocated to Seattle, and tried to offer Carol guidance despite her resistance. She bottomed out when she threw Iron Man through the wing of a passenger jet. She and Iron Man saved the passengers, but Carol finally realized she had a problem and began attending AA meetings. She revealed her identity to governmental authorities and took responsibility for the crash; much to her surprise, the judge gave her a suspended sentence, demanding that she rejoin the Avengers and that they supervise her.

Back with the Avengers and no longer drinking, Carol came into her own. She drew the standoffish Triathlon closer into the team, played a role in ending the Shi'ar conversion of Earth into a "prison planet," led an Avengers contingent against a Deviant army in China, and led a mission to find the Master during Kang's invasion of Earth. On the latter mission she encountered Kang's son Marcus, a virtual duplicate of the Marcus who had once kidnapped her. After her initial revulsion she accepted his aid against the Master's creatures and Carol defeated the Master herself, stabbing him through the chest (Carol would later demand she be court-martialed for this "murder," ultimately being declared innocent of wrongdoing). Carol was central to the defeat of Kang's invasion when she destroyed his orbital Damocles base. Later, after the Avengers helped contain the "Red Zone" disaster, the U.S. President offered Carol a position as Chief Tactical Officer for the Department of Homeland Security (DHS); she accepted, leaving the Avengers.

Carol recruited the Thunderbolts' Dallas Riordan to work with her at the DHS, but chafed at the deskwork and kept slipping into costume — she teamed with Wolverine and Captain America against Rapture and Project Contingency (a renegade SHIELD anti-mutant operation), with the Thunderbolts against Fathom Five and Baron Strucker's Hydra forces, and with several heroes against Titannus. The CSA (Commission on Superhuman Activities) cornered her into approving an assault by the Thunderbolts on the Avengers, and her discontent grew. Eventually, the mad Scarlet Witch altered reality to create a mutant-ruled Earth where Carol, despite her non-mutant status, was that world's greatest hero as Captain Marvel. When the world was restored to normal, Carol retained her Captain Marvel memories, and decided she was wasting her time in a desk job. She resigned from the DHS, resolving to make herself into the hero she now knew she could be.

Carol hired an agent, Sarah Day, to help with her public image, and Day suggested she reassume her Ms. Marvel name. Carol subsequently defeated a Brood army and the Brood-hunting Cru, aided the Avengers against the Collective, was present at the birth of close friend Jessica Jones' baby, and served as the maid of honor at Jessica's wedding. She battled Warren Traveler, a dimension-lost foe from the reality in which she had been Captain Marvel, and battled Titannus again, all while conducting TV interviews and maintaining a very public blog. When the Super Human Registration Act passed, Carol became one of its strongest supporters. With a team of pro-registration friends, Carol apprehended anti-registration heroes like the Prowler, Shroud and

Arachne, and worked to train would-be heroes like Araña. Asked by Iron Man to head a new Avengers roster, she agreed on the condition that she also be given control of her own elite strike force, known as Operation: Lightning Storm. Carol uses this force to right what she sees as the world's wrongs, undertaking missions too quiet or too questionable for the Avengers.

HEIGHT: 5'11"   **EYES:** Blue
WEIGHT: 124 lbs.   **HAIR:** Blonde

ABILITIES/ACCESSORIES: Carol is fluent in English, Russian and another unrevealed Earth language, as well as Kree and Shi'ar languages. She speaks passable Rajaki and has a limited vocabulary in many other languages. Carol is an accomplished pilot, having extensive experience with USAF planes as well as with Kree, Shi'ar and other alien starships. She is extensively trained in armed and unarmed combat, including numerous martial arts. She is immensely strong-willed and able to endure incredible physical pain. As head of Operation: Lightning Storm, she controls an elite team of mostly SHIELD agents, operating from a smaller version of SHIELD's Helicarrier known as a minicarrier.

The Psyche-Magnitron transformed Carol into a peak human, athletically as fit as humanly possible, and also modified her DNA with Kree genes. It gave her the powers of flight, superhuman strength (sufficient to press 70 tons following subsequent genetic alterations), and great resistance to damage, as well as "seventh-sense" precognitive flashes and the ability to change into her costume instantaneously. Six months after her transformation, the Psyche-Magnitron gifted her with a suit which enabled her to survive in space and which was designed to ease her body's continuing transformation; however, this suit was eventually destroyed. After Carol lost her powers to Rogue, she maintained her "peak human" status though she lacked superpowers, save apparently the ability to change instantaneously into costume.

As Binary, Carol tapped into a white hole, channeling its energies through her body to create any form of radiation or gravity. The white hole boosted her strength and endurance levels far beyond her old Ms. Marvel levels, and she could survive indefinitely in space. The subsequent loss of access to the white hole didn't change Carol's powers, merely the level at which they function — she can still fly, can still project photonic blasts, and still possesses extreme strength and the ability to withstand damage at approximately her original Ms. Marvel levels. These powers are maintained by ambient energy absorbed from her environment, and as a result she can have negative effects on sensitive machinery. She can temporarily augment her powers by absorbing energy forms, most notably electromagnetic radiation, plasma and sonics; however, unless Carol is prepared, her energy absorption is rarely instantaneous, so she draws only miniscule power from many energy attacks and can still be damaged by these. Without energy sources, Carol can no longer survive unaided in space.

POWER GRID	1	2	3	4	5	6	7
INTELLIGENCE							
STRENGTH							
SPEED							
DURABILITY							
ENERGY PROJECTION							
FIGHTING SKILLS							

REAL NAME: Clinton Francis "Clint" Barton
ALIASES: Formerly Hawkeye, the Marksman, "Br'er Hawkeye," Seagate Superhuman Cellblock Prisoner 334556, Longbow, Goliath, Father Time, Louis, Robin Hood, the Hawkeye Kid, Golden Archer, "Purple Man"; impersonated Constrictor & Dreadknight
IDENTITY: Secret
OCCUPATION: Outlaw adventurer, revolutionary; former professional super hero, fugitive, unofficial SHIELD operative, federal inmate, CTE security chief, ranch hand, archery tutor, carnival performer, roustabout, butcher shop worker
CITIZENSHIP: USA with a criminal record, pardoned
PLACE OF BIRTH: Waverly, Iowa
KNOWN RELATIVES: Harold & Edith Barton (parents), Charles Bernard "Barney" Barton (brother), Barbara Morse "Bobbi" Barton (Mockingbird, wife), Brett & Mack Barton (ancestors); all deceased
GROUP AFFILIATION: Avengers; formerly Thunderbolts, SHIELD (unofficial), Chain Gang 421-011, Shadows, Great Lakes Avengers, Cross Technological Enterprises, Defenders, Carson Carnival of Traveling Wonders, Tiboldt Circus (a.k.a. Circus of Crime); former partner of Mockingbird, Two-Gun Kid, Black Widow, Trick Shot, Swordsman
EDUCATION: High school (unfinished)
FIRST APPEARANCE: (Hawkeye) Tales of Suspense #57 (1964); (Goliath) Avengers #63 (1969); (Ronin) New Avengers #27 (2007)

HISTORY: The ultimate self-made man, veteran adventurer Clint Barton has reinvented himself repeatedly over the years. Clint and his older brother Barney grew up in the town of Waverly, Iowa, where they worked in their father Harold's butcher shop after school. Successful and popular, Harold had a bad temper that made him physically and verbally abusive with his family; his wife Edith tried to protect her sons, but was not always successful. While Barney grew resentful, Clint compensated by working harder to please his father, trying to be a better son in hopes of spurring Harold to be a better parent. It never worked, and Harold eventually killed himself and Edith in a drunk driving accident when Clint was eight years old. Clint and Barney were placed in the Saint Ignatius Home for Orphaned Boys, but they were too old in the eyes of most prospective parents and spent years being passed over for adoption. Bitter and bored, Barney bullied Clint, who responded by doing all their chores and trying to be a better brother. Clint also found occasional relief in a pile of old Western pulp novels left at the orphanage, the Old West being one of the few subjects that interested him during his early schooling. This interest may have stemmed in part from a family connection, as Clint's ancestor Brett Barton was the sheriff in Tombstone during the heyday of the Two-Gun Kid (Matt Hawk), a legendary masked gunman.

When Clint was fourteen, Barney ran away from the orphanage and Clint reluctantly came along. The fast-talking Barney soon landed the brothers menial jobs with the Carson Carnival of Traveling Wonders, a traveling circus. The Bartons came to regard the carnival folk as their new family, though Clint was oblivious to the fact that the carnival owner's tomboy daughter, Marcy Carson, had a long-standing crush on him. The boys were more interested in the carnival's performers, especially the Swordsman (Jacques Duquesne), a supremely skillful master of bladed weapons. When the Swordsman's assistant quit after deciding their act was too dangerous, Clint eagerly took her place. Impressed by the boy's nerve, Swordsman began teaching him knife throwing so he could become a bigger part of the act. Duquesne gradually became a father figure of sorts to Clint, who worked desperately to earn his mentor's approval.

Trouble arrived in the form of Trick Shot (Buck Chisholm), an unscrupulous archer who fast eclipsed the Swordsman as the carnival's new star attraction. Beating Chisholm badly in a card game, Duquesne offered to forgive Chisholm's debt in exchange for Trick Shot teaching Clint archery, hoping to add some extra appeal to their act. Trick Shot agreed and began tutoring Barton, who proved to have a natural flair for archery. Adopting a buckskin costume and taking the stage name Hawkeye, Clint aspired to be the equal of his partner the Swordsman, but the insecure Duquesne resented Barton's growing skill and became increasingly irritable as his own gambling debts mounted. Meanwhile, Chisholm talked Clint into helping him pull off petty crimes and con games outside the carnival. By this time, Barney had matured somewhat and grew tired of the carnival life, getting his general equivalency diploma. He encouraged Clint to consider leaving the business, and discouraged him from getting mixed up with criminals.

Deeply in debt to a mob-connected loan shark named Marko, the Swordsman robbed the carnival paymaster. When Clint caught him in the act and refused to go along with the crime, Duquesne attacked him, pursuing Clint onto the trapeze and cutting the high wire out from under him. Badly injured by the fall, Clint might have been killed if Barney and Trick Shot had not arrived in time to chase off the Swordsman and take Clint to the hospital. Barney was furious with Clint over his near-fatal association with criminals, though a half-conscious, pain-wracked Clint interpreted his brother's anger as frustration over Clint having passed up the easy money from the payroll robbery. Shunned for a time by Barney, Clint was in hospital with two broken legs when Trick Shot offered to make Clint his new protégé and continue teaching him archery while his injuries healed. Seeing no other options, Clint accepted.

Art by Leinil Francis Yu with John Romita Jr. (inset)

YOUNG HAWKEYE

Trick Shot taught Clint everything there was to know about archery, and also introduced him to the concept of "trick" arrows custom-designed for specific purposes; however, the two archers never grew truly close. Despite Chisholm's cruelty, but Clint stayed with him for the training, and because he had nowhere else to go. Meanwhile, Barney tentatively renewed his relationship with Clint and kept trying to convince his brother to leave the carnival and its criminal element behind. Clint stubbornly refused, and when Barney finally left the carnival to join the military, he left alone.

Once Clint had regained full mobility and become a formidable archer in his own right, Chisholm decided to have Clint earn his keep by moonlighting as Trick Shot's partner in mercenary work — beginning with a mob-sponsored hit targeting Swordsman's creditor Marko, who had been cheating his superiors. Telling Barton they were simply going to rob Marko, Trick Shot slipped into Marko's home and killed Marko and his wife, leaving the unsuspecting Clint outside as a lookout. Attacked by Marko's henchmen, Clint disarmed two of them, but a third gunman shot him, throwing off Clint's aim and resulting in a potentially fatal arrow wound for the third man. Horrified at having hurt someone, Clint was even more shocked upon recognizing the third gunman as his brother Barney. When Trick Shot ordered Clint to leave his brother behind, Clint refused to flee without seeking medical attention for Barney. The two archers fought and Trick Shot easily won, but he spared Clint's life, saying he would return someday to destroy Clint once he had grown into a foe worth killing.

Disappointed in his brother and ashamed of himself, Clint got Barney safely to the hospital and left shortly thereafter, unable to face his sibling. Unbeknownst to Clint, however, Barney had become an undercover FBI agent, and entering Marko's organization was his first field assignment. Upon his recovery, Barney continued to infiltrate organized crime, rising through the ranks to become a notorious gang boss. Clint, meanwhile, returned to the carnival circuit, gradually becoming a star attraction under his stage name Hawkeye and adopting a purple and blue costume similar to Trick Shot's old stage garb. As time passed, however, Clint became bored, desiring bigger challenges and greater fame than carnival performing could provide. He also suffered yet another disillusioning setback while working with the Tiboldt Circus (later known as the Circus of Crime), discovering that its Ringmaster was a criminal and that his accomplice was Clint's own girlfriend, Eden the tattooed lady. Clint turned them in to the police and left the Tiboldt outfit, working for Carson and other carnivals, but show life seemed increasingly empty for him. His few friends were fellow performers such as cyclist Dillon Zarro, who secretly resented Clint's superior skill and showmanship.

Back in his old buckskin suit, Hawkeye was performing in a Coney Island sideshow when he saw the armored superhero Iron Man (Tony Stark) saving patrons from a runaway carnival ride. Impressed and envious, Clint donned a new purple and blue costume with a small arsenal of specially gimmicked "trick" arrows and set out to fight crime as Hawkeye. Successfully thwarting a jewel robbery, he was mistaken for a thief by the police and fled. While escaping,

2ND CARNIVAL OUTFIT

he was rescued from police pursuit by the Black Widow (Natasha Romanoff), a beautiful Russian spy then devoted to sabotaging the scientific and industrial work of genius tycoon Tony Stark. Smitten with the Black Widow, Hawkeye repeatedly fought Stark's supposed bodyguard Iron Man on her behalf, and once clashed with novice hero Spider-Man while trying to rob Stark's business

rival Simon Williams. Sensing a kindred spirit of sorts in Hawkeye, the often-misunderstood Spider-Man urged the misguided archer to abandon crime.

Trying to revive his abortive crime-fighting career, Hawkeye rescued butler Edwin Jarvis and his mother from muggers in the Bronx. Grateful, Jarvis bought Hawkeye dinner and encouraged the archer to aspire to greater things than his fugitive vigilante lifestyle. Meanwhile, the manipulative Black Widow had gradually fallen in love with the dashing Hawkeye despite herself and tried to desert her Russian masters, who nearly killed her in retaliation. Heartbroken, Hawkeye got the wounded Natasha to a hospital and went back into hiding. Deprived of the financial and technological backing of Natasha's former employers, Clint maintained his archery arsenal by robbing criminals, using the funds to buy supplies and paying criminal inventor the Tinkerer to craft some of his more specialized high-tech shafts. Tracking Hawkeye down, Jarvis finally convinced him to abandon life on the run and helped Barton seek a new career with the butler's employers: the Avengers, the world's leading superhero team.

Secretly aided by Jarvis, Hawkeye staged a "break-in" at Avengers Mansion where he offered his services to the Avengers and showed off his skills, partly by freeing a bound-and-gagged Jarvis with a volley of arrows. The Avengers, including Hawkeye's old foe Iron Man, were convinced of Barton's sincerity and impressed by his abilities. Deciding to take a chance on him, they inducted Hawkeye into their ranks as the group's second recruit, filling one of several vacancies that were opening up as Iron Man and the other Avengers founders prepared to take a leave of absence. The other openings were filled by mutant twin siblings Quicksilver and the Scarlet Witch, also former outlaws, while veteran member Captain America (Steve Rogers) stayed on as team leader. The unlikely foursome, nicknamed "Cap's Kooky Quartet" by the media, made for a volatile mix: Hawkeye and the other new recruits often questioned Cap's authority, but Clint soon developed respect for Cap's abilities and character. The two men became close friends, and Hawkeye became one of Captain America's most loyal supporters. Hawkeye also befriended his other early teammates, notably the Scarlet Witch, and he proved to be one of the group's most valuable and longest-serving members.

Hawkeye's past sometimes came back to haunt his Avengers career, but he usually emerged stronger as a result. The Swordsman, now an infamous criminal mercenary, swindled his way into Avengers membership as an agent of the Mandarin and was expelled from the group when the Avengers uncovered his deceptions. The recovered Black Widow was brainwashed into serving her former masters anew, attacking the Avengers and employing the Swordsman and Power Man (Erik Josten) as accomplices. Hawkeye insisted on facing them alone, subduing Josten and defeating the Swordsman in single combat. Unable to bring herself to harm Hawkeye, Black Widow shook off her brainwashing. The lovers resumed their romance, and Black Widow became a recurring ally to the Avengers; however, Natasha's new work with the elite intelligence agency SHIELD came between the couple over time, and they began to drift apart.

1ST SUPER-HERO COSTUME

Feeling insecure since he lacked the superhuman power and genius intelligence of various fellow Avengers, Clint gave up archery and used teammate Hank Pym's growth serum to become the new Goliath, a costumed identity formerly used by Pym himself. Barton continued to serve effectively with the Avengers as the giant-sized Goliath, but he gradually became frustrated with the limitations of Pym's serum; he also realized that he was no more effective as Goliath than he

TRICK ARROWS

had been as Hawkeye, since his archery skills had often proven as valuable as any super-power. In fact, he used archery to win several victories as Goliath, including his single-handed defeat of the Skrulls who had tried to annihilate Earth during the Kree-Skrull War. Having already decided to abandon his Goliath guise, Barton formally resumed his Hawkeye identity after that triumph. Though he briefly resumed his Goliath guise several times in the ensuing years, he generally preferred to operate as Hawkeye, and eventually lost his physical tolerance for size-changing during a conflict with the alien Kosmosians.

During his Goliath phase, Clint was unexpectedly reunited with his brother Barney, who sacrificed his life to save the Avengers from criminal mastermind Egghead. Clint avenged him by bringing Egghead to justice, and soon learned about his brother's FBI career from Barney's partner Allan Scofield. Later, Clint suffered another personal loss when the Black Widow abruptly ended their on-and-off romance. By the time Clint resumed his Hawkeye identity, he had set his romantic sights on the Scarlet Witch; however, she firmly rejected him, having already fallen in love with their android teammate Vision. Bitter over his romantic setbacks and feeling unappreciated by the Avengers, Hawkeye impulsively left the group to work as an archery tutor for eccentric billionaire Imus Champion, but soon teamed with the Avengers to defeat Champion when he turned out to be a dangerous criminal. Despite this victorious reunion, Hawkeye formally quit the Avengers for the first time in hopes of making a name for himself as a solo hero.

Barton briefly tried to renew his relationship with the Black Widow, but this brought him into heated conflict with her then-current lover and partner, the adventurer Daredevil. When the Avengers recruited Black Widow and Daredevil to aid them in a case shortly thereafter, Hawkeye felt further estranged from his former teammates. After helping the Hulk destroy the rampaging monster Zzzax, Hawkeye joined the Hulk and other heroes in the informal Defenders super-team — partly out of curiosity, partly out of a desire to outperform the Avengers, and partly out of attraction to Defenders member Valkyrie. Barton fought several foes alongside the Defenders, and even battled the Avengers when Dormammu and Loki briefly tricked the two teams into fighting; this clash also briefly reunited Barton with the Swordsman, who had reformed and rejoined the Avengers. Realizing he still wasn't making a solo name for himself, Hawkeye quit the Defenders. He subsequently teamed with Spider-Man to defeat the rogue computer Quasimodo, and briefly masqueraded as the Golden Archer as part of a successful ploy to restore a demoralized Captain America's fighting spirit.

GOLIATH

Rejoining the Avengers to help them defeat the time-spanning warlord Kang during the Celestial Madonna affair, Hawkeye witnessed the Swordsman's heroic death in action during that conflict. Barton later left on a time travel quest seeking fellow Avenger the Black Knight, but a chance encounter with Kang en route stranded Hawkeye in the year 1873, where he befriended several of his boyhood heroes: legendary Old West adventurers Kid Colt, Phantom Rider, Rawhide Kid, Ringo Kid and the Two-Gun Kid. Soon joined by the Avengers, Hawkeye helped the cowboys defeat Kang and returned to his own time, accompanied

by the Two-Gun Kid, who wished to explore the future. Clint volunteered to serve as Two-Gun's personal guide to the modern world, and the two friends took an indefinite leave of absence from the Avengers to roam the American southwest in search of adventure, working at the Cheery-O's Dude Ranch in their civilian identities. As Hawkeye and Two-Gun, they defeated the mind-controlling Purple Man, thwarted the alien warlord Kaa with the aid of the Champions, and teamed with Ghost Rider (Johnny Blaze) to foil an attempt on Hawkeye's life by the Manticore.

In time, the duo grew restless and returned to the Avengers, though a homesick and somewhat overwhelmed Two-Gun soon went back to his native time period. After Hawkeye mistakenly attacked the Avengers' new National Security Council liaison, the often-adversarial Henry Peter Gyrich, Agent Gyrich demanded changes to the team's operations and membership — including Hawkeye's removal from the active roster. Demoted to reserve Avengers status, Hawkeye found a new occupation as security chief at scientific R&D firm Cross Technological Enterprises (CTE). Enjoying this high-paying managerial position, Hawkeye protected CTE from threats such as Deathbird and Mister Fear while befriending CTE technician Jorge Latham and dating CTE publicist Shiela Danning. He even rejoined the active Avengers roster, dividing his time between heroics and CTE. At the same time, he was happily reunited with Carson Carnival's current owner Marcy Carson, teaming with Ant-Man (Scott Lang) to save the carnival from Taskmaster.

When the vigilante el Aguila sabotaged an unethical CTE weapons project, Hawkeye assumed this was an isolated incident until the freelance spy Mockingbird (Bobbi Morse) tipped Barton off to massive corruption within the company. When Hawkeye investigated, CTE tried to kill them both, and Danning scornfully revealed that the company had paid her to seduce Clint as a distraction. Crushed by the simultaneous loss of his romance and his job, Hawkeye quickly bounced back and teamed with Mockingbird to fight back, battling their way through mercenaries Silencer, Bombshell and Oddball to bring down CTE and its secret leader, the high-tech subversive Crossfire. Strongly attracted to each other and realizing what a great team they made, the victorious Hawkeye and Mockingbird decided to make their partnership permanent, eloping on the spur of the moment.

Not long afterward, Hawkeye was appointed chairman of the Avengers' new western-based roster in California. As chairman, Hawkeye supervised the preparation of new western headquarters Avengers Compound; they bought the property from retired actress Moira Brandon, who became an honorary Avenger after she helped Hawkeye and Mockingbird recapture an escaped Crossfire. Barton proved to be a highly effective chairman, and his western roster's recruits included Mockingbird, Tigra, Wonder Man, an alternate Iron Man (Jim Rhodes), the original Iron Man (Tony Stark), Thing, Firebird, Doctor Pym, Moon Knight, Wasp, Vision, Scarlet Witch & Mantis. The vigilante Shroud declined an offer of membership from Hawkeye, but became a recurring ally to the group. Also active as a solo adventurer, Hawkeye fought various foes alongside allies such as Silver Sable, Sandman, le Peregrine, Black Crow and reporter Gayle Rogers. Most notably, Trick Shot finally challenged Hawkeye to a death duel, secretly hoping Barton would kill him since he was dying of cancer and wanted to go out facing a worthy opponent. Hawkeye refused to kill Trick Shot, but he offered to help his old enemy cope with his illness and the two men finally reconciled their differences.

When the alien computer entity Dominus exiled the western Avengers to the 19th century using a defective time machine that could only move backward through time, the Avengers teamed with Two-Gun Kid, Rawhide Kid and Phantom Rider to apprehend that era's Iron Mask gang. The Avengers next journeyed further back in time to ancient Egypt to seek the aid of that era's Rama-Tut — but the mad Phantom Rider (Lincoln Slade) abducted Mockingbird as they departed, stranding her in the Old West. He used Indian love potions to brainwash Mockingbird into becoming his lover until she broke his control with Two-Gun's aid and hunted down Slade, who fell to his death in final battle with her. After Hawkeye and the other Avengers found a way back home and rescued Mockingbird en route, she concealed her role in Slade's demise since she feared the idealistic Hawkeye's reaction. When the truth came out months later — as related to Hawkeye by Slade's own vengeful ghost — Clint angrily condemned his wife's conduct, sparking an ideological debate within the Avengers regarding lethal force. Hurt by Clint's reaction, Mockingbird quit the group and left him. A heartsick Hawkeye threw himself into his Avengers work and occasional solo cases, notably his apprehension of the Bullet Biker, who turned out to be Clint's old friend Dillon Zarro.

Returning to spy work, Mockingbird was duped into helping the intelligence coalition Vigilance abduct and dismantle the Vision, further souring her relations with the Avengers in general and Hawkeye in particular. Given this development, and the increasingly take-charge attitude of senior members Doctor Pym and Wasp subtly undermining his leadership, Hawkeye became greatly frustrated. That frustration boiled over when the federal government appointed its abrasive operative USAgent to serve as the western Avengers' new in-house supervisor. Angrily quitting the team, Hawkeye began spending more time with Mockingbird, and the troubled couple mentored the Midwestern novice adventurers known as the Great Lakes Avengers while serving as on-call reservists with the official Avengers. During this period, a vengeful Crossfire placed a rich bounty on Hawkeye's arm which attracted a small army of bloodthirsty super-mercenaries, but Barton defeated Crossfire and company with the aid of Mockingbird and Trick Shot, whose cancer had gone into remission.

Hawkeye eventually rejoined the western Avengers' active roster, where he feuded frequently with teammate USAgent. Clint also flirted with new recruit Spider-Woman (Julia Carpenter), but when the killer robot Ultron kidnapped Mockingbird to use her mind as the programming template for his own robotic bride Alkhema, Barton led the Avengers' successful rescue of Mockingbird and rediscovered how much he loved her. The couple finally fully reconciled their marital differences, Mockingbird rejoined the team, and Clint served as chairman for a time before stepping down to concentrate on his marriage. Mockingbird, meanwhile, considered retiring from adventure altogether since she and Hawkeye had begun to talk of starting a family together. Their plans ended tragically when the Avengers were drawn into a clash between the arch-demons Satannish and Mephisto, who fatally blasted Mockingbird while she was helping Hawkeye and the Scarlet Witch get to safety.

Devastated, Hawkeye left the Avengers to live as a wilderness hermit, but trouble kept finding him. He crippled the Viper's subversive Secret Empire with help from former Avengers teammate War Machine (Jim Rhodes); inventor Mack Mendelson, who helped Hawkeye update and restock his equipment; Trick Shot, who turned against his employer Viper to save Barton; and genetically engineered dog-being Rover, a failed Empire experiment who served as a sort of sidekick to Hawkeye for a time. Parting company with Rover, the troubled Barton developed friendships with Rhodes and old sparring partner USAgent, who had come to respect Barton and tried to recruit him into Force Works, a Stark-sponsored team which had replaced the now-disbanded western Avengers roster. For a time, Hawkeye mentored the U.S. government-sponsored revolutionaries known as the Shadows in the country of San Revilla, but he turned on them and departed after realizing how unethical and dangerous they were.

During his long absence from the Avengers, Hawkeye nursed a grudge against Iron Man (Tony Stark) — partly due to Stark's occasional legal and ethical misconduct as Iron Man, but also due to more personal reasons such as Iron Man's absence during Mockingbird's death, and Stark's arrogant, controlling personality. Perhaps because of this tension, when an Immortus-controlled Stark turned on the Avengers during the elaborate conspiracy known as "The Crossing," he tried to frame Hawkeye for murders Stark himself had committed. In the end, Stark rebelled against Immortus and seemingly sacrificed his life to defeat the villain, and Hawkeye rejoined the active Avengers roster, where he helped guide a teenage version of Stark recruited from an alternate timeline. Clint also befriended mysterious new honorary member Masque, though she soon disappeared.

When Hawkeye and most of the other active Avengers seemingly died while saving humanity from malevolent psychic entity Onslaught. they were secretly displaced into an alternate world created by Franklin Richards, a planet later known as Counter-Earth, where they lived out alternate versions of their lives as that world's Avengers. Eventually returning to their own world, the Avengers regrouped and Hawkeye again joined the active roster, personally recruiting new reservists Firestar & Justice; however, he felt increasingly restless in a non-leadership role after his time with the western Avengers, despite his respect for team leader Captain America. Barton soon quit the team to become the new leader of the Thunderbolts, a group of former super-villains seeking redemption as outlaw heroes.

Aided by sympathetic media coverage from Gayle Rogers — who was later killed by Thunderbolts enemy Scourge (Jack Monroe) — Hawkeye greatly improved the Thunderbolts' public image, and his leadership quickly made them a much more skillful and effective fighting unit. He also became something of an inspirational figure for the team, serving as an example to which they could aspire. He befriended multiple Thunderbolts, notably Songbird, and even shared a risky romance with oft-unscrupulous teammate Moonstone, but he was temporarily estranged from the team when they learned that his work with them had never been government-sanctioned as he originally claimed.

Shortly thereafter, Hawkeye and the Thunderbolts helped foil a massive anti-superhuman conspiracy seemingly masterminded by Commission on Superhuman Activities (CSA) agent Henry Peter Gyrich, who was actually a mind-controlled pawn of Baron von Strucker. Hawkeye offered to keep quiet about the CSA's role in Strucker's conspiracy if the CSA would arrange full criminal pardons for his fellow Thunderbolts. The CSA agreed, though a spiteful Gyrich insisted on an additional condition, that Hawkeye go to jail for operating as an unsanctioned vigilante. Clint accepted the terms and went to prison while the rest of the Thunderbolts went free. Ironically, most of them seemingly died saving the world from Graviton months later, but they actually survived on Counter-Earth.

ARMORED COSTUME

Shortly after his incarceration at Seagate Prison, Barton was secretly recruited by SHIELD officer "Dum-Dum" Dugan for an unofficial mission: to seek out an ultimate weapon developed by the late criminal tycoon Justin Hammer. Over the course of this mission, Clint escaped custody as part of a prison chain gang, later teaming with Songbird and a motley band of super-criminal allies to form a new group of Thunderbolts who neutralized Hammer's weapon and defeated the Crimson Cowl's Masters of Evil. After the Cowl's defeat, Hawkeye and Songbird resisted SHIELD's efforts to take their new teammates into custody, despite the risk of losing their own SHIELD-sponsored pardons. Before the matter could be settled, the new Thunderbolts teamed with the V Battalion, Silver Sable, and the original Thunderbolts to save the world from an all-consuming void emanating from the V Battalion's flagship, the Vanguard. When the two Thunderbolts factions assembled to discuss their collective future afterward, Hawkeye decided to leave the group, convinced he was no longer needed and confident that Songbird and the other members he

trained would be able to keep the group both ethical and effective.

Rejoining the Avengers, Hawkeye spent his off hours touring America's seedier establishments. During one of these trips, he romanced librarian Maryanne Sherbrook. He also helped his old girlfriend Eden make a fresh start after she got out of prison. Meanwhile, the Scarlet Witch went criminally insane and turned against the Avengers, her rampage seemingly killing Vision, Jack of Hearts, Ant-Man and Hawkeye, who was blown up while trying to save his teammates from a Witch-conjured Kree army. She later resurrected Clint when she transformed the world into her "House of M" reality, a mutant-dominated altered reality in which Hawkeye was part of the underground resistance against the oppressive regime of her father, Magneto. Though the Witch seemingly destroyed Hawkeye again when he turned on her, Clint was reborn again when she restored conventional reality.

Disillusioned, confused and overwhelmed after his cycle of death and rebirth, Barton discarded his Hawkeye costume and gear and kept a low profile, informing no one of his return. After consulting sorcerer Doctor Strange (who confirmed that Barton had been lastingly resurrected), Clint decided to seek out and confront the Scarlet Witch despite Strange advising against it. When Barton finally found her, she was living quietly in Transia as an amnesiac Wanda Maximoff, apparently unaware of her past life as the Scarlet Witch. Uncertain of what to do, Clint impulsively shared a brief romance with Wanda before deciding to leave well enough alone and departing.

Clint Barton returned to America just after the super hero civil war fought over the new federal Superhuman Registration Act (SHRA), which required all super heroes to register their identities with the government and submit to federal control. The pro-SHRA forces led by Iron Man (Tony Stark) ultimately prevailed after anti-SHRA resistance leader Captain America surrendered to prevent further violence, though Cap himself was apparently assassinated by agents of the Red Skull while in custody. Most of the anti-SHRA heroes gave up and registered with the SHRA after Cap's surrender, accepting an offer of general amnesty — but a handful of radicals continued to resist the pro-SHRA regime, including an outlaw Avengers team led by Luke Cage. This faction is also allied with some of the teenage Young Avengers, including Kate Bishop, who had assumed Hawkeye's identity as a tribute to the supposedly deceased Barton. Upon returning to New York, Clint secretly confronted Tony Stark, who tried to convince Barton to register with the SHRA and replace the late Steve Rogers as the new Captain America; however, while trying out Cap's costume and shield, Clint met the new Hawkeye and her teammate Patriot (Eli Bradley), helping them escape when Iron Man tried to arrest them. Feeling it was wrong for himself or anyone else to usurp Cap's identity, Clint relinquished the shield and went back into hiding.

Determined to avenge Captain America and carry on Cap's work, Clint has joined Cage's Avengers and adopted a new identity as martial artist Ronin, inheriting a costume and alias formerly used by his new teammate Echo. Where this new life will lead Clint Barton remains to be seen.

HEIGHT: 6'3" **EYES:** Blue
WEIGHT: 230 lbs. **HAIR:** Blond

ABILITIES/ACCESSORIES: A natural athlete, Clint Barton is a highly experienced and formidable unarmed combatant, thanks largely to longtime combat training with Captain America. He also has extensive training as an acrobat and aerialist, skills he has often combined with his natural marksmanship — for instance, training himself to make accurate shots from virtually any angle, physical position or state of motion. Though trained primarily as an archer, Barton is a natural marksman with any thrown or fired weapon, and has a knack for using random objects as makeshift projectiles; in this respect, his abilities are similar to those of the assassin Bullseye, albeit less developed since Barton has concentrated exclusively on archery for much of his career. Barton has an instinctive genius for calculating the angles, velocity and likely impact of objects in motion, and routinely plans and executes complicated ricochet shots using assorted projectiles.

Barton is probably the world's most skillful and accurate archer, albeit currently out of practice. He trained with blades as a youth, notably knife throwing, and has also worked with darts, balls, bolas and boomerangs. He currently employs traditional Eastern martial arts weapons such as swords, throwing stars and nunchakus, and is rapidly becoming more proficient in their use. His phenomenal eyesight, reflexes, manual dexterity and hand-eye coordination make him a natural with most basic weaponry. He is a highly capable and charismatic team leader and a shrewd combat strategist, albeit sometimes reckless.

Barton is a talented weapons designer, particularly well-versed in variations on basic traditional weaponry such as arrows, blades and hand-thrown projectiles. He has designed and crafted crescent darts, boomerangs, throwing irons, bolas and axes. Barton has also built and maintained much of his own custom-made archery arsenal over the years, including a wide array of mechanically gimmicked "trick" arrows, though some of his more high-tech arrows were designed by inventors such as the Tinkerer, Iron Man, Hank Pym, the Black Panther and Mack Mendelson. Highly resourceful, Barton has often proven capable

of constructing makeshift bow-and-arrow sets from random materials within moments.

An experienced motorcycle rider, Barton was one of the most proficient and daring pilots of the Avengers' supersonic Quinjets, with a particular flair for spectacular (and surprisingly survivable) emergency crash landings. For years, Hawkeye also piloted various small, high-tech one-man aircraft or "sky cycles" designed by Jorge Latham (original model) and Mack Mendelson (later model). More recently, Barton had employed a modified flying "Atomic Steed" manufactured by the High Evolutionary's Knights of Wundagore, but later gave this vehicle to the Two-Gun Kid.

As Goliath, Barton could grow to gigantic sizes, gaining superhuman strength in the process. He seemed largely immune to the negative mental and physical side-effects that often plagued other enlarging size-changers, possibly due to Barton's natural athleticism and the powers of concentration that he cultivated via marksmanship. For a time, Barton was 80% deaf due to an injury, but his hearing was restored during his rebirth on Franklin Richards' Counter-Earth.

As Hawkeye, Barton wielded various custom-made bows and specially-gimmicked "trick" arrows, as well as various conventional arrows. His "trick" arrowheads were modular and could be attached to standard target-point arrows, and he usually carried multiple trick arrowheads in his costume. He briefly employed an armored, steel-alloy bulletproof Hawkeye costume.

POWER GRID	1	2	3	4	5	6	7
INTELLIGENCE							
STRENGTH							
SPEED							
DURABILITY							
ENERGY PROJECTION							
FIGHTING SKILLS							

HISTORY: The daughter of Los Angeles police sheriff Morris Walters, Jennifer Walters developed her own strong sense of right from his example. She and her best friend Jill Stevens regularly babysat Jen's next door neighbor, Daniel "Zapper" Ridge, who soon developed a lasting crush on her. Jen spent her summers in Charlestown, Ohio with her maternal cousin, and despite a five year age gap they became as close as siblings. They often spent long evenings reading to one another in the local library; however, they lost touch after Bruce switched degrees to nuclear physics. Though her father hoped she might follow him into law enforcement, Jen wanted to be a dancer. En route to one of Jen's dance recitals, her mother Elaine's car collided head on with another vehicle, killing her; officially the crash was blamed on the other driver's drunkenness, but Morris Walters eventually learned that it had been an attempt on his life arranged by local mob boss Nick Trask. After Elaine's death, both Jen and her father retreated into obsessions with law and justice; Morris poured himself into his work, and Jen into law studies, driving herself to reach the top. Attending Harvard, Jen neither mingled nor partied, graduating summa cum laude. She had her pick of top law firms to join, but she chose to go into private practice; though an excellent lawyer, she often lost cases to cocky Assistant District Attorney Joachim "Buck" Bukowski.

Unknown to Jen, her cousin Bruce had become the monstrous Hulk. Attempting to make contact, Bruce found Jen with a ruptured appendix, and while rushing her to a hospital as the Hulk, was attacked by the Champions. The delay nearly cost Jen her life, and barely conscious during the incident, she did not learn till much later who had saved her life. When Nick Trask framed rival mobster Lou Monkton for murder, Jen took up Monkton's defense. Hoping to shake up Trask, Jen planted a rumor that she had evidence implicating Trask as the killer, shortly before her fugitive cousin Bruce approached her. Jen had just driven him back to her house when Trask's men shot her. Aware Jen had lost too much blood, Bruce gave her an emergency transfusion, then fled moments after the authorities arrived. Recovering in the hospital, Jen hated how vulnerable she felt, unaware of the mutagenic changes her cousin's irradiated blood were making to her body; when Trask's thugs tried to finish her off, adrenaline triggered Jen's transformation into a larger, green-skinned form, dubbed a "She-Hulk" by one of her attackers. Empowered psychologically as well as physically, Jen vowed to herself that whatever Jennifer Walters couldn't handle, the She-Hulk would.

Trying again to eliminate Jen, Trask's men rigged her car to crash; unfortunately, her friend Jill died in her place, and witness Buck Bukowski erroneously thought the She-Hulk had killed her. Jen let the public, her father included, believe she had died, to deter further attempts. Trask blackened She-Hulk's name further, using a murderous green robot, before he finally seemingly died while attacking the She-Hulk with a giant Silver Serpent robot. With the public now aware Jen was alive, the She-Hulk produced the green robot's remains to clear her name for those attacks; however, she continued to be blamed for Jill's death. Having shared her secret with Zapper, now a med student, Jen asked

SAVAGE SHE-HULK

him to analyze a blood sample, worried that she was changing at the slightest provocation and that She-Hulk's increasingly strong personality might engulf her own. Zapper's friend, Ralphie Hutchins, directed Zapper to the former "Living Vampire" Dr. Michael Morbius, working on campus under police guard. He identified a fatal degenerative disease in Jen's blood and provided a serum, which not only cured the condition, but also gave her control over her changes. Jen, in turn, represented Morbius in court, getting multiple

REAL NAME: Jennifer Walters
ALIASES: Jennifer Jameson, Jennifer Smith, Jade Giantess, Nurse Jennifer Emerald, Glamazonia, "Shulkie"
IDENTITY: Publicly known
OCCUPATION: Attorney, adventurer; former SHIELD agent, actress, mine slave
CITIZENSHIP: USA
PLACE OF BIRTH: Los Angeles, California
KNOWN RELATIVES: William Morris Walters (father), Elaine Ann Banner Walters (mother, deceased), Robert Bruce Banner (Hulk, cousin), Elizabeth "Betty" Ross Talbot Banner (cousin-in-law), Rebecca Banner (aunt, deceased), Brian Banner (uncle, deceased), Susan Elizabeth Banner (formerly Susan Drake; aunt, presumed deceased), Cassandra Walters Pike (Brain, aunt), David Pike (Brawn, cousin), John Jameson (husband, marriage annulled); for extended family see Hulk
GROUP AFFILIATION: Initiative; formerly Magistrati, Hulkbusters, SHIELD, Green Cross, Avengers, Defenders (associate), Heroes for Hire, Queen's Vengeance, Fantastic Force, Hulkbusters (Counter-Earth), Brides of Set, Fantastic Four
EDUCATION: Law degree from UCLA
FIRST APPEARANCE: Savage She-Hulk #1 (1980)

murder charges reduced to manslaughter, though her father angrily disowned her for doing so. Soon after She-Hulk met Stargod (John Jameson), indirectly assisting in saving the dying Other-Realm he protected. Jen found she increasingly enjoyed being She-Hulk, preferring battles with foes such as Ultima, Man-Elephant, the Grappler and Man-Killer over dealing with the rival romantic interests of Zapper and new beau Richard Rory, or the growing estrangement from her father. Meanwhile, Buck finally learned the truth about Jill's death and cleared the She-Hulk's name.

Ralphie showed the blood sample Zapper had given him to an ambitious geneticist, "Doc," who duped Zapper into luring She-Hulk into a trap, hoping to use her blood to create a super-villain army; when she broke free, Doc turned Ralphie into a monster, "Brute," to battle her. After escaping, She-Hulk told Zapper his betrayal was the last straw, announced she would never change back to Jen, and departed Los Angeles. Transforming Ralphie into a series of super-villains — Seeker, Radius, Torque and Earth-Lord — Doc used him both to hound the She-Hulk and, through his front man Shade, to muscle in on the LA underworld, but She-Hulk stopped him with the assistance of her penitent friends and father. Having reconciled with those closest to her, She-Hulk set out on a road trip, encountering the hitchhiking Thing (Ben Grimm) and stopping the Negator from causing a meltdown at the Diablo Nuclear Plant.

Eventually reaching New York, she accepted the Wasp's invitation to join the Avengers. She swiftly proved her worth in battles against the Masters of Evil, the Fomor, AIM and T'rannikus' troll army; however, when the Champion of the Universe selected Earth's strongest inhabitants to fight him, she was disappointed that the chauvinistic alien left her off the list. She-Hulk enjoyed her new team's camaraderie, soon becoming close to both the Wasp and Scarlet Witch (Wanda Maximoff), though her relationship with Hawkeye (Clint Barton) was more antagonistic. Meanwhile, her cousin Bruce gained control of his Hulk form, and much to She-Hulk's delight, was given a presidential pardon for his past crimes. When the Avengers aided Hulk against his old foe, the Leader, the cousins had their first chance to talk properly since Jen's transformation. Bruce apologized for turning her into a monster like him, but she told him she viewed the change as a gift, turning her from a victim into someone with the power to do good. Bruce would later admit that he came to see the She-Hulk as one of his few redeeming features, a case where he had not only saved a loved one's life, but had helped to create a hero. During a rematch with the Masters of Evil, the Radioactive Man turned She-Hulk back into Jen with gamma rays; she was initially scared and unable to turn back, but Hawkeye deliberately taunted her until he provoked the transformation, his actions proving the start of a lasting friendship. Later the She-Hulk was kidnapped alongside other heroes by the powerful Beyonder, who transported them to "Battleworld" to fight an assemblage of their foes. When the Wrecking Crew's Bulldozer seemingly slew the Wasp, She-Hulk single-handedly invaded the villains' base, nearly taking down the entire Wrecking Crew before newly created super-villain Titania ("Skeeter" MacPherran) joined in, turning the tide. The two women briefly battled one-on-one, but the assembled villains came to Titania's rescue when She-Hulk got the upper hand. Humiliated, Titania would later become one of She-Hulk's most persistent foes. After the heroes finally won the day and were preparing to return home, the

Thing told She-Hulk he intended to stay behind for a while and asked her to take his place in the Fantastic Four.

Feeling like an intruder in the close-knit team at first, She-Hulk soon became part of their family. During a battle with the extraterrestrial Terminus, she met the FF's old ally Wyatt Wingfoot, who became her boyfriend. A paparazzo working for sleaze magazine "The Naked Truth" photographed She-Hulk sunbathing on the FF's roof; Jen was unable to prevent the pictures seeing print, but the printers, unaware the photos were meant to be green, color corrected them, making Jen unrecognizable. When the Thing finally returned from Battleworld, She-Hulk figured her time with the Four was ending, realizing that what had started as a substituting job had grown into something special; however, Ben decided not to rejoin the team. When the Fantastic Four pursued the evil Psycho-Man into the Microverse, he captured them and imprisoned the She-Hulk in the mines of Nuvidia, artificially conditioned to be too terrified to use her strength against the warders; however, the fugitive Princess Pearla helped her break his brainwashing.

Elements in the US government, worried the She-Hulk might lose control like her cousin had, ordered elite intelligence agency SHIELD to apprehend her for analysis, "Operation Green Genes." They teleported She-Hulk, Wyatt and various passersby from a New York street to the SHIELD Helicarrier, where the sadistic Agent Dooley oversaw a torturous examination; however, one of the other abductees was the host of a malevolent cockroach collective, which fed off radiation. It picked Dooley as its new host and crashed the carrier, hoping to send its power core into meltdown; She-Hulk destroyed the cockroaches and stopped the meltdown, but was exposed to massive levels of radiation. Unable to change back to Jen afterwards, She-Hulk had Mr. Fantastic (Reed Richards) examine her. Finding no physical cause, he secretly brought in psychologist Doc Samson, who concluded that She-Hulk simply didn't want to become Jen again; Reed lied to her and told her the radiation had put a genetic lock on her, an excuse she happily accepted.

The next few months saw the Fantastic Four battle the Skrulls, Dr. Doom (Victor von Doom), the Beyonder, Blastaar and Annihilus. Learning that her cousin Bruce had been separated from the Hulk, She-Hulk rushed to his hospital bed, and later  helped subdue the now mindless Hulk so he and Bruce could be re-merged to save Bruce's life. She-Hulk also went hunting for the Thing, who had gone missing in California, and clashed with his girlfriend Ms. Marvel (Sharon Ventura), but failed to locate him. Her teammates proved more successful, and the Thing rejoined the Fantastic Four. Feeling at loose ends, she returned to the Avengers in time to battle the Olympian gods, whose ruler Zeus unfairly blamed the Avengers for severe injuries his son Hercules had suffered while serving with them. Alongside Thor, She-Hulk personally fought the king of the gods until Hercules recovered sufficiently to make Zeus realize he had acted rashly. After attending the wedding of Johnny Storm and Alicia Masters (secretly the Skrull Lyja), She-Hulk was drawn into the Collector's contest with Death for the life of the Grandmaster, and was killed by Drax the Destroyer, temporarily joining the Legion of the Unliving before being restored to life. When the Super-Adaptoid's robotic Heavy Metal team attacked the Avengers, She-Hulk battled the Mad Thinker's Awesome Android, later to become an important part of her life. After being mentally manipulated by Dr. Druid and Nebula (actually the Terminatrix), She-Hulk quit the team, needing time to be alone. She returned to the courtroom, challenging the constitutionality of the recently enacted Mutant Registration Act on behalf of young mutant Theresa Handel.

She-Hulk went to work for District Attorney Blake Towers, soon learning the job had been partially arranged by his secretary Louise "Weezi" Mason, formerly the World War II heroine Blonde Phantom. She continued to juggle her law career with her heroic one, battling foes such as the Circus of Crime, the Headmen and Dr. Bong. She fought alongside Razorback against Xemnu the Titan, who sought to make her his mate; worked with Nick St. Christopher (Santa Claus) to uncover evidence against a maniacal serial killer; and protected image consultant Lexington Loopner against Pseudo-Man. Having drifted apart after she left the Fantastic Four, She-Hulk looked up Wyatt and renewed their relationship, even briefly getting engaged, but they soon broke it off. Rejoining the Avengers, She-Hulk was among the heroines briefly mesmerized into serving as the "Brides of Set" during Ghaur's failed plot to restore the elder god Set to Earth; she was also among the Avengers who helped sway public opinion against a proposed Super-Powers Registration Act. She battled her cousin David Pike, now the super-villain Brawn, and discovered that Warlord Krang's Major Motion Pictures was making an unauthorized She-Hulk movie; intended to flop so Krang could bilk his investors, it proved a surprise hit, staying sold-out for over 10 weeks. Aided by Howard the Duck, the Critic and the Terror, She-Hulk next prevented Dr. Angst's Band of the Bland from crushing together several realities to create the mundane Insipiverse. As an Avengers member, she helped thwart a breakout from the Vault super prison and battled Terminus, the Outlaws, Stellaris, Ngh the Unspeakable and the Tetrarchs of Entropy. Alongside Nosferata, she took down Jack Serious and the Dorkham Asylum inmates, and the Phantom Blonde (Weezi's daughter Wanda Mason) helped her stop Jasper Keaton's American Purity Party.

After defeating Adrenazon, Spragg the Living Hill, the Mole Man and Black Talon's X-Humed, during which last conflict she inadvertently gained the zombie manservant Garth, She-Hulk renewed her relationship with Wyatt and spent Christmas with her father, temporarily becoming Jen again thanks to Nick St. Christopher's gift. Wyatt helped her battle the Living Eraser from Dimension Z and Mahkizmo before She-Hulk and Weezi ventured into space to battle Spragg and Xemnu again, rescuing Razorback, Tayrn O'Connell and Rocket Raccoon from the D'Bari Vuk and the Xartans/Carbon Copy Men. Captured during this last escapade,

She-Hulk had an Ovoid in an adjacent cell give her the power to switch minds; intending to swap with Weezi so she could update her other allies, She-Hulk instead found the gamma radiation in her blood interfered with the process, so they switched physiques instead. The pair returned to Earth, where Weezi enjoyed a brief stint as the new She-Hulk before normality was restored.

The robot War Zone attacked She-Hulk, introducing a toxin into her bloodstream to gradually remove her powers. She sought the help of Zapper, now a brilliant hematologist, unaware that War Zone had been sent by Zapper's father-in-law, Hector DeVasquez, who believed killing her would remove his daughter's competition for Zapper's affections. Arriving in LA, She-Hulk battled the Rumbler, who killed her; discovering the gamma rays were preventing her brain's post-mortem decay, Zapper revived She-Hulk with an infusion of gamma rays, briefly turning her into a more muscular, "savage" form. Attacked again by War Zone and DeVasquez, the latter's gamma tank overloaded She-Hulk, causing her to revert to Jen; the Hulk voluntarily provided another transfusion to restore her powers. She later fought alongside her cousin against the Bi-Beast, battled Electro and the Scarlet Beetle, and broke up with Wyatt.

Diablo mind-controlled She-Hulk into stealing the Guardsman of Chthon statue, but Fantastic Force freed her and she joined the team for a while. After helping Doc Samson hunt the gamma-powered serial killer Patchwork, who briefly turned her into Jen again, she fought Onslaught alongside the Avengers, the Fantastic Four and other heroes. When most of the active Avengers seemingly died in that battle, She-Hulk was offered a full-time slot but declined, concentrating on her legal work. Lured away from Tower's office to become a private partner in Jeryn Hogarth's practice, Jennifer became the attorney for Heroes for Hire, aiding them against the Master's Strike Force One, Exodus' Acolytes and the Man Beast, and enjoying a short romance with Luke Cage. The heroes Onslaught had "killed" were saved by Franklin Richards' immense psychic powers and transported to his Counter-Earth, reborn, initially without powers or memories of their past lives, alongside counterparts of friends and family back home. The displaced heroes eventually returned home, accompanied by the Counter-Earth She-Hulk whom they erroneously believed was the original. When they entered their home reality, the second She-Hulk was absorbed into her counterpart. Rejoining the shorthanded Avengers, She-Hulk battled Template, Kulan Gath and Count Nefaria before joining the Human Torch's temporary Fantastic Four (with Ant-Man and Namorita) to battle the Gideon Trust and the Awesome Android. After the Hulk and other senior members of the Defenders were driven insane and became the tyrannical Order, Nighthawk assembled their female counterparts, including the She-Hulk, to defeat them and restore them to normal. She also returned to her old job as one of Tower's prosecutors.

When the Avengers investigated the bio-weapon Bloodwash's release near Mount Rushmore, She-Hulk was exposed to the virus. Her teammate Jack of Hearts tried to evacuate her, but his energy powers unintentionally transformed her into a more savage She-Hulk, who bounded off in search of Bruce. Her transformations were now triggered by fear, and she was brutish and destructive as She-Hulk. Jen headed to Bone, Idaho, where the Hulk had recently been sighted, but the Avengers caught up with her and she changed, demolishing much of the town in her rampage; she was eventually subdued with the Hulk's help, and Jack of Hearts corrected the gamma radiation balance within her; however, She-Hulk's guilt over Bone saw her changing unintentionally back to Jen during her sleep and partying hard during the day. Her hedonistic lifestyle ultimately forced the Avengers to evict her from their mansion, and Blake Tower to fire her. Prestigious law firm Goodman, Lieber, Kurtzberg and Holliway hired her to work in their Superhuman Law Section, though Holden Holliway insisted he wanted Jennifer Walters, not the She-Hulk. Feeling a target since her dual identity was public knowledge, she received a protective spell from the Scarlet Witch so that no one who wished the She-Hulk harm could see her as Jen. She moved into the Excelsior Apartments alongside other GLK&H employees, including Awesome Andy (the reformed Awesome Android) and fellow lawyer Augustus "Pug" Pugliese, who developed a massive crush on her; however, GLK&H's top lawyer Mallory Book was less welcoming, seeing her as a rival rather than colleague. While suing J. Jonah Jameson for years of libeling Spider-Man, Jen renewed her friendship with his son John, and they began dating, much to Pug's annoyance. After Holden's granddaughter, the super delinquent Southpaw, was arrested, he arranged for her to be released into a reluctant Jen's custody. When the Scarlet Witch went mad and attacked the Avengers, she transformed Jen into her savage persona, hospitalizing Captain Britain (Kelsey Leigh) and killing the Vision. Though aware she had been under another's control, Jen remained guilt-ridden over this.

MAGISTRATI ROBES

She-Hulk was soon recruited into the cosmic Living Tribunal's Magistrati to administer universal law, silencing the Watcher Qyre at the behest of an extremely reclusive race he had observed, a ruling that angered Qyre's friend Zoma. Sent to Skardon to free it from the Champion's rule, She-Hulk fought him in the boxing ring, swiftly losing the first bout; she appealed the decision and trained as Jen for three months, building her strength and being taught to fight by Gamora. Transforming for the rematch, her improved strength as Jen was exponentially increased as She-Hulk; after forcing the Champion to remove his strength-enhancing Infinity Power Gem as a disallowed weapon, She-Hulk soundly beat him and made him swear never to wear the gem again. Returning home, she found it difficult to control her increased might, borrowing John Jameson's strength-controlling Jupiter Suit; however, the vengeful former Champion, directed by Zoma, gave his gem to Titania, who smashed up the Excelsior and GLK&H's Timely Plaza offices looking for her nemesis. Titania easily knocked She-Hulk out, and she turned back into Jen, whom Titania couldn't see thanks to Wanda's protective spell. Stealing the gem from Titania, Jen used it to knock Titania out, but found herself unable to change back into the She-Hulk.

While Timely Plaza was being rebuilt, an incognito Jen helped rebuild Bone, while Doc Samson worked on a gamma charger to allow her to become the She-Hulk despite the mental blocks; Dr. Strange eventually restored her ability to transform at will by removing Wanda's protection spell. Returning to GLK&H, Jen worked on a time-travel murder case, but learned that jurors called from the past included her recently deceased friend Hawkeye. Jen attempted to slip him a note warning him of his demise, and was arrested by the Time Variance Authority (TVA). Threatened with complete removal from the timestream, and shown a probable future where something she had already done triggered the cosmos-devastating Reckoning War, Jen was given the lesser sentence of having another TVA prisoner, the Two-Gun Kid, remanded into her custody. Back on Earth, her client Starfox saw her arguing with John and tried to help by surreptitiously using his mind powers to send her head-over-heels in love with John.

In the wake of the Stamford disaster, where 612 innocents died during a superhuman battle, She-Hulk represented Speedball, the sole survivor, and came out in favor of the proposed Superhuman Registration Act (SHRA), perhaps changing her past stance in part because of her own recent transgressions; however, she also took on the Act's strongest proponent, Iron Man, challenging him on the stand during a trial to close down a hate site exposing the identities of former New Warriors. John Jameson proposed, and the couple immediately wed, but Pug revealed Starfox's action and the villainous Alistaire Smythe transformed John back into Stargod. With Starfox's influence removed, She-Hulk realized she didn't love John and she asked for an annulment. Drafted into SHIELD via the SHRA's small print, she joined agent Clay Quartermain's Hulkbusters in rounding up her missing cousin's old foes, and worked as a trainer for the new Initiative program; however, when she discovered that Iron Man had fired the Hulk into deep space, She-Hulk confronted him, only to be stripped of her powers by a nanite injection. Warning Iron Man that she could do more damage as a lawyer than as She-Hulk, she promised to destroy him. Outlaw boy genius Amadeus Cho ("Mastermind Excello") offered to restore her powers by blocking Stark's nanites if she helped him against Iron Man, but Jen declined, wanting to do things legally; however, with the Hulk's return at the head of an alien gladiator army, Jen used Cho's treatment to restore her powers, and when talking failed to work, fought her cousin, only to end up a prisoner. Following the Hulk's defeat, Jen was freed; having used up her supply of Cho's formula, she continues to fight Stark in the courts, and has obtained an injunction preventing him from using the nanite technology on anyone else until the case is heard.

JUPITER SUIT

HEIGHT: (Jen) 5'10"; (She-Hulk) 6'7", variable
WEIGHT: (Jen) 150 lbs.; (She-Hulk) 700 lbs., variable
EYES: Green   **HAIR:** (Jen) Brown; (She-Hulk) green

ABILITIES/ACCESSORIES: She-Hulk possesses immense superhuman strength, now able to lift in excess of 100 tons; this has varied much higher during "savage" periods and immediately after battling the Champion. She possesses a high degree of imperviousness to injury and disease, regenerates from injuries, and is resistant to extreme temperature variations and radiation, although gamma rays can trigger unstable transformations. She can leap over 600 feet up or 1000 feet across. She can swap physiques with other humans using Ovoid mind techniques, and seems to have the ability to sense extradimensional viewers observing her, a power perhaps related to her cousin's ability to see astral forms; Jen tends to downplay this last trait, as speaking to an unseen audience tends to unsettle those around her. A spell formerly prevented those who intended She-Hulk harm from seeing Jen, but this has been recently removed. She is a highly skilled lawyer, a trained fighter and owns a modified, spaceworthy, flying 1959 Dodge.

POWER GRID	1	2	3	4	5	6	7
INTELLIGENCE							
STRENGTH							
SPEED							
DURABILITY							
ENERGY PROJECTION							
FIGHTING SKILLS							

HISTORY: Designed by billionaire industrialist/financier Anthony "Tony" Stark (an Avengers founder in his dual identity as Iron Man), the Stark Tower Complex is also informally known as "Avengers Tower" since it currently houses the Avengers super hero team. A gleaming beacon of modern architecture located in the vicinity of Manhattan's Columbus Circle (approximately 10 blocks north of the Fantastic Four's Baxter Building), the complex was completed after four years of excavation and construction; by that time, Stark's personal fortune had been severely depleted for various reasons. When the Avengers temporarily disbanded after the destruction of their original Avengers Mansion headquarters, Stark could not afford to help them rebuild; however, when he helped reorganize the team months later, he donated Stark Tower's upper floors (originally intended as his personal Manhattan residence) to serve as the team's new headquarters. Their presence made it more difficult for the complex to attract conventional renters, but this had already been a problem due to prospective office tenants fearing that Stark's Avengers ties would make the building a target. The complex originally consisted of three main buildings: the 93-story Main Tower, the 55-story North Building and the 35-story South Building.

The Main Tower's top three floors are dedicated exclusively to Avengers operations. Most of the 93rd floor and portions of the 92nd floor house the War Room — a sprawling conference center outfitted with transponder "windows" which allow a full, panoramic view of New York City. The 93rd floor features an automated operating system capable of generating holographic images; receiving transmission bands from over 50 television stations simultaneously; displaying schematics; housing the Avengers' entire crime/forensics files library; and providing live video links to organizations and agencies such as SHIELD, the Commission on Superhuman Activities (CSA) in Washington D.C., and the Fifty State Initiative Training Program at Camp Hammond in Stamford, Connecticut. Floors 91 and 92 contain spacious living quarters for Avengers members and their families as well as a state-of-the-art kitchen facility and a community recreation room. The 92nd Floor also houses Stark's private office suite while the 90th floor houses his Major Robotics/Electronics Fabrication Laboratory, where Stark continually upgrades his Iron Man armor. The Tower's Aircraft Support Hangar houses the Avengers' various helicopters and Quinjets, connected to the roof by a diagonal tunnel for rapid deployment. Tony Stark's longtime butler Edwin Jarvis lives in one of the building's many private suites and maintains the floors dedicated to Avengers operations.

The lower levels of the Main Tower as well as the entirety of the South Building and North Building are largely occupied by Stark's own subsidiaries and non-profit organizations. The Independent Subway System (IND) Division of the New York City Subway maintains a station below the complex's base, accessible from both the street and the complex's sub-basements. Multiple sub-basements house secure parking facilities as well as regional offices for various federal government agencies and programs such as the CSA and the Initiative, which oversee the paperwork associated with local superhuman registration operations.

When the super hero Sentry (Robert Reynolds) returned to prominence as a member of the Avengers after years of subconsciously erasing the world's memories of him, his long-hidden Watchtower suddenly rematerialized atop the Stark complex's Main Tower, fully integrated into the building's existing architecture. Serving as both the Sentry's headquarters and as the private residence of Robert Reynolds and his wife Lindy, the massive, 20-story Watchtower is operated and maintained by CLOC (Centrally Located Organic Computer), a near-sentient computer of the Sentry's own design. "Helioscopes" created by the Sentry monitor locations around the world and provide live video feeds to his Monitor Room, located near the Watchtower's domed top. Travel through the Watchtower is facilitated by a series of seven interior "turbovators," a tube-like system of the Sentry's own design based on pneumatic technology. Turbovator G is the main vertical turbovator tube and runs from the highest level of the Watchtower (the Monitor Room) to the lowest level (the Sub-Basement/Lower Vault).

HEIGHT (MAIN TOWER): 1138 feet (1707 feet including the Sentry Watchtower)
STORIES (MAIN TOWER): 93 (113 including the Sentry Watchtower)
FIRST APPEARANCE: New Avengers #3 (2005)

Art by Frank Cho

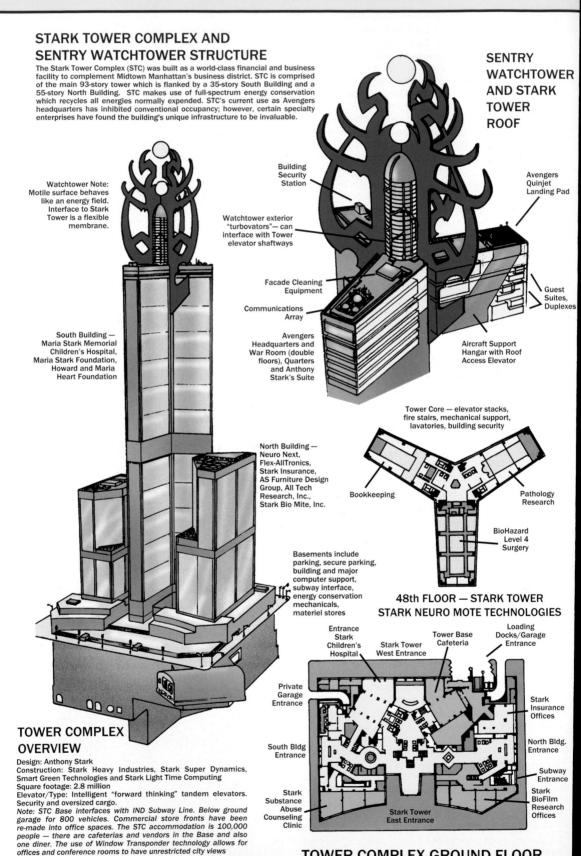

STARK TOWER COMPLEX AND SENTRY WATCHTOWER STRUCTURE

The Stark Tower Complex (STC) was built as a world-class financial and business facility to complement Midtown Manhattan's business district. STC is comprised of the main 93-story tower which is flanked by a 35-story South Building and a 55-story North Building. STC makes use of full-spectrum energy conservation which recycles all energies normally expended. STC's current use as Avengers headquarters has inhibited conventional occupancy; however, certain specialty enterprises have found the building's unique infrastructure to be invaluable.

SENTRY WATCHTOWER AND STARK TOWER ROOF

Building Security Station

Avengers Quinjet Landing Pad

Watchtower Note: Motile surface behaves like an energy field. Interface to Stark Tower is a flexible membrane.

Watchtower exterior "turbovators" — can interface with Tower elevator shaftways

Facade Cleaning Equipment

Communications Array

Guest Suites, Duplexes

South Building — Maria Stark Memorial Children's Hospital, Maria Stark Foundation, Howard and Maria Heart Foundation

Avengers Headquarters and War Room (double floors), Quarters and Anthony Stark's Suite

Aircraft Support Hangar with Roof Access Elevator

North Building — Neuro Next, Flex-AllTronics, Stark Insurance, AS Furniture Design Group, All Tech Research, Inc., Stark Bio Mite, Inc.

Tower Core — elevator stacks, fire stairs, mechanical support, lavatories, building security

Bookkeeping

Pathology Research

BioHazard Level 4 Surgery

Basements include parking, secure parking, building and major computer support, subway interface, energy conservation mechanicals, materiel stores

48th FLOOR — STARK TOWER STARK NEURO MOTE TECHNOLOGIES

TOWER COMPLEX OVERVIEW

Design: Anthony Stark
Construction: Stark Heavy Industries, Stark Super Dynamics, Smart Green Technologies and Stark Light Time Computing
Square footage: 2.8 million
Elevator/Type: Intelligent "forward thinking" tandem elevators. Security and oversized cargo.
Note: STC Base interfaces with IND Subway Line. Below ground garage for 800 vehicles. Commercial store fronts have been re-made into office spaces. The STC accommodation is 100,000 people — there are cafeterias and vendors in the Base and also one diner. The use of Window Transponder technology allows for offices and conference rooms to have unrestricted city views

Entrance Stark Children's Hospital

Stark Tower West Entrance

Tower Base Cafeteria

Loading Docks/Garage Entrance

Private Garage Entrance

Stark Insurance Offices

South Bldg Entrance

North Bldg. Entrance

Subway Entrance

Stark Substance Abuse Counseling Clinic

Stark Tower East Entrance

Stark BioFilm Research Offices

TOWER COMPLEX GROUND FLOOR

HISTORY: A flighty young woman who would grow into an extraordinary heroine, Janet Van Dyne was a frivolous socialite when she first met brilliant biochemist Hank Pym, secretly the shrinking super hero Ant-Man. Janet's father, eminent scientist Vernon Van Dyne, was then developing a gamma ray projector designed to make contact with alien life forms; Vernon sought to consult with Pym regarding the gamma device, but Pym declined since the project seemingly fell outside his area of expertise. Having accompanied her father during his meeting with Pym, Janet found Hank handsome but felt a scientist would be too dull for her, preferring more adventurous men. Pym, meanwhile, was smitten with Janet and struck by her resemblance to his late wife Maria Trovaya, but he felt she was too young for him. Pym and the Van Dynes parted politely, and Vernon returned to his gamma beam research.

Vernon made a fatal breakthrough when his projector accidentally freed Pilai, a prison inmate from Kosmos, the same other-dimensional realm which spawned the "Pym Particles" that Hank Pym used in his size-changing technology. Manifesting on Earth via the gamma projector, Pilai killed Vernon and fled. Finding her father dead and realizing it had something to do with his research, Janet called Pym for help. He initially dismissed this as a prank, but his insect allies confirmed her story and Pym investigated as Ant-Man. Impressed by Jan's surprising strength of character and her determination to avenge her father, Ant-Man advised her to consult Hank Pym. As Pym, he asked if she was serious about her new sense of mission, and she indicated her eagerness to hunt down not only her father's killer, but also criminals in general. Convinced of her sincerity, Pym revealed his secret identity to her and offered to make her his partner. She accepted, Pym shared his shrinking formula with her, and he also implanted synthetic specialized cells beneath her skin that would produce wings from her back and antennae from her forehead when she shrank. Cobbling together an outfit from alternate costumes Pym had crafted for himself, Janet Van Dyne adopted a new costumed identity as the Wasp. Together, she and Ant-Man defeated and seemingly destroyed the rampaging "Creature from Kosmos," Pilai.

Pym initially insisted that their relationship should remain strictly professional, citing Van Dyne's youth and his fear of losing a loved one again, but they soon settled into an uneasy groove as successful crime-fighting partners and somewhat dysfunctional romantic partners. Pym often retreated into his work and neglected Jan, but the more serious he seemed, the more flighty the Wasp would act. Pressuring Pym to be more romantic and outgoing, she also flirted incessantly with other men, mostly in an effort to make Hank jealous. Unbeknownst to her, this exacerbated Pym's chronic insecurity, as did her family's wealth. Pym often secretly felt as if he were out of Jan's league, unable to see himself as worthy of a beautiful high society girl. His feelings of insecurity escalated when he and Wasp teamed up with Thor, Iron Man (Tony Stark) and the Hulk (Bruce Banner) to found a super hero team, which the Wasp dubbed the Avengers. The far greater might of his new teammates made Pym feel inadequate, even after he added growth powers to his repertoire and adopted a new identity as Giant-Man.

Wasp and Pym defeated a wide array of criminals such as the robotic Cyclops, hypnotic musician Trago, the other-dimensional Living Eraser, the medieval-inspired Black Knight (Nathaniel Garrett), dictator el Toro, the alien giant Colossus, Giant-Man impersonator Second-Story Sammy, protection racketeer the Wrecker, Atlantean warlord Attuma, power-mad size-changer Madam Macabre, and the extraterrestrial Supramor the Hidden Man. They even mistakenly battled the misunderstood hero Spider-Man, later a longtime ally; there was an instinctive, long-standing animosity between Spider-Man and the Wasp, which they attributed to the natural antipathy between wasps and spiders, but he and Van Dyne gradually became friendlier with each other over the years. Pym's and Van Dyne's most persistent foes included evil scientist Egghead, the armored Porcupine, the tricky Magician and the super-swift Human Top

REAL NAME: Janet "Jan" Van Dyne
ALIASES: Formerly Giant-Woman, Pixie, Janet Pym, Dr. Spectrum, Invisible Girl
IDENTITY: Publicly known
OCCUPATION: Adventurer, fashion designer, president of Van Dyne Industries, board member of Nevell Industries, independently wealthy socialite; former screenwriter, hardware store clerk, debutante
CITIZENSHIP: USA
PLACE OF BIRTH: Cresskill, New Jersey
KNOWN RELATIVES: Vernon Van Dyne (father, deceased), Hank Pym (Yellowjacket, ex-husband), Ruth (aunt), Bertram (uncle), Jennifer (cousin)
GROUP AFFILIATION: Avengers, the Initiative; formerly Lady Liberators, Defenders associate
EDUCATION: Unrevealed
FIRST APPEARANCE: Tales to Astonish #44 (1963)

Art by Frank Cho

(David Cannon), later known as Whirlwind, who developed a sinister romantic obsession with the Wasp.

Pym and the Wasp also battled many villains alongside the Avengers, including corrupt nobleman Count Nefaria, whose henchmen gave Van Dyne a nearly fatal gunshot wound. Surgical specialist Dr. Hjarmal Svenson saved her life, but the incident left both Pym and Van Dyne badly shaken. Pym had already been nursing serious doubts about their adventuring career, and Van Dyne's near-death experience had forced her to realize the risks of her new life for the first time. The couple stepped down from active Avengers duty, and soon retired from crime-fighting altogether.

Bored and restless in retirement, Jan was happy when conflicts with Attuma and the Collector drew her and Pym back into the Avengers. Trying to make a fresh start, the uneasy Pym adopted a new costumed guise as Goliath while battling serious health problems associated with his size-changing powers. Despite his difficulties, he and the Wasp became mainstays of the Avengers, including a period during which they and new recruit Hawkeye (Clint Barton) were the team's only consistently active members. While Pym quietly struggled, Jan relished her adventures with the Avengers and reveled in her newfound control of the multi-million Van Dyne fortune, which she had inherited in full upon her 23rd birthday. Her new wealth further increased Pym's feelings of insecurity, and his emotional problems only worsened after he created the robot Ultron, which went rogue and became one of the Avengers' deadliest enemies. Pym, Wasp and their teammates also failed repeatedly to apprehend their old foe Whirlwind, who was secretly hiding in plain sight as Jan's chauffeur, "Charles Matthews."

Pym's feelings of guilt and shame over Ultron, his long-term sense of inadequacy, and the pressure of serving as Avengers leader all left him in a very fragile emotional state, made worse by his troubled romance with Van Dyne. She wanted and expected him to propose marriage, but he felt too unworthy of her than ever. Smashing his lab equipment in a moment of frustration, Pym accidentally exposed himself to mind-altering chemicals and suffered a major mental breakdown (his second), deluding himself into thinking he was a different person known as Yellowjacket — a more daring, assertive personality, and a role more compatible with the Wasp.

In his new costumed identity as Yellowjacket, Pym claimed he had "killed" Goliath, and that he was taking Pym's place — both in the Avengers and in Jan's affections. Wasp and the other Avengers immediately saw through Yellowjacket's disguise, but they played along with him at the urging of SHIELD psych expert Special Agent Carver, who warned that challenging Pym's delusion might trigger a full-blown psychotic break. Jan even went so far as to stage her own wedding to the delusional Yellowjacket, though Pym regained his memory shortly after the ceremony when he saved Wasp from the Circus of Crime using his Goliath powers. The couple took a leave of absence from the Avengers while Hank recovered, calling it a honeymoon and making their marriage official; however, Pym refused to seek psychiatric treatment, stubbornly

insisting that he was cured, and he even opted to keep the Yellowjacket guise as his long-term costumed identity.

Despite his outward confidence, Pym privately continued to feel inadequate in comparison to Wasp and his fellow Avengers. He also felt like a personal and professional failure since his scientific career had stalled and he was living off the wealth of Van Dyne, who had started a successful career of her own as a fashion designer. After the couple both survived near-fatal health crises and finally exposed "Charles" as the Whirlwind, Pym began to scale back his involvement in the Avengers, opting for reserve status while Jan served with the active roster. Perhaps trying to compensate for his less active role in their adventuring, Pym developed a serum that enhanced Jan's powers by harnessing the energy of her size-changing, using that energy to increase her physical strength and to power her bioelectric sting. By this time, Jan had begun consulting psychiatrist Michael Reilly for advice on how best to handle the troubled Hank, acting as supportive and affectionate with Pym as possible, but her efforts were soon undone. Attacked and brainwashed by Ultron, Pym suffered a third mental breakdown, assaulting Wasp and the other Avengers.

Pym soon regained his sanity, but his underlying mental problems remained, and he gradually became ill-tempered and verbally abusive with Jan. When he rejoined the active Avengers roster, he was so eager to prove himself that he acted recklessly during a mission and was charged with misconduct. Descending into his fourth and worst mental breakdown, Pym plotted to redeem himself by building a robot designed to attack the Avengers at his disciplinary hearing, a robot that Pym himself would be able to defeat using a secret cut-off switch. When Wasp discovered Pym's plan, he angrily forbade her to interfere and even physically struck her. Pym's subsequent misconduct court martial went badly, especially after his teammates spotted Van Dyne's black eye and realized how she got it. Seeing the group turn against him, Pym activated his robot, but it worked too well and seriously threatened most of the Avengers, including Yellowjacket himself. Pym was almost killed before Wasp deactivated his robot using the secret cut-off switch.

Pym left the Avengers in disgrace, and Jan swiftly divorced him — but to everyone's surprise, she emerged from the crisis stronger than ever. She had long regarded Pym as a sort of substitute father figure, and for years Pym had been the primary focus of her life. With Pym gone, Van Dyne redefined herself as an independent adult for the first time. She threw herself into her fashion designs and her other business interests with renewed vigor, enjoying even greater success than before. She also strengthened her commitment to the Avengers, successfully running for chairwoman and proving to be one of the most effective and capable leaders in the team's history. Wasp helped recruit new members such as Starfox, Captain Marvel (Monica Rambeau) and She-Hulk, who became one of Jan's closest friends. Van Dyne also made peace with ex-husband Pym and came to regard him as a friend after he regained his mental stability. Meanwhile, Wasp found new loves in her life. She shared a brief, intense romance with wealthy playboy Tony Stark, but ended it after Stark confessed he was her longtime teammate Iron Man. She later began dating the dashing mercenary adventurer Paladin, a longer-lasting and more light-hearted relationship.

WASP WITH BOOPSIE

Van Dyne's stint as Avengers leader, while successful, was also highly stressful. Killed and resurrected twice during the cosmic Beyonder's original Secret Wars, the still-recovering Wasp was briefly manipulated into letting Vision take over the team as chairman before she reclaimed the post. She later led the group through one of the most traumatic crises in its history, the occupation of Avengers Mansion by Baron (Helmut) Zemo's Masters of Evil. Shortly after the Masters' defeat, Jan decided she needed a vacation and stepped down as Avengers chair, taking an indefinite leave of absence; however, when the Avengers' new western roster was shorthanded, Wasp began assisting them. She also became friendlier with Pym, who had joined the western group as the plainclothes Doctor Pym after rebuilding his confidence and revamping his methods. Wasp soon became a fully active member of the team's western division, and she and Pym even briefly served as interim co-chairs of the western roster.

Jan and Hank toyed with renewing their romance during their western Avengers stint, but they eventually decided to part as friends. Pym returned to pure research, while Van Dyne left the team to travel and pursue her new sideline as a screenwriter, shopping around a script for an Avengers movie. Neither lover had fully let go of the other, though. Upon returning to America, she began therapy sessions with psychologist Dr. Vincent Rossi and threw herself into her long-neglected fashion design career, making a critically acclaimed comeback. When Pym sought her out to congratulate her, the pair started growing closer again — an intimacy that intensified after Pym's B.I.G. experimental size-changing project led them into a conflict with a gang of criminal Kosmosians. In the end, the Kosmosians were defeated while Pym and Van Dyne were romantically reunited, though Wasp's size-changing powers may have been temporarily neutralized as a result.

This affiliation led to a double tragedy for Janet Van Dyne. First, the bulk of her fortune was stolen by longtime teammate Tony Stark, who was then Immortus's mind-controlled pawn in an elaborate plot against the Avengers known as "the Crossing." Later, during a battle between the Immortus-controlled Iron Man and the other Avengers, Stark fatally wounded Jan. Pym saved her life by subjecting her to a renewed application of the mutation processes that created her Wasp powers in the first place, but this rescue also mutated Van Dyne into a bizarre bug-woman form that made her look rather like an oversized human butterfly. Jan seemed to take this in stride and rejoined the Avengers, though she was estranged from Pym when she learned that the overanxious Giant-Man had planted a monitoring device on her without her knowledge in order to better analyze her new physical state. Still, this latest breakup did not stop the couple from declaring their love for each other while they and most of the other Avengers seemingly died battling the psionic monster Onslaught.

With most of the active Avengers seemingly dead, the remaining members disbanded the team. Meanwhile, Pym, Wasp and the other supposedly dead Avengers had been hurled into an alternate world created by Franklin Richards, a world later known as Counter-Earth. The lost Avengers lived out alternate versions of their past lives in this new world, including another incarnation of the Pym-Wasp romance. By the time the Avengers finally returned to their own Earth, Franklin's power had instinctively "fixed" any Avengers who needed it, such as returning Wasp to her human form and restoring her standard powers.

Upon returning, Pym, Wasp and the other Avengers founders promptly reassembled the team. Like Pym, however, Wasp initially opted for reserve membership so she could concentrate on rebuilding her depleted fortune and renewing her romance with Pym. She soon succeeded in both respects (presumably with some financial help from a repentant Stark on the business front), though Pym's emotional problems endured and made their romance uneasy. Despite this, they continued to participate in Avengers adventures, notably the cosmic conflict known as the Destiny War, during which Wasp led a squad of Avengers from assorted timelines in a successful effort to save humanity from the Time Keepers.

When the Avengers were suffering bad publicity during the Triune Understanding's smear campaign against the team, Wasp accepted an invitation to resume her old post as team leader. She quickly repaired the group's image and assembled a new and effective roster, though there were problems — notably Pym, who had rejoined as Goliath. During the Avengers' battle with the sorcerer Kulan Gath, one of Gath's spells accidentally split Pym into two separate beings: a Goliath embodying Pym's intellect and a Yellowjacket embodying his passions, representing all the wilder emotions Pym had repressed since his long-ago abuse of Van Dyne. After she discovered what was happening, Wasp helped Hank merge his two warring halves with the assistance of Triune Understanding founder Jonathan Tremont, and also helped Hank to accept himself as a whole person, a flawed but worthwhile individual. Determined to confront and master his inner demons for good, Pym resumed his Yellowjacket identity and continued to serve with the Avengers under co-chairs Wasp and Captain America.

Together, Wasp and Cap led a reorganization of the Avengers, rebuilding and refitting their headquarters and equipment, and launching an ongoing series of operations designed to better monitor and contain potential threats. Despite these expanded and improved operations, the group suffered one of its worst setbacks ever when they failed to prevent Kang from slaughtering the population of Washington, DC, after which the Avengers were forced to formally surrender to Kang on behalf of the world. In the end, though, the Wasp and Captain America led the Avengers and many other warriors in overthrowing Kang's rule and liberating the people of Earth.

After the war, the Wasp became more preoccupied with her personal development rather than team issues. While vacationing with Pym, she declined his proposal of remarriage but reaffirmed her commitment to their romance. Soon afterward, she began experimenting with new applications of her size-changing power, mimicking Pym's longtime ability to assume gigantic sizes. Given the often-negative mental and physical side-effects of such growth powers, this may have played a role in Jan's somewhat erratic behavior during that same period. She became increasingly quarrelsome with Pym, suddenly preoccupied with his abusive past and personal shortcomings. At the same time, she shared a brief relationship with longtime teammate Hawkeye, leaving Pym shocked and crushed after he found them together.

When a criminally insane Scarlet Witch turned against the Avengers, Wasp was among the injured and Hawkeye was among the slain. Pym stayed by Wasp's bedside throughout her recovery, which convinced her to give their romance yet another chance. When the Avengers disbanded following the Scarlet Witch disaster, Wasp and Pym left together, briefly settling in Britain while Pym did some work at Oxford. Their latest attempt at reviving their romance failed, however, and they had already split up when they were among the super-beings sent to Battleworld by the alien Stranger as part of his latest experiment. Taking charge of the random band of heroes and misfits the Stranger had abducted, Wasp helped the group make their way back to Earth. She also firmly rejected new romantic overtures from Pym, having realized anew how unhealthy their on-and-off connection was, though Pym quickly found comfort in a new romance with Avengers reservist and fellow Battleworld escapee Firebird.

When the federal Superhuman Registration Act (SHRA) was passed following the Stamford disaster, a super hero civil war broke out between factions supporting and opposing the legislation. While Jan had vocally opposed similar legislation in the past, she and Pym were both among the Avengers members and associates who sided with the pro-SHRA faction, led by Tony Stark. As part of Stark's inner circle, they participated in several battles with the anti-SHRA forces led by Captain America, including a fight which cost the life of their longtime friend Goliath (Bill Foster), Pym's old research partner. Despite this tragedy, Wasp and Pym remained loyal to the pro-SHRA cause until the civil war ended with the surrender of Captain America. Since then, like many of her peers, Wasp has registered with the federal government's Initiative program, which oversees, regulates and coordinates the activities of America's super heroes, as managed by new SHIELD director Tony Stark. She was also recruited into a new Initiative-backed Avengers roster assembled by Stark and led by Ms. Marvel.

WASP USING ANTENNAE

WASP IN GIANT FORM

Art by Olivier Coipel

HEIGHT: 5'4" (variable) **EYES:** Blue
WEIGHT: 110 lbs. (variable) **HAIR:** Auburn

ABILITIES/ACCESSORIES: The Wasp is able to alter her own physical size, though she generally uses this power more for shrinking than for growing. Through concentration, she can reduce herself to as little as a half-inch in height ("wasp size") or restore herself to normal human size at will. She has also demonstrated the capacity to enlarge herself to gigantic sizes (up to fifty feet), but very seldom employs this ability. Her size-changing power stems from Pym Particles, exotic subatomic particles discovered by Henry Pym which originate in the other-dimensional alien world of Kosmos. When people or objects tap into Pym Particles, they change size by "hyperphasing" with matching quantities of Pym Particles in the Kosmosian dimension. Shrinking temporarily shunts much of a size-changer's normal mass into the particle-suffused mists of Kosmos, and growing beyond normal size requires the temporary absorption of excess mass from the Kosmosian realm. The Wasp's size-changing originally depended on repeated doses of Pym Particles to activate her powers: for instance, she initially wore cylinders of Pym Particle-derived gas on her belt, which would reduce or increase her size upon release. She later wore a cartridge belt filled with Pym Particle-derived, color-coded pills or capsules formulated to reduce or enlarge her form to specific pre-set sizes. For

a time, her size-changing could also be triggered by cybernetic devices worn by herself or Pym; however, long-term exposure to Pym's size-changing process has long since permanently infused her body with Pym particles, such that she can now change sizes at will.

Compared to other Pym-powered size-changers, the Wasp has experienced relatively few negative side-effects stemming from her size-changing powers, perhaps in part because she has concentrated almost exclusively on shrinking; Pym-derived growth powers have long been associated with greater health risks such as mental instability or dangerous physical strain, which probably explains why Van Dyne has mostly avoided giant sizes. In fact, during the one brief period when she frequently assumed gigantic sizes, her behavior was more emotional and erratic than usual. Perhaps suspecting this link herself, Van Dyne has not experimented with gigantic sizes again since then. Shrinking is almost effortless for her, as is resuming her normal size, though too many changes back and forth between sizes within a short span of time can be fatiguing. Growing to gigantic sizes is more of a physical and mental strain, and switching directly from giant size to insect size or vice versa has taxed her to the point of fainting on occasion. Her exceptionally strong will may partially explain her adapting well to the mental strain of size-changing. She probably also benefits from an additional mutation that Henry Pym induced years ago, which harnesses the energy of her size-changing process and uses it to enhance her strength, presumably easing the physical strain of size-changing.

Thanks to the aforementioned secondary mutation, Van Dyne actually grows stronger as she shrinks, channeling the energy of the shrinking process into enhanced physical strength — for instance, when she is reduced to her one-foot height, she has slightly superhuman strength and can easily bend a two-inch diameter steel bar nearly double. Even at her smallest half-inch size, she retains strength equal to or slightly greater than that of her normal-sized form. On the rare occasions when she assumes gigantic sizes, she seems able to grow taller and stronger than most Pym-powered size-changers with comparatively less physical strain — again, presumably aided by the secondary mutation which uses energy from the size-changing process to enhance her physical strength. During her "Giant-Woman" phase, she could assume heights of forty or fifty feet with relative ease, and was able to lift at least 30 tons at her maximum stature.

Synthetic specialized cells implanted beneath her shoulder blades expand into functional, insect-like wings as she shrinks; when she returns to normal size, the wings disappear beneath a nearly undetectable layer of genetically engineered callous. She could initially manifest her wings only at insect size, but the bioengineered wing cells gradually multiplied over the years, enabling her to manifest her wings at larger sizes. She can now sprout wings at a height of 4'4" or smaller; however, she is slightly less maneuverable at larger sizes, tires more rapidly and makes an easier target, so she usually prefers to fly at sizes smaller than her maximum winged height. She is also far more practiced in the art of flying at tiny sizes, having learned to fly at larger sizes only in recent years. Her wings remain proportionately the same size relative to the rest of her body as she changes sizes, apart from their disappearance beneath her skin at heights above 4'4". At her maximum winged size, she can fly at speeds of up to 38 mph for up to an hour before tiring. It takes more energy to achieve top flight speed at smaller sizes, but her physical strength and endurance increase as she shrinks, so this more or less balances out. Her wings' efficiency is sometimes negatively affected by extremes of temperature or humidity. Able to maneuver in flight much like a real wasp, she can hover and dart forwards and backwards in addition to sustained forward flight. She has also trained herself to fly upside down if need be. Her reaction time using her wings is exceptional, sufficient to evade even rapid-processing targeting computers. Her wings are grafted to her spinal column and rib cage by a series of supporting rings that serve as artificially placed ligaments. Composed of inert unstable molecules, these rings smoothly expand and contract as needed.

Synthetic specialized cells implanted beneath the Wasp's temples originally expanded into functional, insect-like antennae as she shrank; when she returned to normal size, the antennae would disappear beneath an undetectable layer of genetically engineered callous. The Wasp's antennae enable her to communicate with and command higher insects such as ants, wasps and bees; they also enable two-way mental communications with cybernetic devices such as the various artificial antennae worn by Pym over the years. In addition, her antennae have sometimes proven hypersensitive to exotic stimuli, enabling her on rare occasions to detect an alien or malevolent presence in her vicinity. While her similar wing cells have multiplied over the years, her antennae cells soon atrophied; they never died out completely, but the antennae cells have been dormant for much of Van Dyne's career as the Wasp, no longer growing when she shrinks. After her natural antennae atrophied, she replaced them with various cybernetic devices worn as a helmet, cowl or collar. Like Pym's various cowls and helmets, these devices enabled her to communicate with and command insects, but she generally had less enthusiasm for this function than Pym and used her cybernetic accessories less frequently over time. The Wasp's antennae were later revitalized by a fresh infusion of Pym Particles from Pym himself, and she was again able to manifest her antennae as she shrank for some time thereafter; however, she has seldom manifested her antennae in recent times, suggesting that the antennae cells have

probably become dormant again.

While the Wasp has generally used her antennae and cybernetic devices to command random swarms of wasps, bees and ants, she has also employed and trained specific insects as partners for brief periods. For instance, she briefly employed a trained bee as her personal steed, and later replaced the bee with a similarly short-lived sidekick, a trained wasp dubbed "Boopsie." While she has sometimes used bees, wasps and flying ants as steeds to avoid straining her wings, she has done this much more infrequently in recent years as her wings have grown stronger and her bond with the insect world has grown weaker. Unlike Pym, she has seldom formed long-term attachments to specific insects.

In her earliest adventures, the Wasp wielded a large stick pin as a makeshift "sting" with which to jab her opponents. She soon replaced this with forearm-mounted compressed air guns designed by Pym; triggered by a finger-drawn pull cord, these new stingers could fire one long continuous burst of compressed air or a series of shorter bursts. These air blasts struck with a concussive force of 75 pounds per square inch. She sometimes loaded her compressed air stingers with pellets or needles which she could fire with tremendous force. Later, Pym provided her with wrist-mounted stingers that fired bursts of electrical energy. He eventually modified these stingers so they could tap the energy of her body's size-changing process and convert it into blasts of bioelectricity, greatly enhancing her firepower. While making these modifications, Pym altered the Wasp's powers such that her size-changing increased her body's natural bioelectrical charge, enabling her to act as a more powerful battery for her stingers. This ability gradually increased over time, and she can now generate powerful blasts of bioelectrical energy without any mechanical aids — enabling her, for instance, to blast through solid concrete rapidly enough for her to fly through it without slowing down. She can even generate her bioelectric "sting" blasts while she is full-sized, presumably through a bioelectric energy reserve built up during recent size-changing.

An athletic woman of above normal intelligence, the Wasp has trained extensively in unarmed combat with the Avengers, most notably under the tutelage of Captain America. She was also trained in specialized size-changing combat by Hank Pym, learning to use her variable size to her advantage (for instance, enlarging from below to punch a larger opponent above her, exploiting the momentum of her size change and the element of surprise). She has long since grown accustomed to the potentially overwhelming sensation of being tiny within vastly larger surroundings. She is a gifted, experienced and charismatic team leader, a highly capable combat strategist and a keen student of public relations. A gifted fashion designer, she has designed costumes for fellow heroes and has designed and worn well over two hundred unique costumes of her own. All of her costumes and most of her civilian clothes and jewelry are treated with unstable molecules so that they change sizes along with her when she shrinks and grows.

When she was more drastically mutated during the "Crossing" crisis, Wasp became taller, orange-skinned and inhuman-looking, with large antennae, larger and more colorful wings, and elongated clawed fingers. She seemed unable to change sizes during this period, but was able to use her wings and antennae at full size. She was restored to her normal form during her rebirth on Franklin Richards' Counter-Earth.

POWER GRID	1	2	3	4	5	6	7
INTELLIGENCE							
STRENGTH *							
SPEED							
DURABILITY							
ENERGY PROJECTION							
FIGHTING SKILLS							

*STRENGTH INCREASES AS SHE SHRINKS OR GROWS

HISTORY: The younger son of munitions manufacturer Sanford Williams, Simon was a bookish lad who loved math, chess and jazz and preferred reading to sport. His father demanded the best from both Simon and his brother Eric, becoming abusive if they achieved anything less than straight A's. Desperate for parental approval, young Simon excelled in the sciences but never satisfied his perfectionist father; the less academic Eric responded to Sanford's abuse by bullying Simon. Eric drifted into crime, but Simon resisted pressure to follow suit, instead taking over Williams Manufacturing around the age of 20 after their father died, renaming it Williams Innovations. Simon's inexperienced leadership landed the company in debt, partly due to rival firm Stark Industries constantly outdoing them on the R&D front. Simon pinned his hopes on developing a new missile targeting system for the US government, but when novice hero Spider-Man (Peter Parker) tried to stop the criminal Hawkeye (Clint Barton) from stealing the system designs, their battle destroyed the lab, pushing the company closer to bankruptcy. Simon turned to Eric, but his brother's intimidation tactics failed to garner contracts; in desperation, Simon embezzled money, hoping to invest it in Eric's Maggia ventures for a quick profit. Caught by the authorities, Simon admitted his guilt.

Before his sentencing, Simon's bail was paid by Asgardian sorceress Amora the Enchantress. Her ally, Nazi scientist Baron (Heinrich) Zemo, offered Simon superhuman powers and a chance for revenge in return for helping Zemo's Masters of Evil destroy the Avengers, who were funded by Simon's rival Tony Stark (secretly Avengers founder Iron Man). Simon accepted, but after Zemo's ionic ray treatments granted him superhuman strength and durability, Zemo revealed that the treatment would also kill Simon without weekly doses of an antidote. Believing Simon's loyalty thus ensured, the Masters lured the Avengers into battle and Simon came to the heroes' aid as Wonder Man. After the Masters fled, Simon asked to join the Avengers, who took him in and helped seek a cure for his terminal condition, just as Zemo had planned. Briefly snatched out of time to serve in Kang the Conqueror's Legion of the Unliving against a future incarnation of the Avengers, Simon was soon returned to his proper time by Immortus, with his departure unnoticed and his memories of the incident wiped. Touched by the Avengers' concern and respect for him, Simon nevertheless lured them into the Masters' ambush a few days later. When he realized Zemo would kill his captives rather than ransom them off as Simon had presumed, Simon switched sides, freeing the Avengers. The Masters fled, but Simon collapsed and seemingly died moments later, noting that he was happy to have done one noble thing in his life.

Simon had actually entered a deep hibernative state as his ionic energies triggered a body-wide transformation. Unaware of this and hoping to restore him someday, the Avenger Giant-Man (Henry Pym) hurriedly recorded Simon's brain patterns and stored his body. Unable to accept Simon's failings, Eric claimed responsibility for the embezzling and blamed the Avengers for Simon's death, targeting them as the costumed Grim Reaper. Intrigued by Simon's story, Reaper's robotic ally Ultron stole Simon's brain patterns and used them to form the artificial mind of his android pawn, the Vision, who soon joined the Avengers. Initially embracing the Vision as his resurrected brother, the Reaper stole Simon's inert body and offered to transfer the android's mind into it, but the Vision declined. Still seeking vengeance, Eric paid the voodoun Black Talon to revive Simon's body as a Zuvembie, delivered to Avengers Mansion and instructed to slay the Avengers. Simon instead collapsed, and the heroes soon apprehended the Black Talon, though they remained unaware of Eric's involvement. The team kept Simon under observation in their mansion, monitoring his stabilizing lifesigns, until his consciousness fully awoke when the Living Laser used the Serpent Crown to take over Simon's mind temporarily.

Simon remained with the Avengers while Vision's wife Scarlet Witch (Wanda Maximoff) tried to help him acclimatize, but the Vision himself proved hostile, his sense of identity shaken by the return of the man he had believed himself to be. Having likewise presumed the Vision was

REAL NAME: Simon Williams
ALIASES: "Wundy," John Porter, Dethblo the Diabolical, Hal Canutt, Corporal Mitchell, Monster Man, Black Bart, Mr. Muscles
IDENTITY: Publicly known
OCCUPATION: Adventurer; formerly actor, stuntman, security troubleshooter, industrialist, inventor
CITIZENSHIP: USA with a criminal record, pardoned
PLACE OF BIRTH: Paterson, New Jersey
KNOWN RELATIVES: Sanford Williams (father, deceased), Martha Williams (mother), Eric Williams (Grim Reaper, brother), Thomas, William (nephews, apparently destroyed), extended family through in-laws
GROUP AFFILIATION: Avengers, Operation: Lightning Storm, the Initiative; formerly Legion of the Unliving, Force Works, Masters of Evil (unofficial)
EDUCATION: Advanced degree in electrical engineering
FIRST APPEARANCE: Avengers #9 (1964)

Simon, the Reaper captured the Avengers and put both men on trial, determined to identify his true brother and slay the imposter. The Vision admitted he had once hoped he was the true Simon Williams, but was now content to be his own, unique, person. Simon, meanwhile, revealed his newly glowing eyes, a visible sign of his now energy-permeated body. When the Vision hypothesized that Simon had stepped beyond humanity and that he and Simon were the true brothers, an enraged Eric decided to kill them all, but the mutated Simon proved resistant to Eric's

Art by Roberto De La Torre with Don Heck (top inset)

weapons and he easily subdued the Reaper. Wonder Man's next opponent, however, made Simon question his apparent invulnerability: discovering Ultron's attacks could hurt him, Simon was overwhelmed by a fear of dying again. He began freezing up in combat repeatedly, despite scientific studies indicating he was now a being of living energy and had not truly died the first time around. Soon after facing Ultron, Simon battled Power Man (Erik Josten), who had also been empowered by Zemo's ionic equipment, and then Count Nefaria, who copied and refined the process; both would become recurring opponents.

Growing somewhat closer to his new "brother" Vision, Simon found other friends amongst his new peers, such as Ms. Marvel (Carol Danvers), whose advice Simon sought in trying to work past his fears. He was also reunited with Hawkeye, now a long-reformed Avengers veteran. Wonder Man developed a strong friendship with the apelike Beast, whose extroverted personality complimented the more introspective Simon. When the Avengers and the Guardians of the Galaxy faced the cosmically powerful Korvac, who killed most of the heroes with ease, Wonder Man finally overcame his death phobia and attacked; though Simon, too, fell, his relentless onslaught gave the surviving heroes a vital chance to rally, and all the fallen heroes were later restored by their foe. Despite nearly dying a second time, and occasional brief relapses of fear when reminded of his own mortality, Simon was never again ruled by the terror of dying.

A cinema trip with the Beast inspired Simon to do something beyond living off his Avengers stipend, and he decided to become an actor. When the government ordered the Avengers to limit their team size to seven members, Simon moved out, though he was granted formal membership in the team's reserves and pardoned for his past crimes. He landed his first acting role as the lead in an off-Broadway play, City of Angst, by a producer who hoped having an Avenger in the cast would boost box office; however, Simon's complete lack of training saw the play close the same night it opened, leaving Simon a laughing stock.

The only acting job Simon could get was that of "Mr. Muscles" on cable's The Uncle Elmer Show, as the caveman-clad victim of Elmer's abusive jokes. He began assisting the Avengers more often, fighting the Taskmaster, Red Ronin (during which battle he earned a lifelong fan by rescuing teenager Cindy Knutz), and the Brotherhood of Evil Mutants. Joining the Avengers fulltime to replace the departing Falcon, Simon lost his acting job after accidentally humiliating Uncle Elmer's star, Waylon Wilkie, during filming. He soon landed the lead on Ted Silverberg's television show, Monster Man; however, the series was canned mid-season after the Thing, unhappy about Monster Man being based on him, discovered the alien Xemnu was using the show as a means of mind control. When the Avengers reorganized and reduced their roster again, Simon quit the team and departed with fellow ex-Avenger Hercules, who offered to introduce him to Hollywood directors and producers.

Hercules' contacts proved unreliable and Simon remained in New York, struggling to pay his rent. When the Vision lost an arm, Simon provided an energy transfusion which saved his life, battling the Grim Reaper yet again as a result. Simon's career finally turned around when his agent booked him on a popular network talk show, on the condition that Simon brought along some fellow Avengers; when the show's taping was attacked by rogue inventor Fabian Stankowicz, Simon helped defeat Fabian. A West Coast producer saw Simon in action and tracked him down, locating him soon after he had lost his latest job as a Cordco Incorporated security troubleshooter, offering him stunt work in films

such as the unfinished The Demon That Devoured Hollywood and Decimator 2. Simon soon gained his own fanclub, the Wonderfans, who followed his every career move.

Simon relocated to Los Angeles, where Hawkeye invited him to join the Avengers' new West Coast roster. Dividing his time between his movie career and battling menaces such as the Blank, Graviton and Maelstrom, Simon also helped talk the Vision out of staging a benevolent takeover of the world's computer networks. Soon afterward, the Avengers overturned Dr. Doom's own brief conquest of the world, largely because Wonder Man proved immune to the mind-control pheromones of Doom's pawn, the Purple Man. Eric returned, plotting to copy both Simon and the Vision's minds, delete all but the shared memories, and then download this "pure" Simon into a zombie surgically altered to resemble a pre-superhuman Simon. Confronting the Reaper alongside Vision, Wonder Man finally convinced Eric that he was the real Simon by revealing he knew Eric had falsely taken the blame for Simon's embezzling; fleeing in shame, Eric fell to his death, but soon returned as a zombie to plague Simon anew.

Craving absolution, Simon confessed his embezzlement on television. His confidence was boosted by the public's favorable response, and as a result of his newfound fame, he was offered the role of leading villain in the A-list movie Arkon IV. The normally insecure Simon became cocky and arrogant, no longer willing to play second string either on screen or off. His ego caused problems when he repeatedly challenged both Hawkeye and Iron Man's leadership during a time travel mission, and he considered quitting the Avengers. Returning home, Simon drew unwanted attention from Mephisto when the demon clashed with the Avengers and X-Men; Mephisto noted Simon's immortal status and stained soul with interest. Simon finally regained some perspective after defeating Tyrannus (in the Abomination's body), only to find his show biz peers assuming it had been a publicity stunt. Humbled, Simon stayed on with the Avengers, battling Yetrigar, Eastern European villains, the High Evolutionary's Sensors, the Night Shift and Super-Nova.

Meanwhile, Immortus was manipulating events to turn the Scarlet Witch into his reality-altering tool. The coalition of intelligence agencies "Vigilance" kidnapped and disassembled the Vision; he was quickly rebuilt, but his mind had been wiped. Partly because he was secretly in love with Vision's wife, Simon refused to let his brain be used as a template to restore the android's personality. Wanda was enraged at his decision, and Simon felt increasingly guilty as a series of new misfortunes further traumatized her, notably the loss of her children. Hoping to ease her pain, Simon agreed to let his brain patterns be replicated; however, the now-emotionless Vision rejected the offer, noting this would merely create a new copy of Simon, not restore the old Vision. Descending into outright criminal insanity under the influence of her father Magneto, Wanda turned on the Avengers, seemingly killing Simon, then restoring him to life. Believing Wanda was finally ready for his purposes, Immortus revealed himself and his plans, only to have them thwarted when the witch Agatha Harkness restored Wanda's sanity. Simon was supportive of Wanda during her subsequent recovery, but she eventually made it clear that his romantic interest in her was not mutual, and relations between them became tenser.

Under the watchful eye of his agent Neal Saroyan, Simon got parts in films such as Damage Control: The Movie, but "serious" roles still eluded him. Neal set him up with both

an unwanted sidekick, Spider, and a fake girlfriend, Ginger Beach, though Simon was more interested in screenwriter Alex Flores. Regarding Simon as a threat to her operations, would-be LA crimelord Lotus Newmark swore to destroy him. When a Kree/Shi'ar interstellar war menaced Earth, the Avengers intervened; during the conflict, Simon tried and failed to disarm a Nega-Bomb, but its detonation wiped out much of the Kree Empire. Caught in the blast, Simon and Vision survived, but the radiation mutated Simon's powers, which became unstable. Returning to Earth, he began leaking ionic energy, unintentionally empowering the rage-filled Angkor and eight of his own friends and neighbors, including Spider, Ginger and Alex. Simon's eight empowered associates briefly formed the crimefighting Crazy 8. Simon had to kill Angkor to stop him, embracing his own rage and learning that it fueled his unstable powers.

Wonder Man quit the Avengers and was going to give up acting, but changed his mind when Neal promised him the lead in a big-screen

version of *Hamlet*, unaware Lotus had arranged it to get Simon out of LA while she took over. When the Crazy 8 opposed her, Lotus sent Splice and Rampage to kill them. Simon returned in time to save most of his friends, but Alex was critically injured, forcing Simon to reconsider his recent actions. Mephisto then assailed Simon with illusions and fake memories to weaken his will; one illusion revealed how Lotus had been involved in much of Simon's recent woes. Mephisto's ambitious son, Blackheart, interfered, and alongside Eric, Simon became a pawn in both their games and was drawn into Hell, but Simon ultimately rejected both demons, and convinced Blackheart to heal Alex. Back on Earth, he reabsorbed his ionic energy from the Crazy 8, stripping most of them of their powers. Soon after, he and Alex became engaged. Learning the Avengers' western roster had disbanded in his absence, Simon joined Iron Man's new Force Works group, only to be targeted by Kree forces blaming him for the Nega-bomb disaster. When the Kree's ion cannon ruptured during this battle, Simon carried it into space to save Earth, but was apparently killed when it exploded.

Simon survived as discorporated energy, holding onto life through his love for Wanda. When the sorceress Morgan Le Fay used Wanda as a conduit to reshape the world, the imprisoned Wanda reached out for help, and her powers re-formed Simon as pure ionic energy. He helped defeat Morgan, and over the next few months Wanda summoned him repeatedly, each time finding it easier, until he manifested to protect her even when she was rendered unconscious. A ghostly Grim Reaper raised Simon and other dead Avengers, compelling them to attack the living Avengers, but Wanda restored the dead heroes' true personalities and they turned against Eric. Also, by finally accepting her own long-repressed love for Simon, Wanda restored him to full life; he, in turn, resurrected Eric. Simon began working with the Avengers again but declined fully active status, feeling unworthy of the group and his new life due to his various past misdeeds and mistakes.

Simon's new romance with Wanda strained his relationship with the Vision, who had recently regained his capacity for emotion, including his feelings for her. Simon also felt guilty over unfinished business left from before he died, notably his engagement to Alex. Accompanied by the Beast, he returned to LA to make amends but found nobody blamed him, and he discovered Alex was happily married. After apprehending Lotus,

Simon met his fan Cindy Knutz, who told him how much he had changed her life; inspired by this, Simon set up a non-profit Second Chances foundation to help those overwhelmed by circumstances beyond their control. Returning from LA, he was ambushed by Count Nefaria, now both an ionic being and an energy vampire; Nefaria took control of both Simon and Atlas (Erik Josten), planning to explode a Nega-bomb which would turn humanity into ionic beings upon whom he could feast. Simon and Atlas escaped his control in time to carry the bomb into space, and this time Simon survived the explosion. Simon moved to LA, the long-distance relationship eventually ending his involvement with Wanda.

He accepted a challenge to reform the assassin Lady Killer, unaware this was part of a ploy by his former agent Neal Saroyan, secretly head of the Nobility assassins' group, to destroy the Avengers. Simon's charge, renamed Ladyfair, accompanied him to an Avengers party, where Neal had her poison the drinks; however, she resisted Neal's control long enough to prevent anyone imbibing. Simon flew to LA to confront Neal, but found him already slain by his own people. After the Super-human Registration Act was passed, Simon teamed with Ms. Marvel and others to battle anti-registration rebels, helping capture his former teammate Arachne. Intelligence agency SHIELD also blackmailed him into helping them investigate Atlantean subversives during the conflict. In the aftermath of this Civil War, Simon has joined Iron Man's new Avengers.

HEIGHT: 6'2"
WEIGHT: 380 lbs.
EYES: Red (permeated with shifting spots of ionic energy, no visible irises); formerly gray
HAIR: Gray, sometimes dyed black

ABILITIES/ACCESSORIES: Wonder Man's ionic energy-permeated body possesses greatly enhanced strength, durability, reflexes and stamina; he can lift in excess of 100 tons, is impervious to virtually any form of penetration wound, and does not tire. He does not require food, water or air, and does not age. He can fly at speeds in excess of 700 mph, or leap hundreds of feet from a standing jump. For a time, he shifted into an energy form while using his powers, but his conventional physical form now seems to be his constant state. During past periods when his powers were destabilized, his strength increased when angry, and he could alter his physical appearance, grow to giant stature, fire energy beams from his eyes, explode and reform at will, and empower others with ionic energy; he has apparently lost these abilities for now. He can control his internal energy flux to make his eyes appear normal temporarily; his eyesight extends beyond the normal human visible spectrum, and his hearing is also enhanced. He formerly wore a rocket belt or jetpack powered by his own ionic energies, but no longer requires these to fly.

POWER GRID	1	2	3	4	5	6	7
INTELLIGENCE							
STRENGTH							
SPEED							
DURABILITY							
ENERGY PROJECTION							
FIGHTING SKILLS							

CAPTAIN AMERICA

STORM

HULK

SPIDER-MAN

GIANT-GIRL

IRON MAN

WOLVERINE

FINDING ZEMO

JEFF PARKER
CRANIUM

MANUEL GARCIA
HYPOTHALAMUS

SCOTT KOBLISH
CORPUS CALLOSUM

VAL STAPLES
COLORHEAD

DAVE SHARPE
BRAINTRUST

AARON LOPRESTI
and GURU eFX
COVER

BRAD JOHANSEN
HEADCASE

NATHAN COSBY
GRAY MATTER

MARK PANICCIA
TEMPORAL LOBE

JOE QUESADA
OVERMIND

DAN BUCKLEY
COSMIC CONSCIOUSNESS

Captain America created by Joe Simon and Jack Kirby

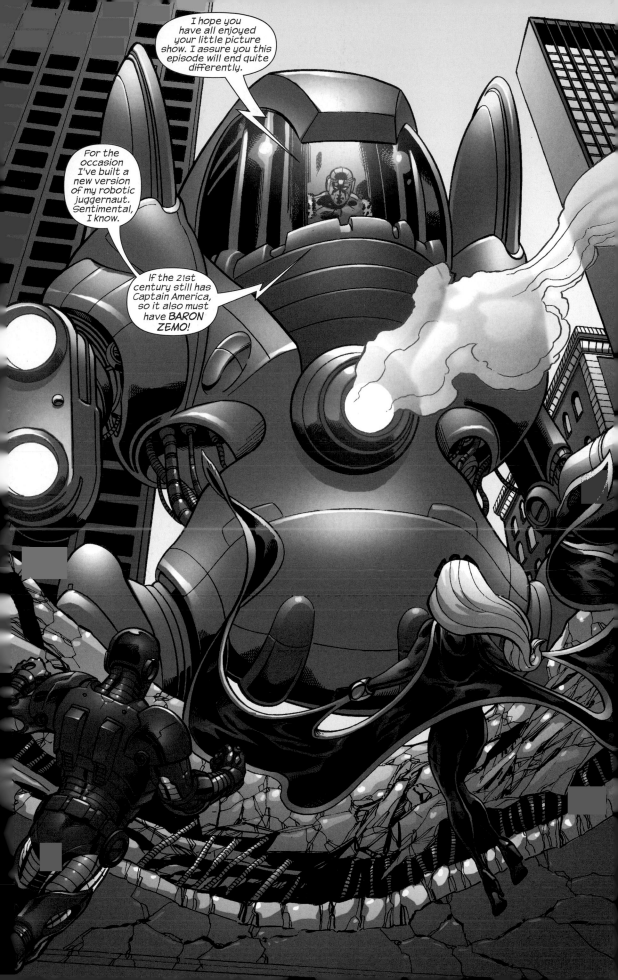

So how in the world could Baron Zemo be back after all these years?

Maybe he ended up in suspended animation like Captain America?

That's so unlikely, I can't believe you'd mention it.

A guy who turns into a green giant just said something was unlikely.

We've gotta get out and look for Cap--this sitting around is killing me!

You wouldn't mind sitting if you just had to carry a 12-ton robot across the city.

We can't do anything until Iron Man is through examining that thing. I don't even know where to start.

Calm down, Spider-Man. We're up against a very methodical planner, and we're not going to beat him unless we use our brains, too.

We should know soon. Iron Man is tracking energy signals that match the robot's equipment.

But Cap could be--

Thank you, Jarvis.

I don't think this is the same Baron Zemo from World War II. He's just as brilliant, but even more calculating.

I've found this much weaker signal coming from the Austrian border.

You think the other one is a fake?

I'm sure it's a trap. Zemo has spent too much time orchestrating this abduction not to cover his trail.

He's probably expecting us to act rash because we're worried about our teammate.

Exactly. Do we still have the discontinued Quinjet in storage?

Stripped of all the good parts, but it still flies.

Good. Bruce, since you need to recuperate, you can remote-pilot that Quinjet to the source of the first signal.

Fine, but I'd still be in fighting shape once I "Hulk out."

I know, but we need a subtle approach for this, and The Hulk doesn't do subtle.

Y'know, it's easy to see why you're the other team leader, besides Cap.

I believe we are equals in leadership, but I will say this...

...my posters sell better.